Governors State University
Library Hours:
Monday thru Thursday 8:00 to 10:30
Friday 8:00 to 5:00
Saturday 8:30 to 5:00
Sunday 1:00 to 5:00 (Fall
and Winter Trimester Only)

Cognitive Therapy
for Suicidal Patients

Cognitive Therapy for Suicidal Patients

Scientific and Clinical Applications

Amy Wenzel

Gregory K. Brown

and Aaron T. Beck

American Psychological Association
Washington, DC

Published by
American Psychological Association
750 First Street, NE
Washington, DC 20002
www.apa.org

To order
APA Order Department
P.O. Box 92984
Washington, DC 20090-2984
Tel: (800) 374-2721; Direct: (202) 336-5510
Fax: (202) 336-5502; TDD/TTY: (202) 336-6123
Online: www.apa.org/books/
E-mail: order@apa.org

In the U.K., Europe, Africa, and the Middle East, copies may be ordered from
American Psychological Association
3 Henrietta Street
Covent Garden, London
WC2E 8LU England

Typeset in Goudy by Stephen McDougal, Mechanicsville, MD

Printer: Edwards Brothers, Ann Arbor, MI
Cover Designer: Watermark Design Office, Alexandria, VA
Technical/Production Editor: Tiffany L. Klaff

The opinions and statements published are the responsibility of the authors, and such opinions and statements do not necessarily represent the policies of the American Psychological Association.

Library of Congress Cataloging-in-Publication Data

Wenzel, Amy.
   Cognitive therapy for suicidal patients : scientific and clinical applications / Amy Wenzel, Gregory K. Brown, and Aaron T. Beck. — 1st ed.
      p. ; cm.
   Includes bibliographical references and index.
   ISBN-13: 978-1-4338-0407-6
   ISBN-10: 1-4338-0407-7
   1. Suicidal behavior—Prevention. 2. Cognitive therapy. I. Brown, Gregory K., Ph. D.
II. Beck, Aaron T. III. Title.
   [DNLM: 1. Suicide—prevention & control. 2. Cognitive Therapy—methods.
WM 165 W482c 2009]
   RC569.W475 2009
   616.85'8445—dc22
                                                                        2008021597

British Library Cataloguing-in-Publication Data
A CIP record is available from the British Library.

Printed in the United States of America
First Edition

CONTENTS

ACKNOWLEDGMENTS

We would like to offer our heartfelt thanks to the many researchers and clinicians who influenced our thinking as we developed cognitive therapy for suicidal patients. Our research staff worked tirelessly to administer the cognitive intervention, recruit and assess patients at follow-up intervals to monitor their progress, and provide the necessary services to retain patients in our clinical trials. Our postdoctoral fellows and faculty who served as therapists and assessors in these studies include Michele Berk, Sunil Bhar, Jason Chapman, Danielle Farabaugh, Randy Fingerhut, Evan Forman, Dara Friedman-Wheeler, Gregg Henriques, Marjan Holloway, Julie Jacobs, Elizabeth Jeglic, Willem Kuyken, Kenneth Laidlaw, Jennifer Mayer, Christine Ratto, Sabine Schmid, Ian Sharp, Megan Spokas, Shannon Stirman, Debbie Warman, and Joseph Wright. Clinicians and faculty who have facilitated the recruitment of participants for our studies include Dwight Evans, Joseph J. Gallo, Judd Hollander, Ira R. Katz, David Oslin, Susan Rappaport, Frank Sites, Jeffrey Staab, and the many other physicians, nurses, and academic associates within the University of Pennsylvania Health System and the U.S. Department of Veterans Affairs. We also appreciate the assistance from law enforcement, emergency medical services, and crisis response centers in the Philadelphia area.

Other research staff who have contributed to our studies include Mark Carey, Sarah Charlesworth, Michael Crooks, Amy Cunningham, Brian Dearnley, Maureen Endres, Nicholas Finstrom, Allison Fox, Carly Gibbons, John Guerry, Jessie Handelsman, Pamela Henderson, Nathaniel Herr, Heath Hodges, Ellen Jørstad-Stein, Bambi Juryea, Rachel King, Kathryn Lou, Brianna Mann, Joseph Moldover, Carly Romeo, Carlene Ryan, Daniella Sosdjan, Lisa Starr, Sarah Tarquini, Rolando Vega, Robert Wheeler, Blair Wisco, James Yadavaia, and David Zembroski. Moreover, our studies would not have been possible without our dedicated executive administrator, Barbara Marinelli.

We extend a special thanks to Amy Cunningham for her extensive editing of several drafts of this book.

The clinical chapters of this volume were based, in part, on the unpublished treatment manual, *Cognitive Therapy Treatment Manual for Suicide Attempters*, which was used in our clinical trials at the University of Pennsylvania. We would like to thank the many clinicians to whom we have offered ongoing supervision on this intervention and who are using this intervention in community mental health settings throughout Philadelphia. Other clinicians throughout the country have participated in workshops and provided excellent feedback about the manner in which the intervention would work in their practice settings. We also acknowledge the cognitive behavior therapy team of the Treatment of Adolescent Suicide Attempts study, including David Brent, John Curry, Tina Goldstein, Jennifer Hughes, Betsy Kennard, Kim Poling, Margaret Schlossberg, Barbara Stanley, and Karen Wells, as well as other colleagues who have made valuable contributions to our work, including David Jobes and M. David Rudd. The thoughtful insights from all of these clinicians often inspired us to modify our specific strategies, develop new strategies, and adapt our strategies for special populations.

Many sponsoring agencies have supported the research described in this volume. The agencies that have supported our recent studies include the American Foundation for Suicide Prevention, Centers for Disease Control and Prevention (National Center for Injury Prevention and Control), National Alliance for Research on Schizophrenia and Depression, National Institutes of Health (National Institute on Drug Abuse and National Institute of Mental Health), and the Department of Veterans Affairs. We especially appreciate the support of Jane Pearson at the National Institute of Mental Health.

Our acknowledgments would not be complete without mentioning the staff of the American Psychological Association Books Department, particularly Susan Reynolds. You made this writing experience a very positive one for all of us.

Finally, we would like to thank our families for supporting us as we undertook this major endeavor. We are grateful for your love and commitment. We dedicate this book to those who continue to struggle with suicidal desire, and our hope is that this work can help to alleviate their pain and suffering and, ultimately, to save lives.

Cognitive Therapy
for Suicidal Patients

INTRODUCTION

Suicide is a major public health problem, accounting for more than 32,000 deaths in the United States in 2005. It is the 11th leading cause of death among all age groups and the 2nd among adults between the ages of 25 and 34 (Centers for Disease Control & Prevention, 2008). The number of deaths by suicide reflects only a limited portion of the effect of suicidal acts on society. Although there is no national database of suicide attempts, epidemiological survey studies have indicated that approximately 2.7% of the U.S. population have made a suicide attempt with the intent to die (Nock & Kessler, 2006), and approximately 13.5% of the U.S. population have experienced suicidal thoughts or wishes at some point in their lives (Kessler, Borges, & Walters, 1999).

These cold statistics show nothing of the tragic effects on the lives of those close to the victims of suicide. Friends and family agonize, "How could we have missed the signs?" and "What could we have done to prevent it?" Clinicians who treated these patients ask themselves the same questions. The present volume is designed to address both of these issues, including ways to detect patients at risk for suicide and ways to prevent suicide through psychotherapy. Our material is drawn from the cumulative body of knowledge built by our group and by other investigators. Until the middle of the past century, suicide prevention approaches were based largely on clinical lore. However, the more recent approaches to suicide prevention are based on scientifically sound empirical evidence, and it is the latter approach that is emphasized in this volume.

This introduction was written for three purposes. First, I provide some historical background regarding the development of an empirically based approach to understanding suicidal behavior. Second, I outline the major contributions by my research group in understanding many of the psychological variables that contribute to suicidal behavior. Finally, I describe the organization of the volume and highlight the chapters to come.

HISTORICAL BACKGROUND

The first major institutional program of this discipline in the United States was at the Los Angeles Center for Suicide Prevention, established in 1958. Among the leading figures were Edwin Shneidman, generally considered the father of suicidology, Robert Litman, and Norman Farberow. I was most impressed at that time by their attempt to provide an organized research agenda to understand the psychological and clinical aspects of suicidal behavior and, particularly, completed suicides. They refined the investigative tools used in explaining the motives leading to suicide with the development of the "psychological autopsy," which involves in-depth interviews with the relatives of the decedent and the collection of data regarding the circumstances surrounding the attempt, including the analysis of suicide notes (if any).

Almost concurrently, considerable progress in the empirical approach to this problem was being made in other countries, particularly in the United Kingdom. In their volume *Attempted Suicide: Its Social Significance and Effects*, Stengel and Cook (1958) emphasized the importance of assessing intent in evaluating suicidal behavior because intent is a central variable that is used to determine whether a person who engaged in self-injury behavior indeed attempted or committed suicide. In keeping with the approach of social behaviorists, however, Norman Kreitman in Edinburgh, Scotland, applied the term *parasuicide* to describe a broad category of self-injury, which includes what would generally be considered as "genuine" suicide attempts and deliberate self-injury or self-poisoning without suicidal intent (Kreitman & Philip, 1969). In contrast to Stengel and Cook (1958), Kreitman and his group noted that suicidal intent as a subjective, unobservable state could not be reliably assessed, in contrast to the overt behavior of self-injury. After our group demonstrated the utility of the Suicide Intent Scale (SIS), Kreitman's group acknowledged that suicidal intent could indeed be evaluated (Dyer & Kreitman, 1984). Nonetheless, the controversy over whether suicidal intent can be identified as a way of classifying "true" suicide attempts has not as yet been fully resolved, and the terms *parasuicide* and *self-harm* are still widely used in Europe and occasionally in North America to include all instances of self-poisoning or self-injury regardless of the person's degree of intent to kill him- or herself.

The scientific investigation of suicidal behavior received an enormous boost in the United States when the Center for the Study and Prevention of Suicide was established within the National Institute of Mental Health, with Shneidman as its first director, and provided with sufficient funds to launch a number of initiatives for promoting the infant discipline and giving grants for individual projects. One of the projects initiated by Harvey Resnik, the second director of the center, was an exploration of the causes of the relatively high rate of suicide among the Papago Indian Tribe in Phoenix, Arizona, representative of a generalized high rate among southwestern Native American tribes. Alcoholism was identified as the most common precursor of suicide attempts in this population. Several recommendations were made and subsequently implemented to reduce the suicide rate. Concurrently, Resnik convened a conference of various investigators interested in the study of suicide to assess the current state of the field and to make policy recommendations. Among the various committees that were formed was one on the classification of suicidal behavior, which I chaired. The members of the task force came to several conclusions: (a) that the welter of terms, such as *hysterical suicide, pseudo-suicide,* and *histrionic attempts,* were confusing and hindered progress not only in helping individual patients but also in establishing a framework for research and (b) that there was no satisfactory system for classifying suicidal behaviors (completed suicides were frequently linked with suicide attempts in the research literature) and that a new system separating suicide ideation, suicide attempt, and completed suicide should be constructed. We also suggested that the descriptive variables, degree of suicidal intent and medical lethality, should be added to the system (with medical lethality applied, of course, only to the attempters).

I then embarked on a long journey through the maze of problems associated with research in this area. One of my main objectives was to place the various factors associated with suicidal behavior on a quantitative foundation, in contrast to the existing qualitative approach. In this I was aided substantially by a talented group of researchers. My plan was to focus successively on classification, assessment, prediction, and intervention. Much of our time and energy was devoted to developing and validating a variety of instruments to measure the relevant variables.

We initially conducted a number of studies designed to measure the relevant descriptive variables of the classification system. To implement this goal, we developed the 20-item clinician-administered SIS (see chap. 1 for a comprehensive description of this measure). The SIS items were derived from self-descriptions of patients' states of mind before a suicide attempt and their actual behavior at the time of the attempt. The first 8 items assess the objective circumstances surrounding the suicidal act, such as writing a suicide note, taking precautions against discovery, and making recent threats of suicide. This subscale can also be used to infer the degree of intent for people who have died to determine whether their death could be classified as a suicide. The other subscale assesses patients' subjective perceptions about their suicidal behavior, including variables such as expectation of lethality and reaction to the attempt.

There were a number of specific issues that we addressed with our empirical data to clarify the role of suicidal intent in suicidal behavior. For example, we were initially puzzled by the poor correlation between suicidal intent and medical lethality. However, when corrections were made to take into account patients' expectations regarding the potential lethality of the attempt, the scale correlated well with medical lethality (A. T. Beck, Beck, & Kovacs, 1975; G. K. Brown, Henriques, Sosdjan, & Beck, 2004); that is, when patients had accurate expectations about the degree of lethality of their attempt, then intent correlated strongly with lethality. In addition, we wondered whether individuals who had made attempts with a strong intent to die had the same characteristics as those who died by suicide. We found this to be the case (Lester, Beck, & Mitchell, 1979), which suggests that one can extrapolate findings from attempts associated with a strong intent to die to completed attempts. Another question that we raised was whether those who made interrupted attempts (i.e., when patients started but did not complete the attempt, usually because of interference by another person) were at risk for eventual suicide. We found that their risk was just as great as for those who carried out their attempt. During the period of time that we were studying the characteristics of individuals who had made suicide attempts, there was a popular belief that suicide attempts represented a cry for help. We assessed this hypothesis by examining communication of intent (an item on the SIS). We found that whether the attempters communicated a wish to die (a) was more a function of their personal communication style than a generalized motive for a suicide attempt and (b) was not related to the actual wish to die (Kovacs, Beck, & Weissman, 1976). However, a follow-up study showed that patients who did not communicate suicide intent were at greater risk of eventual suicide than those who did (A. T. Beck & Lester, 1976). Together, these studies demonstrated that suicidal intent is a crucial component of suicide attempts and completed suicides.

The next step in our investigation was to evaluate the validity of the suicide ideation category in the classification system. To assess suicidal intent among patients who were hospitalized for suicide ideation rather than after making a suicide attempt, we adapted the items in the SIS that we had been administering to attempters. We found that this Scale for Suicide Ideation (SSI) also had good concurrent and construct validity (see chap. 1 for a comprehensive description of this measure). In short, both of these new scales substantiated the adequacy of the new classification system. We also believed that they could also serve as useful research and clinical instruments in themselves.

PSYCHOLOGICAL CHARACTERISTICS OF SUICIDAL BEHAVIOR

A major theme of our research was not simply to validate the classification system but also to identify those psychological variables contributing to suicidal intent that were amenable to modification. As clinicians as well as investigators, we were eager to find ways to reduce the risk of suicide in our patients. Early in my work, I became aware of the central role of hopelessness, or negative expectations for the future, in my depressed suicidal patients. I observed that the greater the hopelessness, the greater these patients' wish to kill themselves. I also found that if I successfully targeted patients' hopelessness in therapy, their suicidal wishes appeared to subside. To confirm these clinical observations, it was important to develop a measure of hopelessness. I assembled a list of pessimistic statements from the patients, culled them, and prepared a 20-item scale (i.e., the Beck Hopelessness Scale [BHS]) with 10 items keyed positively (e.g., "My future seems dark to me") and 10 keyed negatively (e.g., "I look forward to the future with hope and enthusiasm"). The psychometric properties of the BHS were adequate, with a high internal consistency and 1-week test–retest reliability (A. T. Beck & Steer, 1988) and significant associations with clinical ratings of hopelessness (A. T. Beck, Weissman, Lester, & Trexler, 1974), suicidal intent (e.g., A. T. Beck, Steer, & McElroy, 1982), and suicide ideation (e.g., A. T. Beck, Steer, Beck, & Newman, 1993).

We then investigated whether the BHS correlated with suicidal intent in a sample of individuals who had attempted suicide. We found that the intensity of suicidal intent was more highly correlated with hopelessness than with depression (Minkoff, Bergman, Beck, & Beck, 1973). A validation study found that hopelessness accounted for 76% of the association between depression and suicidal intent in 384 patients who were hospitalized for a suicide attempt (A. T. Beck, Kovacs, & Weissman, 1975). When patients who had been hospitalized for depression or suicidal risk rather than for a recent suicide attempt were studied, we found that hopelessness, rather than depression per se, was a determinant of suicidal intent (Bedrosian & Beck, 1979). Hopelessness also correlated more strongly with suicidal intent than with depression among individuals who attempted suicide and were diagnosed with alcohol dependence (A. T. Beck, Weissman, & Kovacs, 1976) and among individuals who had made a suicide attempt and were diagnosed with drug dependence (Weissman, Beck, & Kovacs, 1979).

Because the prediction of eventual suicide was and continues to be a significant public health issue, I wondered whether high hopelessness at baseline interviews could forecast completed suicide attempts some time in the future. To investigate this problem, we intensively studied 207 patients hospitalized between 1970 and 1975 for suicide ideation, rather than for a recent suicide attempt, at the time of admission. During a follow-up period of 5 to 10 years, 14 patients committed suicide. Of all the data collected at the time of hospitalization, only the BHS and the pessimism item of the Beck Depression Inventory predicted the eventual suicides. A score of 10 or more on the BHS correctly identified 91% of the eventual suicides (A. T. Beck, Steer, Kovacs, & Garrison, 1985). Taken in conjunction with previous studies showing the relation between hopelessness and suicidal intent, these findings indicate the importance of hopelessness as an indicator of long-term suicide risk in previously hospitalized depressed patients.

We also addressed the question of whether hopelessness could predict suicide in an attempter sample; 413 patients who were hospitalized for suicide attempts between 1970 and 1975 were followed until 1982. We used a multiple logistic regression analysis to predict the risk of eventual suicide. The diagnosis of alcoholism was the best predictor of eventual suicide—the risk of alcoholic patients eventually committing suicide was more than five times greater than that of nonalcoholic patients. A newly formed subscale of the SIS—Precautions—also predicted eventual suicide, which indicated that patients who had carefully planned their unsuccessful attempt to prevent interruption were at high risk of being successful at a later attempt. The BHS, however, was not predictive of suicide in this study of individuals who had attempted suicide (A. T. Beck & Steer, 1989). This finding was a surprise and perplexed me for many years. In the discussion section of the A. T. Beck and Steer (1989) article, however, we proposed that many attempters might have experienced a decrease in depression and hopelessness after an unsuccessful suicide attempt, which could account for this null finding. Some patients, for example, express feelings of euphoria at still being alive after an attempt. This observation suggested that the patients' feelings regarding the attempt might have confounded the results.

On reviewing this article 15 years later, Gregg Henriques determined that we had information in our database that could address this question. He found that by analyzing patients' reaction to the attempt—either sad or glad that it was unsuccessful—the problem was solved. Hopelessness was high in the sad group, and this group was significantly more likely to commit suicide than the glad group (Henriques, Wenzel, Brown, & Beck, 2005).

My research team and I also investigated psychological variables associated with eventual suicide in outpatient samples. Two overlapping cohorts at the Center for Cognitive Therapy (CCT) at the University of Pennsylvania were studied from 1978 to 2004. These two samples (ns = 1,958 and 6,891) consisted of patients who presented at CCT for evaluation and treatment. A study of the first cohort at CCT found that an optimal cutoff score of 9 or above on the BHS correctly identified 16 of the 17 patients who committed suicide. The high-risk group was 11 times more likely to commit suicide than the low-risk group (A. T. Beck, Brown, Berchick, Stewart, & Steer, 1990). These results confirmed the earlier findings with suicidal and depressed inpatients. A later study by G. K. Brown, Beck, Steer, and Grisham (2000) of the second cohort identified 49 deaths by suicide. Univariate survival analyses revealed that the severity of hopelessness, suicide ideation, and depression were significant risk factors for eventual suicide. The consistent finding of hopelessness as a predictor of future suicide led to the speculation that hopelessness in these patients had "trait" characteristics. If hopelessness is high at one point, it is likely to be high just before a completed suicide. Indeed, we found a correlation of .69 between successive administrations of the BHS separated by 1 week (A. T. Beck & Steer, 1988).

Integrating the findings of hospital and outpatient ideators and of suicide attempters, we concluded that these psychological and clinical variables were significant risk factors for suicide across the lifetime of the patients and, more important, that they could be a main focus for a therapeutic intervention. Before embarking on a clinical trial to prevent suicidal behavior, however, we decided to examine several other clinical–psychological risk factors. It occurred to me that many of the patients who were not especially suicidal at the time of admission to the clinic might have been more suicidal in the past, and that it might be this past history of suicidality that is particularly strong in predicting future suicidal behavior. To test this hunch, I reworked the time frame of the SSI to apply to the most suicidal period in the patient's life (i.e., the SSI—Worst Point, or SSI–W). On long-term follow-up of 3,701 patients, we found that high scorers on the SSI–W were more likely to commit suicide than were low scorers. In fact, the SSI–W was a better predictor of eventual suicide than current suicide ideation and hopelessness (A. T. Beck, Brown, Steer, Dahlsgaard, & Grisham, 1999).

I also noticed in my work with patients that the suicidal wishes were not unidimensional. Suicidal patients were frequently conflicted about reasons for living and for dying, and this conflict was expressed as an internal struggle between the wish to live and the wish to die. I reasoned that those patients for whom the wish to die exceeded the wish to live would be at high risk for eventual suicide. This observation had been supported by Kovacs and Beck (1977) in a study of an inpatient sample of patients who had recently made a suicide attempt. A further replication was made on an outpatient sample at CCT (G. K. Brown, Steer, Henriques, & Beck, 2005), in which patients who endorsed a greater wish to die than to live were approximately six times more likely to kill themselves.

A significant clinical question is whether the association between these psychological variables, particularly hopelessness, and suicide can have significance in terms of treatment. An application of the cognitive model to therapy was conducted by Rush, Beck, Kovacs, Weissenburger, and Hollon (1982). We found that cognitive therapy had a significant impact on reducing hopelessness. I then speculated that a poor response to cognitive therapy might be predictive of eventual suicide. In a retrospective analysis, we found that those patients who eventually committed suicide had shown minimal improvement—they had high and stable scores on the BHS and dropped out of treatment prematurely against their clinicians' wishes (Dahlsgaard, Beck,

& Brown, 1998). This finding suggests that hopelessness should be a key target in treatment and that a vigorous attempt should be made to keep this high-risk group in treatment.

In looking back over 35 years of research, I believe we have not only established the validity and practicality of a classification system of suicidal behavior with its qualifying variables (i.e., intent and lethality) and a number of measures to tap various aspects of suicidal behavior, but we have also provided a number of strategies for evaluating suicidal risk. Of special value for identifying high-risk individuals is the use of the SSI–W and the BHS. Moreover, questioning individuals with suicide ideation regarding their wish to live versus their wish to die and asking individuals who have attempted suicide about their reaction to the attempt are efficient methods available to any professional. We have also found that patients whose hopelessness does not improve during therapy require special attention and long-term monitoring.

There are also promising applications of therapeutic interventions for suicidal patients. It is now well established that cognitive therapy reduces depression and suicide ideation as well as pharmacotherapy and reduces the probability of relapse significantly better. What effect this has on the suicide rate remains to be seen. In our recent work with individuals who had recently attempted suicide, we devised a 10-session outpatient intervention to serve two purposes: (a) to focus the therapy primarily on suicide ideation and provide the patient with strategies to deal with suicidal crises and (b) to structure the therapy so that it can be administered in a relatively brief number of sessions to make it compatible with the duration of treatment generally available at mental health centers. We found that the reattempt rate in the treatment group was reduced by almost 50% relative to patients who were receiving usual care (G. K. Brown, Tenhave, et al., 2005). It is this intervention that is described extensively in Part II of this volume.

THE CURRENT VOLUME

The current volume crystallizes our basic, clinical, and therapeutic investigations of suicidal behavior over several decades. We have included our own studies within a comprehensive review of the literature relevant to the classification, assessment, prediction, and treatment of suicidal behavior. For the first time, we present our cognitive model of suicidal behavior, which serves as a blueprint for therapy and research. Because patients who have previously attempted suicide are at the highest risk for eventually killing themselves, we have concentrated particularly on this group in our presentation of the plan and strategies for treatment. The same procedures, however, can be adapted for the treatment of any patients who endorse suicide ideation.

This volume is divided into three sections. In the first section, we review and integrate the scientific literature that provides the rationale for areas of focus in our treatment. Chapter 1 describes the classification system I discussed earlier and the corresponding inventories to assess the important constructs in the classification system. Chapter 2 summarizes the extensive literature on correlates of and risk factors for suicidal behavior, focusing on the broad categories of demographic variables, diagnostic variables, psychiatric history variables, and psychological variables. In chapter 3, we apply the literature on risk factors for suicidal behavior, particularly those that are psychological in nature (e.g., hopelessness), in the development of a cognitive model of suicidal behavior. Finally, chapter 4 describes interventions for reducing suicidal behavior that have been evaluated to date and foreshadow aspects of those interventions that are included in our own cognitive therapy approach. After reading this section, the reader should have a solid understanding of contemporary empirical literature on suicidal behavior and a grasp of aspects of suicidal behavior that require further study.

The second section of the volume provides an extensive guide for clinicians who wish to apply our intervention with their adult suicidal patients. Chapter 5 provides a basic overview of cognitive therapy's general principles, including the manner in which sessions are structured and common cognitive and behavioral strategies. Chapters 6 through 9 describe the four phases of the intervention, from the early phase of treatment to cognitive case conceptualization, and on to the intermediate and later phases of treatment. Throughout these chapters, we present the case of "Janice," who represents a composite of many of the suicidal patients who have gone through our clinical trials. This section concludes with chapter 10, which presents common challenges in treating suicidal patients experienced by cognitive therapists and the manner in which cognitive therapy strategies can be used to address these challenges.

The final section of the book describes ways in which the protocol presented in Part II can be applied to special populations, including adolescents (chap. 11), older adults (chap. 12), and patients with substance dependence disorders (chap. 13). The modifications described in these chapters are currently being evaluated in clinical trials in our own unit and in others across the United States. Case examples representing composite patients who have received these interventions are presented to illustrate the application of cognitive therapy strategies. At the end of the book, we place our research within the larger national agenda of suicide prevention and identify future directions for the field.

The chapters in this volume have been prepared by my two collaborators, Amy Wenzel and Gregory K. Brown. We have worked together on many investigations and are pleased to be able to share the fruits of our labor with the professional community. I have contributed my own ideas to each chapter and have been personally gratified by the overall results. We hope that clinicians will be able to draw on our investigations and experience to prevent suicide and that researchers will be stimulated to build on the scientific foundations and expand the work into new areas. Finally, I want to express my appreciation to the large group of brilliant professionals, including Drs. Wenzel and Brown, who have collaborated with me over the years in the investigation and therapy of suicidal behavior.

—Aaron T. Beck

I

COGNITIVE THEORY AND EMPIRICAL RESEARCH

1

CLASSIFICATION AND ASSESSMENT OF SUICIDE IDEATION AND SUICIDAL ACTS

Janice, a 35-year-old woman who has recurrent major depressive disorder, ingested approximately 20 sleeping pills after a minor conflict with her stepfather. Her mother and stepfather were home when she swallowed the pills. In the days after she was medically stabilized, Janice reported that she became so discouraged by her life circumstances that she believed suicide was the only way out. She expressed ambivalence about making the attempt; although she indicated some relief that she had survived, she continued to report hopelessness about her ability to make positive changes in her life. This is the first time Janice has been hospitalized following a suicide attempt, although she reported that she had made three previous attempts that did not require medical attention.

Nick, a 25-year-old man with polydrug dependence, has made several suicide attempts since the age of 15. In his most recent attempt, he jumped off of a bridge after smoking crystal methamphetamine. Nick often indicates that he expects to die before he turns 30 and that he is not afraid of death. Even when he denies feeling suicidal, he engages in risky behavior such as excessive drug use, speeding on the highway while driving his motorcycle, and getting in fights at bars. Nick had trouble remembering what he was thinking at the time of the incident and could not deny that he had made a suicide attempt. He was uncooperative with the medical staff who treated him following his recent attempt and refused to answer many of their questions, asking, "Can I just get out of here now?"

Chad is a 13-year-old who was taken to the emergency department after his mother saw him making minor lacerations on his left wrist. The wounds were superficial, so he was released from the hospital after only a short while, with referrals to outpatient mental health professionals. Although his attempt caused no physical damage, Chad clearly indicated that he was trying to kill himself because he was tired of being bullied at school. He is the smallest boy in his class and for several years has been taunted and beaten up by other boys in the neighborhood as he walks home from school. Chad reported that he will try to kill himself again if he continues to be bullied.

These are but a few representations of the circumstances surrounding self-injury behavior that bring people to the emergency department. Given that this is a book on cognitive therapy for suicidal patients, the reader will likely view these vignettes as three descriptions of different kinds of suicide attempts. However, as will be seen in this chapter, there is quite a bit of variability in the manner in which clinicians determine whether an instance of self-injury actually constitutes a suicide attempt. For example, Janice knew her mother and stepfather were in the house at the time she ingested the pills; does this indicate that she was hoping that they would find her before it was too late? Nick has a history of suicide attempts, drug abuse, and other risky behavior, but he claimed he could not remember what prompted him to jump off the bridge; did he truly wish to die with this attempt, or was this an instance of risky behavior prompted by an altered state of consciousness? Chad, on the other hand, was the most explicit of the three cases in his intention to commit suicide; however, his wounds were only surface scratches. Can this instance really be called a suicide attempt if it did not result in any physical damage? Researchers have found that clinicians, even those who specialize in working with suicidal patients, show very little agreement in their determination of who did and did not attempt suicide (Wagner, Wong, & Jobes, 2002).

In this chapter, we present accepted definitions for various manifestations of suicide ideation and suicidal acts. Of course, a standard nomenclature is imperative for the reader to understand the terms used in the remaining chapters of this book. But in a larger context, experts in suicidology have called for the development of a standard nomenclature to facilitate (a) precise and systematic risk assessments, (b) accurate communication between clinicians and between clinicians and patients, and (c) the ability to compare research findings between studies that are presumably attempting to study similar phenomena (O'Carroll, Berman, Maris, Mościcki, Tanney, &

Silverman, 1996; Rudd, 2000; Silverman, 2006). In addition, we discuss a system that can be used to classify suicide-relevant behaviors (cf. A. T. Beck, Resnik, & Lettieri, 1974). Finally, we describe assessment tools with established psychometric characteristics that quantify a patient's standing on several dimensions of this classification scheme.

A STANDARD NOMENCLATURE FOR SUICIDOLOGY

According to O'Carroll et al. (1996), *nomenclature* is "a set of commonly understood, logically defined terms. The terms of any nomenclature may be considered a type of shorthand by which communication about classes of more subtle phenomena is facilitated" (p. 240). In other words, nomenclature facilitates communication by using language that will be recognized widely by clinicians, researchers, health care administrators, family members of individuals who have engaged in suicidal acts, and patients themselves. In contrast, a *classification* scheme is typically more involved, including

> comprehensiveness; a systematic arrangement of items in groups or categories, with ordered, nested subcategories; scientific (e.g., biologic or etiologic) validity; exhaustiveness; accurately sufficient for research or clinical practice; and an unambiguous set of rules for assigning items to a single place in the classification scheme. (O'Carroll et al., 1996, p. 240)

In this section, we focus on a recent attempt to provide a standard nomenclature for the field, and we consider one approach to classification in the next section.

Exhibit 1.1 summarizes terms and definitions that capture the range of suicide-relevant behaviors. We define *suicide* as death caused by self-inflicted injurious behavior with any intent to die as a result of the behavior (Crosby, 2007). This definition illustrates three important components—(a) that the person is dead, (b) that the person's behavior caused his or her own death, and (c) that the person *intended* to cause his or her own death. The third criterion, the intent to kill oneself, has been the source of considerable controversy in the field, but is likely the most precise variable that distinguishes between those who have died by suicide and those who have died by other causes (Andriessen, 2006). Similar definitions of suicide have been described in the literature (Silverman, Berman, Sanddal, O'Carroll, & Joiner, 2007; see Silverman, 2006, for a comprehensive review).

The concept of suicidal intent is also central to our definition of a *suicide attempt*, which is a nonfatal, self-inflicted, potentially injurious behavior with any intent to die as its result (Crosby, 2007). A suicide attempt may or may not result in injury. Furthermore, evidence of the intent to die can be explicit or implicit. Explicit intent is the person's direct communication of the intent to end his or her own life. Implicit intent can be inferred from the

EXHIBIT 1.1
Definitions of Terms

Term	Definition
Suicide	Death caused by self-inflicted injurious behavior with any intent to die as a result of the behavior.[a]
Suicide attempt	A nonfatal, self-inflicted, potentially injurious behavior with any intent to die as a result of the behavior. A suicide attempt may or may not result in injury.[a]
Suicidal act	A self-inflicted, potentially injurious behavior with any intent to die as a result of the behavior. A suicidal act may or may not result in death (suicide).
Suicide ideation	Any thoughts, images, beliefs, voices, or other cognitions reported by the individual about intentionally ending his or her own life.

Note. The term *suicide* may be used interchangeably with the terms *completed suicide* or *death by suicide.* [a]Source data from Crosby (2007).

circumstances of the behavior or from the person's belief that the behavior could have resulted in death (Crosby, 2007). As with other definitions of a suicide attempt (e.g., O'Carroll et al., 1996; Silverman et al., 2007), this definition indicates that there are two separate dimensions that need to be considered in identifying suicide attempts: (a) the degree to which there was a potential for actual injury and (b) the degree of intent to commit suicide at the time of the behavior. Both of these dimensions require further discussion, given the difficulty in the assessment of suicidal intent and medical lethality.

Suicidal intent can be evaluated simply by asking people to recall whether they intended to kill themselves at the time of the act. The presence or absence of suicidal intent, however, is sometimes difficult to determine because people may report ambivalence about whether they wished to live or die at the time they attempted suicide or because their recollection of their intent is inaccurate or unreliable. One approach to assessing intent is to infer intent from the circumstances surrounding the execution of the suicidal act, such as attempting suicide so that one is less likely to be rescued or discovered, making final preparations in anticipation of death (e.g., completion of a will or purchasing guns), or leaving a suicide note (A. T. Beck, Resnik, et al., 1974). However, the assessment of inferred intent from objective circumstances is also subject to assessment bias. For example, people may purposefully make preparations for suicide or engage in self-injury behavior to make it appear that they attempted suicide when there was actually no intent (Freedenthal, 2007). Inferring intent from the medical lethality of the act is also problematic. As was mentioned in the Introduction to this book, our research group found a minimal association between the degree of suicidal intent and the extent of medical lethality for patients who attempted suicide (A. T. Beck, Beck, & Kovacs, 1975; G. K. Brown, Henriques, Sosdjan,

& Beck, 2004). It was only those patients who had accurate expectations about the likelihood of dying from their attempt who exhibited the expected pattern, such that the resulting degree of danger to their lives was proportional to the degree of suicidal intent.

One important feature of our definition of a suicide attempt is the presence of *any* suicidal intent. Patients would be regarded as having made a suicide attempt even if there was only a slight desire to kill themselves. In other words, professionals who are called on to classify an instance of self-injury behavior make their assessment of intent on the basis of whether there was any intent to die versus absolutely no intent to die. A suicide attempt is distinguishable from *nonsuicidal intentional self-injury behavior*, which is a self-inflicted potentially harmful behavior with no intent to die as its result. When a person either attempts or commits suicide with some intent to die, we say that person engaged in a *suicidal act*.

Another aspect of our definition of a suicide attempt that deserves further discussion is the degree of physical injury that occurs as a result of the behavior. Specifically, the definition indicates that actual physical injury does not necessarily need to occur for a behavior to be classified as a suicide attempt; rather, the definition indicates that there needs to be the *potential* for self-injury. Consider the case in which a person places a loaded gun in his or her mouth and pulls the trigger, but the gun jams and fails to discharge. This behavior would be classified as a suicide attempt according to this definition even though no actual self-injury occurred.

These definitions can be applied to understanding the cases presented at the beginning of this chapter. During her assessment with a clinician, Janice indicated that she had many motivations for swallowing the pills, including wanting to escape, wanting to punish her mother and stepfather, and wanting to die because she did not see a solution to her problems. Although the escape motive was perhaps the most salient of these reasons, her self-injury behavior was classified as a suicide attempt because she had some intent to die. Nick, in contrast, did not remember his intent at the time he jumped from the bridge because of his altered state of consciousness. However, there was indirect evidence to infer that he had some intent to die when he jumped off the bridge, such as his history of multiple attempts, his prediction that he would die before he reaches age 30, and the fact that others were not present, making rescue unlikely. Moreover, during his psychological evaluation, Nick would not deny that his behavior was a suicide attempt. Thus, Nick's behavior is also regarded as a suicide attempt, albeit with less certainty than there is with Janice's suicide attempt. Chad clearly indicated that he wanted to die at the time that he made the superficial wounds on his arms. Although Chad did not inflict medically significant injury on himself, his clinician regarded him as making a suicide attempt because (a) cutting his skin had the potential to cause an injury and (b) he had the intent to kill himself at the time of the act.

As listed in Exhibit 1.1, we define *suicide ideation* as any thoughts, images, beliefs, voices, or other cognitions reported by the person about ending his or her own life (i.e., committing suicide). However, we caution readers in concluding that a patient is characterized by suicide ideation simply because thoughts of killing him- or herself are evident, as there are instances in which a person has an intrusive thought of killing him- or herself (e.g., a person with obsessive–compulsive disorder) but does not have any desire or intent to commit suicide. Thus, suicide ideation is regarded as being more closely related to suicidal acts when it is accompanied by a desire to end one's life. Furthermore, as noted earlier in this chapter, *suicidal intent* refers to having the desire to kill oneself *and* having any intention to act on this desire to kill oneself.

There are several other suicidal behaviors that have recently been used in analyses of clinical trial data (Posner, Oquendo, Stanley, Davies, & Gould, 2007) that are exploratory in nature and in need of further research. These behaviors involve any intent to kill oneself that is not classified as a suicide attempt or a suicide. A person has made an *interrupted attempt* when he or she begins to engage in a potentially self-injurious act with the intent of ending his or her life but is interrupted by another person or external circumstance. In this instance, a suicide attempt would have occurred if the potentially self-injurious act had not been interrupted or prevented. An example of an interrupted attempt is when a person has a gun pointed toward himself and intends to pull the trigger to kill himself but the gun is taken away by someone else. A person has made an *aborted attempt* when he or she intends to kill him- or herself and begins to take steps toward making the attempt but stops before actually engaging in any self-injury behavior. An example of an aborted attempt is when a person is poised to jump from a bridge with the intent to kill herself but turns around and walks away of her own accord. *Preparatory behavior* occurs when a person engages in a behavior with the intention of getting ready to kill him- or herself, such as assembling a specific method of suicide (e.g., stockpiling pills, purchasing a gun) or making other preparations to end his or her life (e.g., giving away important objects, writing a suicide note). We consider the mental activity of planning for an attempt as associated with suicidal desire and intent to commit suicide.

One term that is not part of a standard nomenclature but that we use throughout this book is *suicidal crisis*. We define a suicidal crisis as a discrete, intense episode of suicide ideation accompanied by suicidal desire, a suicide attempt, or other suicide-relevant behavior. Our cognitive therapy protocol is designed to prevent future suicidal acts in patients who have had any type of suicidal crisis.

CLASSIFICATION OF SUICIDE IDEATION AND SUICIDAL ACTS

Classification presupposes an established nomenclature, much in the same way that validity presupposes reliability. Because suicidologists continue to revise the nomenclature that captures suicide ideation and suicidal acts, there is no classification scheme that is widely adopted and implemented by clinicians working with suicidal patients. Nevertheless, there is one approach to classification, devised more than 30 years ago, that has had tremendous influence on the field of suicidology (A. T. Beck et al., 1972). At present, it is this scheme that has the largest body of empirical research supporting its importance in understanding and defining the parameters of suicidal acts. According to this scheme, suicidal phenomena are described as *completed suicides*, *suicide attempts*, or *suicide ideation*. Most contemporary suicidologists now refer to completed suicide as *suicide* or *death by suicide* (cf. Silverman et al., 2007). Each construct is qualified by specific variables, including the certainty of the rater, the lethality of the attempt, intent to die, mitigating circumstances, and method.

A. T. Beck et al. (1972) regarded *certainty* as being useful mainly for research purposes, to establish the reliability between raters. In this scheme, certainty is rated on a continuous scale ranging from 1% to 100%. *Lethality* is defined as "danger to life in a medical, biological sense" and refers to the "deadliness of the suicidal act or contemplated act" (A. T. Beck et al., 1972, p. 9). The rating is based on the objective medical danger associated with the act, not the degree of harm the person anticipated would be associated with the act. It is associated with a past suicide attempt rather than with the risk of future suicidal acts and is rated on a 4-point scale (*zero*, *low*, *medium*, and *high*). In the next section, we describe a measure that quantifies the degree of lethality associated with suicide attempts.

As stated previously, *intent* to die is a key feature that distinguishes between suicidal and nonsuicidal acts. Like lethality, intent is measured on a 4-point scale (*zero*, *low*, *medium*, and *high*). Although a verbal indication of intent might be the most straightforward manner in determining the degree to which the person intended to die as a result of his or her suicide attempt, it has the potential to be of questionable accuracy because of reporting biases. Thus, intent should also be considered in the context of other characteristics, such as the behaviors associated with the suicidal act (e.g., whether the person took precautions so that others would not find him or her), the person's disposition in the time leading up to the suicidal act (e.g., depression, hopelessness), and the person's relevant history that provides a background for the suicidal act (e.g., avoidant problem solving style, history of previous attempts). In the next section, we describe a measure that quantifies many of these aspects of intent.

The final two dimensions of classification proposed by A. T. Beck et al. (1972) are *mitigating circumstances* and *method of attempt*. According to A. T. Beck et al. (1972), mitigating circumstances include "those aspects of age, intelligence, toxicity, and organic or functional illness that might alter the awareness of the patient to the consequences of his action or could temporarily aggravate his propensity toward willful self-destructive behavior"

(p. 10). The presence of a mitigating factor implies that the suicidal act might not otherwise have taken place. Like lethality and intent, it is rated on a 4-point scale (*zero, low, medium,* and *high*). Finally, A. T. Beck et al. (1972) indicated that the method of the attempt should be documented because some methods of attempt are associated with different degrees of lethality, intent, or mitigating circumstances. For example, it is well established that people are much more likely to die by suicide if they use firearms than if they overdose on medications (Shenassa, Catlin, & Buka, 2003). The method of attempt is a descriptive indicator (e.g., "firearms") rather than a rating made on a continuous or ordinal scale.

Table 1.1 summarizes the manner in which the suicidal acts of the three cases presented at the beginning of this chapter would be classified according to this scheme. Janice admitted that she made a suicide attempt with some intent to die by overdosing on sleeping medication; thus, we are 100% certain in designating her behavior as a suicide attempt. There were no mitigating circumstances, as she is a middle-aged woman of average intelligence who was not under the influence of alcohol or drugs and would be expected to understand the consequences of her actions. Her level of intent was rated as medium. On the one hand, her attempt was serious, and she experienced an exacerbation of hopelessness and desperation immediately before the attempt. She indicated that she saw suicide as the only way out of her problems. On the other hand, after she was medically stabilized she admitted that she did not think the dose of medications she took would be lethal. Moreover, she clearly knew her mother and stepfather were in the house, which raises the possibility that she held out some hope that she would be found.

Although Nick's jump from the bridge had the potential to be highly lethal, he was assigned a rating of medium lethality because the only injury he sustained was a minor fracture to his leg. He was rated as having a high level of intent because (a) he has a history of multiple attempts, (b) he anticipates that he will die at a young age and is not afraid of death, and (c) he engages in many risky behaviors that could be construed as being consistent with suicidal desire. However, there are also mitigating circumstances surrounding this attempt, as Nick was under the influence of drugs and does not actually remember the events leading up to the attempt. Thus, the level of mitigation was rated as high, and as a result, the clinician's level of certainty was rated as 50%. Although many aspects of Nick's history would suggest that he made a suicide attempt, it is likely that drug intoxication significantly influenced his behavior.

Finally, Chad's case is one that is often seen by clinicians who specialize in working with children and adolescents. Although Chad made it clear that he intended to kill himself by bleeding to death, the level of lethality was designated as zero because he produced only surface scratches with no bleeding, which required very little wound care. As is discussed at greater length in chapter 11, children and adolescents who make suicide attempts

TABLE 1.1
Classification Scheme: Application

Dimension	Classification
Janice	
Main class	Suicide attempt
Lethality	High
Intent	Medium
Mitigation	Zero
Method	Overdose
Certainty	100%
Nick	
Main class	Suicide attempt
Lethality	Medium
Intent	High
Mitigation	High
Method	Jumping
Certainty	50%
Chad	
Main class	Suicide attempt
Lethality	Zero
Intent	High
Mitigation	Medium
Method	Cutting
Certainty	100%

Note. Source data from Beck et al. (1972).

associated with no or low lethality should be monitored closely for future suicidal behavior, as children often underestimate the lethality of their suicidal acts (H. E. Harris & Myers, 1997). Thus, Chad's clinician rated him as making an attempt with 100% certainty because he clearly expressed intent, but she indicated that his young age is a mitigating circumstance because his stage of cognitive development likely prevented him from fully understanding the consequences of his actions. His level of mitigation was rated as medium because his attempt was clearly associated with a mitigating factor, although he also claimed to have made a conscious, reasoned decision.

ASSESSMENT OF SUICIDE DIMENSIONS

Beck and his colleagues designed several standardized measures that correspond to the classification dimensions, including the degree of intent associated with a previous attempt, the lethality of a previous attempt, and the severity of suicide ideation. Although these scales have been used primarily in research settings, we encourage clinicians to consider implementing them in a standard assessment of high-risk patients because they provide a systematic approach to determining the characteristics of suicide ideation and suicidal acts.

Suicidal Intent

The Suicide Intent Scale (SIS; A. T. Beck, Schuyler, & Herman, 1974) is a clinician-administered measure of the seriousness of the intent to commit suicide among patients who have attempted suicide. The SIS consists of 20 items that quantify a person's verbal and nonverbal behavior before and during the most recent suicide attempt. Each item is rated on an ordinal scale ranging from 0 to 2, and the first 15 items are summed to obtain a total score ranging from 0 to 30. The first part of the SIS (Items 1–8) covers objective circumstances surrounding the suicide attempt and includes items on the preparation and manner of execution of the attempt, the setting, and prior cues given by the patient that could facilitate or hamper the discovery of the attempt. The second part of the SIS (Items 9–15) covers the attempter's subjective perceptions of the method's lethality, expectations about the possibility of rescue and intervention, the extent of premeditation, and the alleged purpose of the attempt. The interview takes about 10 minutes to administer. A self-report version of this scale, the Suicide Intent Questionnaire, is also available and correlates strongly with the interviewer-administered version ($r = .87$; Strosahl, Chiles, & Linehan, 1992).

The SIS has sound psychometric properties, including high internal consistency ($\alpha = .95$; A. T. Beck, Schuyler, et al., 1974) and high interrater reliability, ranging from .81 (Mieczkowski et al., 1993) to .95 (A. T. Beck, Schuyler, et al., 1974). Several studies have found that the objective circumstances section of the SIS differentiates fatal from nonfatal suicide attempts (A. T. Beck, Schuyler, et al., 1974; R. W. Beck, Morris, & Beck, 1974). Further evidence of validity is found in its moderate correlations with measures of depression ($rs = .17–.62$; Minkoff, Bergman, Beck, & Beck, 1973; Silver, Bohnert, Beck, & Marcus, 1971) and hopelessness ($rs = .31–.41$; Kovacs, Beck, & Weissman, 1975; Weissman, Beck, & Kovacs, 1979).

Numerous investigators have conducted factor analyses of the SIS to identify meaningful subscales. For example, A. T. Beck, Weissman, Lester, and Trexler (1976) identified four factors: (a) Expectancies and Attitudes, (b) Premeditation, (c) Precautions Against Intervention, and (d) Oral Communication. Although this factor structure was later replicated (Wetzel, 1977), Mieczkowski et al. (1993) conducted analyses suggesting that the SIS is composed of two dimensions—a Lethal Intent factor and a Planning factor. A. T. Beck and Steer (1989) created subscales for three of the four factors identified by A. T. Beck, Weissman, Lester, et al. (1976): (a) Seriousness, (b) Precautions, and (c) Planning. The Seriousness subscale was calculated by summing ratings on items assessing alleged purpose, expectations of fatality, seriousness of the attempt, attitude toward dying, and conception of rescuability. The Precautions subscale was calculated by summing ratings on items assessing isolation, timing, and precautions against discovery. The Planning subscale was calculated by summing ratings on items assessing final acts, active preparation, writing a suicide note, overt communication of intent, and degree of premeditation. The coefficient alphas for the Seriousness, Precautions, and Planning subscales were .86, .73, and .61, respectively.

The predictive validity of the SIS for suicide has been investigated in a number of studies that included epidemiological community samples (De Leo et al., 2002; Hjelmeland et al., 1998) and hospitalized patients (A. T. Beck & Steer, 1989; Harriss, Hawton, & Zahl, 2005; Hawton & Harriss, 2006; Holmstrand, Niméus, & Träskman-Bendz, 2006; Lindqvist, Niméus, & Träskman-Bendz, 2007; Niméus, Alsen, & Träskman-Bendz, 2002; Pierce, 1987; Samuelsson, Jokinen, Nordström, & Nordström, 2006; Skogman, Alsen, & Ojehagen, 2004; Tejedor, Diaz, Castillon, & Pericay, 1999). Several of these studies found that scores on the SIS predicted death by suicide (Harriss et al., 2005; Hawton & Harriss, 2006; Niméus et al., 2002; Pierce, 1987). Although A. T. Beck and Steer (1989) found that the SIS total score did not predict eventual suicide, they determined that the Precautions subscale of the SIS was associated with an increased risk of eventual suicide. Moreover, there is some evidence that suicide is more strongly associated with scores on the objective circumstances section of the SIS than with scores on the section on patients' perceptions of the attempt (e.g., Harriss et al., 2005).

The SIS can be used as a guide in determining the level of intent associated with the suicide attempts described at the beginning of this chapter. There are no established cutoffs on the SIS that indicate zero, low, medium, and high levels of intent. However, the objective data yielded by this scale can facilitate the application of sound clinical judgment. For example, Janice's responses during the administration of the SIS indicated that she made an attempt characterized by medium intent. Although she was isolated in her room when she made the attempt, her family members were nearby, and intervention was probable. Because she had not contemplated making the attempt ahead of time, she did not make final acts in preparation for death or compose a suicide note. However, she knew that death was a possibility, and she wanted to die to escape her problems. Nick's responses during the administration of the SIS indicated that he made an attempt characterized by high intent. Nobody was in contact with him when he jumped from the bridge, and intervention was unlikely. Although the certainty of his perceptions is questionable because he was under the influence of drugs at the time of his attempt, he could not deny that he intended to commit suicide (and, later in the interview, conceded that it was likely), and he expected that death was certain even if he was rescued by others. Chad's responses during the administration of the SIS also indicated that his attempt was characterized by high intent. He prepared for his attempt by stealing a knife from the kitchen and storing it in the bathroom in the basement, away from traffic. He contemplated suicide for several days and composed a brief suicide note. Moreover, he repeatedly indicated that he wanted to die because he could not stand to be bullied any longer.

The SIS is a widely used measure of the degree of intent to commit suicide during a suicide attempt and assists the clinician in determining whether a patient made a suicide attempt that is consistent with the nomenclature described in this chapter. The research described in this section supports the use of the SIS as part of a suicide risk assessment. In fact, we view suicidal intent as one of the most important variables to consider in determining the suicide risk of individual patients.

Lethality

The Lethality Scales (LS; A. T. Beck, Beck, et al., 1975) were developed to measure the medical lethality of the injury. This instrument consists of eight separate scales that are rated by the clinician according to the method of the attempt (e.g., shooting, jumping, drug overdose). Each scale ranges from 0 (e.g., fully conscious and alert) to 10 (e.g., death). The ratings are based on an examination of the patient's physical condition on admission to the medical, surgical, or psychiatric service and are determined by a review of the medical charts and consultation with the attending physician. Lester and Beck (1975) reported that the LS have high interrater reliability ($r = .80$). Although fewer studies have used the LS than have used the other measures described in this chapter, we advocate for their use in clinical settings, provided that medical records are available, because they provide an objective and systematic approach to quantifying the dimension of lethality.

The LS were used to determine the lethality of Janice's, Nick's, and Chad's suicide attempts. Janice was administered the Lethality Scale for Coma-Producing Drugs. Her mother discovered her a few hours after she made the attempt, at which time she was comatose and unresponsive but breathing normally. These circumstances led the clinician to assign a lethality rating of 8, which corresponds to a highly lethal attempt. Lower ratings are assigned on this scale for attempters who are lethargic or blunted but not unconscious or who are asleep but are easily aroused. As stated previously, Nick's attempt resulted in a minor fracture that required casting, but there was no major tendon damage, and a complete recovery was expected. These injuries corresponded to a lethality rating of 4 using the Lethality Scale for Jumping. A higher rating would have been assigned if Nick had sustained tendon damage, internal bleeding, or major damage to vital areas or if complete recovery was not expected. Chad, in contrast, was assigned a 0 on the Lethality Scale for Cutting because he made only surface scratches. Higher ratings on this scale are assigned to attempters who damage major vessels or who sustain extensive blood loss.

Suicide Ideation

The Scale for Suicide Ideation (SSI; A. T. Beck, Kovacs, & Weissman, 1979) is a 21-item clinician-administered rating scale that measures the current intensity of patients' specific attitudes, behaviors, and plans to commit suicide on the day of the interview. Each item consists of three options graded according to the intensity of suicide ideation on a 3-point scale ranging from 0 to 2. The ratings for the first 19 items are summed to yield a total score ranging from 0 to 38.

The first five items of the SSI are considered screening items. Three of these items assess the wish to live and the wish to die, and the remaining two items assess the desire to attempt suicide by active or passive methods (e.g., overdosing vs. stopping medication that is required to live). Both of these items are consistent with the definition of suicide ideation reported in Exhibit 1.1. If the patient reports any active or passive desire to commit suicide, then the 14 additional items are administered. These items assess characteristics of suicidal thoughts and preparatory acts, such as the duration and frequency of ideation, sense of control over making an attempt, number of deterrents, and amount of actual preparation for a contemplated attempt. Two additional items not included in the total score are the incidence and frequency of previous suicide attempts. The SSI takes approximately 10 minutes to administer. A self-report version of this scale, the Beck Scale for Suicide Ideation (A. T. Beck & Steer, 1991), correlates with the clinician-administered version ($rs = .90–.94$) and has good internal consistency and concurrent validity with measures of related constructs (A. T. Beck, Steer, & Ranieri, 1998; Steer, Rissmiller, Ranieri, & Beck, 1993).

The SSI is a particularly versatile instrument and has been tested in many settings. Specifically, the SSI has been standardized with adult psychiatric patients in inpatient (A. T. Beck, Steer, Kovacs, & Garrison, 1985) and outpatient (A. T. Beck, Brown, & Steer, 1997) settings. It has also been applied in primary care practices, emergency departments, rehabilitation programs, and private practices (e.g., Bruce et al., 2004). In addition, the SSI has been administered to individuals representing many age ranges such as college students (e.g., Clum & Curtin, 1993), adolescents (e.g., de Man & Leduc, 1994), and older adults (e.g., Bruce et al., 2004; Szanto et al., 1996).

The SSI has excellent psychometric properties. For example, it has good internal consistency, with coefficient alphas ranging from .84 (A. T. Beck et al., 1997) to .89 (A. T. Beck, Kovacs, et al., 1979). The SSI also has high interrater reliability, with correlations ranging from .83 (A. T. Beck, Kovacs, et al., 1979) to .98 (Bruce et al., 2004). The SSI correlates positively with the suicide items from the Beck Depression Inventory and the Hamilton Rating Scale for Depression (e.g., A. T. Beck, Kovacs, et al., 1979; Hawton, 1987), with previous suicide attempts, with severity of depression (e.g., A. T.

Beck et al., 1997), and with daily monitoring of suicidal ideation (Clum & Curtin, 1993). The SSI discriminates suicidal inpatients from depressed outpatients (A. T. Beck, Kovacs, et al., 1979) and suicide attempters from nonattempters (Mann, Waternaux, Haas, & Malone, 1999). Moreover, changes in SSI scores correlate moderately with changes in levels of depression ($r = .65$) and hopelessness ($r = .57$) from pretreatment to posttreatment (A. T. Beck, Kovacs, et al., 1979).

The SSI is one of the few measures of suicide ideation with established predictive validity for completed suicide. In a prospective study, we found that patients who scored greater than 2 on this inventory were approximately seven times more likely to commit suicide than those who scored a 2 or below (G. K. Brown, Beck, Steer, & Grisham, 2000). Although suicide ideation is a criterion for a diagnosis of major depressive episode, the G. K. Brown et al. (2000) study determined that the presence of suicide ideation is an independent estimate of suicide risk above and beyond the risk associated with major depression.

The SSI was used to assess suicide ideation in the three cases presented at the beginning of this chapter. Although this measure was administered after their attempts, all three individuals continued to score in a manner suggesting persistent suicide ideation that requires careful monitoring (i.e., Janice's SIS score = 19; Nick's SIS score = 26; and Chad's SIS score = 28). All three individuals endorsed a strong wish to die and that their wish to die outweighed their wish to live. Janice and Nick reported a weak desire to make another suicide attempt, and Chad indicated a strong desire to do so if he continues to be bullied. Janice indicated that she experiences only brief, fleeting suicide ideation, whereas Chad experiences suicide ideation for longer periods, and Nick experiences suicide ideation almost continuously. Both Janice and Nick believed that nothing would deter them from making another attempt, whereas Chad expressed some concern that he would hurt his mother by attempting suicide. Janice and Nick had ideas of how they would attempt suicide in the future, but the details were not well planned. In contrast, Chad had a well-formulated plan (i.e., to cut his wrists). Janice was unsure whether she had the courage to make another attempt, whereas Nick and Chad were confident that they would be able to carry out an attempt.

As mentioned in the Introduction, the SSI has been adapted for measuring the intensity of specific attitudes, behaviors, and plans to commit suicide during the time period that the individual was the most suicidal (Scale for Suicide Ideation—Worst Point [SSI–W]; A. T. Beck, Brown, Steer, Dahlsgaard, & Grisham, 1999). Patients are instructed to recall the approximate date and circumstances when they were experiencing the most intense desire to commit suicide. They are then asked to keep this experience in mind while the clinician rates their responses to the 19 SSI items regarding how suicidal they were at that time. The predictive validity of the SSI–W for suicide has been established, such that psychiatric patients who scored in the higher risk category (i.e., SSI–W total score greater than 16) are 14 times more likely to commit suicide than patients who scored in the lower risk category (A. T. Beck et al., 1999).

Suicide ideation can also be screened using the single Suicidal Thoughts and Wishes item from the Beck Depression Inventory—II (A. T. Beck, Steer, & Brown, 1996). Patients assign one of four ratings to characterize their desire to commit suicide—0 (i.e., "I don't have any thoughts of killing myself"), 1 (i.e., "I have thoughts of killing myself, but I would not carry them out"), 2 (i.e., "I would like to kill myself"), or 3 (i.e., "I would kill myself if I had the chance"). A rating of 2 or higher on this item is consistent with our definition of suicide ideation with suicidal desire. Our research group has found that the psychiatric outpatients from G. K. Brown et al.'s (2000) study who scored a 2 or higher on this measure were 6.9 times more likely to die by suicide than patients who scored below 2. Although the SSI and the Beck Scale for Suicide Ideation provide a more comprehensive picture of a patient's suicide ideation, this single item has the potential to be useful in screening for suicidal thoughts and wishes when the clinician does not have the means to conduct a comprehensive psychological assessment.

SUMMARY AND INTEGRATION

This chapter has presented the standard nomenclature that is used throughout the remainder of the book. Suicide ideation, suicide attempts, and suicide are mutually exclusive categories that are differentiated by (a) whether the person engaged in an act to kill him- or herself (i.e., whether harm actually occurred) and (b) whether the person is still alive. In contrast, other terms presented in this chapter are dimensional in nature and characterize the degree of seriousness of the suicidal thought or act, such as intent and medical lethality. All of these variables are important to assess in a clinical context, as the higher a patient's loading on these dimensions, the higher the probability that he or she will engage in a future suicidal act.

Research has demonstrated that there is much disagreement among clinicians when they are called on to determine whether a patient made an attempt (Wagner et al., 2002). Our experience tells us that many clinicians do not have operational definitions of these constructs to guide their clinical decisions. Adherence to the definitions presented in this chapter is one important step clinicians can take in identifying suicidal patients. We also encourage the use of the standardized assessments to quantify the full range of suicide ideation and intent in individual patients. In addition to the measures described in this chapter, there are many other instruments available in the field that assess these constructs for children (see Goldston, 2003, for a review), adults, and older adults (see G. K. Brown, 2002, for a review) that can be easily administered in clinical settings. Many items on these instruments assess aspects of suicidal thoughts and wishes that may not immediately come to a clinician's mind (e.g., whether a person would take precautions to keep him- or herself alive, such as taking prescribed medications for a medical illness). Although these measures take time to administer, we find that they provide valuable information that will help the clinician to arrive at a judgment with confidence about a patient's risk for engaging in future suicidal acts and the level of care that is required to keep the patient safe.

2

CORRELATES OF AND RISK FACTORS FOR SUICIDAL ACTS

How does the clinician determine who is at risk to attempt suicide? This question has been a central one in the suicide literature for more than 50 years. As is shown in this chapter, there are many characteristics that distinguish between those who do and those who do not engage in suicidal acts. No single one of these variables is sufficient to trigger a suicidal act, and in fact, these factors accumulate and interact to increase a person's vulnerability for suicidal behavior (Mościcki, 1999). Unfortunately, a working knowledge of these variables is often difficult to apply in an evaluation of any one patient because the vast majority of individuals characterized by them do not go on to attempt or commit suicide (Murphy, 1984; Paris, 2006).

Nevertheless, a sound assessment of the degree to which a patient is characterized by variables associated with suicidal acts can accomplish two important clinical goals. First, it can guide the clinician in selecting the appropriate level of care (e.g., weekly outpatient visits, partial hospitalization program, inpatient hospitalization) on the basis of the number and severity of these variables that a particular patient endorses or exhibits. Second, it provides the clinician with the beginnings of the cognitive case conceptualization of patients' clinical presentation (see chap. 7), such that distal background factors and immediate precursors for suicidal acts can be hypothesized. This framework, in turn, provides logical points of intervention in subsequent treatment. We discuss variables relevant to suicide attempts and deaths by suicide in adults that fall into four main categories: (a) demographic variables, (b) diagnostic variables, (c) psychiatric history variables, and (d) psychological variables.

The astute reader will notice that we have avoided using the term *risk factor* to this point in the chapter. According to Kraemer et al. (1997), a risk factor is a "measurable *characterization* of each *subject* in a specified *population* that precedes the outcome of interest and which can be used to divide the population into 2 groups (the high-risk and the low-risk groups that comprise the total population)" (p. 338). Inherent in this definition is that the characteristic must precede the outcome. In contrast, a great deal of the research examining variables unique to suicidal patients uses cross-sectional or retrospective research designs, such that researchers compare individuals who have and have not attempted or committed suicide to determine what is different about the suicidal patients. These studies are valuable and provide rich information about the concomitants of suicidal acts. However, they do not necessarily identify factors that put individuals at risk for suicidal acts because risk factors can only be labeled as such if they are demonstrated empirically to be present before the event under observation (i.e., a suicide attempt or death). Instead, we regard these factors as *correlates* of suicidal acts, or as variables that have been found in empirical research to be associated with suicidal acts. We use the term *risk factor* when variables are investigated in prospective designs, in which research participants are assessed at the time they enroll in the study and are tracked over time to determine the degree to which particular variables predict those who eventually engage in suicidal acts (Kraemer et al., 1997). We encourage clinicians to give established risk factors the greatest weight in determining suicide risk in their individual patients.

DEMOGRAPHIC VARIABLES

Demographic variables associated with suicidal acts are, perhaps, of least interest to the clinician because many of these factors cannot be modified in treatment (e.g., age, gender). Nevertheless, clinicians should be aware of these high-risk demographic groups so that they can consider this knowledge as they determine the appropriate level of monitoring and care for individual patients. For example, it is well established that men are more likely to die by suicide than are women (e.g., Oquendo et al., 2001; Suokas, Suominen, Isometsä, Ostamo, & Lönnqvist, 2001), perhaps because men are more likely than women to use lethal means (Denning, Conwell, King, & Cox, 2000). Although many studies have found that more women than men attempt sui-

TABLE 2.1
Suicide Rates by Gender and Ethnicity in the United States: 1999–2003

Race/ethnicity	Gender	
	Male, all ages	Female, all ages
Non-Hispanic White	21.1	5.0
Non-Hispanic Black	9.8	1.8
Hispanic	9.8	1.7
American Indian or Alaskan Native	16.7	3.9
Asian/Pacific Islander	8.3	3.0

Note. All values are reported in terms of number of suicides per 100,000 people. Source data retrieved from http://www.cdc.gov/nchs/health_data_for_all_ages.htm

cide (e.g., Roy & Janal, 2006), other research has demonstrated that men make more attempts than women when the behavior is motivated by the intent to die rather than by the intent to communicate something to others (Nock & Kessler, 2006). In addition, death by suicide is more common in older (Loebel, 2005), lower socioeconomic status (Beautrais, 2001; Kreitman, Carstairs, & Duffy, 1991), and veteran (Kaplan, Huguet, McFarland, & Newsom, 2007) populations. There are no national statistics for death by suicide as a function of sexual orientation because sexual orientation is not indicated on state death certificates. However, results from empirical research have shown that men who had at least one same-sex partner over the past 5 years are 2.4 times more likely to have attempted suicide than men who report having only opposite-sex partners over the past 5 years. In contrast, there is no difference in the prevalence of attempts in women as a function of their partner's gender over the past 5 years (Gilman et al., 2001).

Epidemiological research has demonstrated that death by suicide varies tremendously by race and ethnicity. Table 2.1 displays suicide rates as a function of gender and ethnicity in the United States between 1999 and 2003. Across all racial and ethnic groups, the rate of suicide for men is substantially higher than the rate of suicide for women, with rates consistently higher in non-Hispanic White individuals than in individuals of other ethnicities. However, some research has suggested that suicide rates are increasing dramatically among young African American men (see Joe & Kaplan, 2001, for a review). As seen in Table 2.1, the suicide rate in American Indian and Alaskan Native individuals is higher than that for any other non-Caucasian racial or ethnic group, although it should be acknowledged that rates vary among tribes, with some tribes reporting as many as 150 suicides per 100,000 people and others reporting zero suicides per 100,000 people (L. M. Olson & Wahab, 2006).

Variables such as age, gender, socioeconomic status, sexual orientation, race, and ethnicity have been identified as risk factors in several prospective research designs, and even when they emerge as correlates in cross-sectional or retrospective designs, they are generally viewed as risk factors for suicidal acts because they are obviously in place before the suicidal act is observed. Kraemer et al. (1997) referred to these variables as fixed markers. We regard these risk factors as important but distant background variables, in contrast to those that exert great influence in the time immediately preceding the attempt.

Some demographic variables that distinguish between suicidal and nonsuicidal individuals can change over the course of a person's life, although they are much less malleable than the psychological variables that we discuss later in this chapter and that are often targeted in psychotherapy. For example, several prospective studies have found that unemployment predicts suicide above and beyond many other established risk factors (A. T. Beck & Steer, 1989; G. K. Brown, Beck, Steer, & Grisham, 2000). Some studies have demonstrated that individuals who attempt suicide (Mann et al., 1999) and those who die by suicide (Beautrais, 2001) have fewer years of education than nonsuicidal individuals. In addition, many studies have shown that suicidal patients are more likely to be single (Pokorny, 1983), divorced (Cantor & Slater, 1995), or widowed (Stroebe, Stroebe, & Abakoumkin, 2005) relative to nonsuicidal patients receiving psychiatric care. Data from the National Longitudinal Mortality Study, a large epidemiological study using a nationally representative sample of adults, indicated that individuals who are divorced or separated are twice as likely to commit suicide than married persons (Kposowa, 2000). It is possible that the relation between the absence of a marital partner and suicidal acts can be explained by a broader problem, such as social isolation. Empirical research has demonstrated that social isolation is strongly associated with death by suicide (see Trout, 1980, for a review). Unlike many of the other variables discussed in this section, social isolation is a problem involving many psychological factors that can be addressed in psychotherapy. As is seen in Part II of this volume, one major component of our treatment program involves assisting suicidal patients to develop their social support networks, which we expect will reduce their sense of social isolation.

Thus, research on demographic variables associated with suicidal acts has suggested that older men who are of low socioeconomic status and who are single, divorced, or widowed are at especially high risk for suicide. Of course, the vast majority of individuals characterized by these demographic variables do not engage in suicidal acts, suggesting that a model of suicidal acts informed only by these factors would be far from complete. Moreover, the identification of demographic variables associated with suicidal acts does not speak to the specific mechanism by which suicidal crises are activated in these vulnerable individuals. Therefore, it is imperative to interpret these demographic risk factors in the context of the psychological symptoms and processes that are known to be at work in suicidal patients.

DIAGNOSTIC VARIABLES

Medical illnesses, such as AIDS, cancer, chronic obstructive pulmonary disease, chronic pain, end-stage renal disease, and severe neurological disorders, are associated with an increased risk for suicide ideation, suicide attempts, and death by suicide (Hughes & Kleespies, 2001; Levenson & Bostwick, 2005). In their review of suicide and medical illness, Hughes and Kleespies (2001) indicated that between 30% and 40% of individuals who die by suicide have a medical illness; however, these rates vary according to age, such that they are lower in younger adults who have committed suicide and higher in older adults who have committed suicide. Although the presence of a medical illness rarely increases suicide risk in and of itself, it often increases vulnerability to suicide through the activation of hopelessness, perceived lack of meaning in life, and loss of important social roles (Levenson & Bostwick, 2005), as well as through the onset of comorbid psychiatric symptoms (E. C. Harris & Barraclough, 1994; Suominen, Isometsä, Heila, Lönnqvist, & Henriksson, 2002).

The presence of one or more type of psychiatric disturbance is a central variable in explaining suicidal acts, as 90% or more of individuals who die by suicide are diagnosed with one or more psychiatric disorders (e.g., Beautrais et al., 1996; Bertolote, Fleischmann, De Leo, & Wasserman, 2003; Suominen et al., 1996). We define *psychiatric disturbance* as an instance in which a person meets criteria for one or more psychiatric disorders or reports or exhibits psychiatric symptoms associated with life interference, subjective distress, or both. Psychiatric disturbance can be determined either by a diagnostic interview that establishes psychiatric diagnoses or by an inventory that yields a score on a dimension of psychiatric symptoms (e.g., the Beck Depression Inventory). Perhaps the most comprehensive analysis of suicide risk associated with psychiatric disturbance was conducted by E. C. Harris and Barraclough (1997), who assembled studies published between 1966 and 1993 that had followed cohorts of patients with at least one psychiatric disorder for at least 2 years. They calculated standardized mortality ratios for each major psychiatric disorder by averaging observed rates of suicide deaths relative to expected rates of suicide deaths.

Of all of the types of psychiatric disturbance, the relation between depression and suicidal acts has been studied the most extensively (Lönnqvist, 2000), perhaps because suicide ideation and suicide attempts are implicated in one criterion that contributes to the diagnosis of major depressive disorder. Approximately 15% of patients with major depressive disorder report that they have made a suicide attempt at some point in their lives (Chen & Dilsaver, 1996). Between 2% and 12% of individuals with major depressive disorder die by suicide (Bostwick & Pankrantz, 2000), and conversely, more than 50% of individuals who die by suicide are diagnosed with major depressive disorder (Bertolote et al., 2003). In their meta-analysis of suicide risk associated with various psychiatric disorders, E. C. Harris and Barraclough (1997) determined that the risk of a depressed individual dying by suicide is 20 times greater than that which would be expected for nondepressed individuals with similar demographic characteristics.

Bipolar disorder is also strongly associated with suicidal acts. For example, Chen and Dilsaver (1996) found that 29% of their bipolar sample reported that they had made at least one suicide attempt, and E. C. Harris and Barraclough (1997) calculated that the risk of suicide in bipolar patients was approximately 15 times greater than that which would be expected for nonbipolar individuals with similar demographic characteristics. Results from Hawton, Sutton, Haw, Sinclair, and Harriss's (2005) meta-analysis suggested that the subset of bipolar patients who are admitted to the hospital for depression, present for treatment with a mixed affective state, or are diagnosed with a rapid cycling disorder are most likely to attempt suicide after they are released from the hospital. In other words, bipolar disorder is associated with suicidal behavior, but it appears that bipolar patients are at greatest risk to engage in suicidal acts when they are in the depressive or mixed affective phase of their illness (Maser et al., 2002). In contrast, some research has shown that bipolar patients treated with lithium prophylaxis have comparatively low rates of suicide (Müller-Oerlinghausen, Muser-Causemann, & Volk, 1992).

In addition to mood disorders, substance use disorders are frequently identified as diagnostic factors that put individuals at risk for suicidal acts. According to Inskip, Harris, and Barraclough (1998), between 7% and 8% of individuals with alcohol dependence die by suicide. A diagnosis of alcohol abuse or dependence is associated with a suicide risk that is almost six times greater than that which would be expected in nonalcoholic individuals with similar demographic characteristics (E. C. Harris & Barraclough, 1997). Some research has shown that the suicide risk is particularly high for heavy drinkers, whereas the suicide risk for moderate drinkers is only slightly elevated (e.g., Andréasson & Romelsjo, 1988). E. C. Harris and Barraclough (1997) also determined that the risk for suicide in individuals with a drug abuse or dependence disorder is, depending on the particular drug under consideration, between 4 and 20 times that which would be expected for non–drug-dependent individuals with similar demographic characteristics. The risk for suicidal acts increases even more in the context of polydrug use (E. C. Harris & Barraclough, 1997; Vingoe, Welch, Farrell, & Strang, 1999) and comorbidity with another psychiatric disorder (Prigerson, Desai, Lui-Mares, & Rosenheck, 2003). We revisit the issue of suicidal acts in patients with substance use disorders in chapter 13.

Schizophrenia and schizophrenia spectrum disorders are also associated with elevated risk of suicide attempts and deaths; according to E. C. Harris and Barraclough (1997), patients with schizophrenia have a risk of suicide that is 8.5 times greater than would be expected for nonschizophrenic individuals with similar demographic characteristics. As many as 40% of patients with psychotic disorders attempt suicide at some point in their lives (Meltzer, 2003), and 9% to 13% eventually die by suicide (e.g., Caldwell & Gottesman, 1990). Variables that make schizophrenic patients especially vulnerable to suicidal acts include depression (e.g., Heila et al., 1997; Steblaj, Tavcar, & Dernovsek, 1999), hopelessness (Drake & Cotton, 1986), positive symptoms (e.g., Fenton, McGlashan, Vistor, & Blyer, 1997), social withdrawal (Steblaj et al., 1999), lack of insight (Steblaj et al., 1999), and acute onset (Mortensen & Juel, 1993). Command hallucinations to harm oneself have also been associated with self-injury behavior (e.g., Rogers, Watt, Gray, MacCulloch, & Gournay, 2002). Thus, it is possible that the risk of suicidal acts is elevated in two types of psychotic patients—those who are depressed and those who experience florid positive symptoms.

Research has also shown that risk for suicidal acts is high in patients with certain Axis II diagnoses (e.g., Allebeck & Allgulander, 1990; Mann et al., 1999). For example, in one longitudinal study, approximately 20% of patients with borderline personality disorder made a suicide attempt in a 2-year period (Yen et al., 2003). Patients with this diagnosis report an average of three lifetime suicide attempts (Soloff, Lis, Kelly, Cornelius, & Ulrich, 1994). In addition, individuals with antisocial personality disorder who exhibit the specific feature of antisocial deviance are at increased risk to engage in suicidal acts (e.g., Verona, Patrick, & Joiner, 2001). It is possible that a common variable, such as impulsivity, could explain the high prevalence of suicide attempts and deaths in patients with these disorders.

Anxiety is the only type of psychiatric disturbance for which there is mixed evidence that it elevates the risk of suicidal acts. In their meta-analysis, E. C. Harris and Barraclough (1997) determined that "anxiety neurosis" was associated with a suicide risk 6 times that which would be expected in the general population, that obsessive–compulsive disorder was associated with a suicide risk 10 times that which would be expected, and that panic disorder was associated with a suicide risk 10 times that which would be expected. However, these rates were based on the results of only one to two studies associated with each type of anxiety disorder. In contrast, A. T. Beck, Steer, Sanderson, and Skeie (1991) found evidence suggesting that panic disorder is only an indirect risk factor for suicidal acts, as the suicide risk increases only in those panic patients with a comorbid mood or substance use disorder.

Thus, a number of types of psychiatric disturbance are associated with attempted suicide and suicide, including major depression, bipolar disorder, substance dependence disorders, psychotic disorders, and some Axis II disorders, particularly those in Cluster B. In fact, E. C. Harris and Barraclough (1997) concluded that "virtually all mental disorders have an increased risk of suicide excepting mental retardation and possibly dementia and agoraphobia" (p. 222). Despite the fact that empirical research has established a close association between diagnoses of psychiatric disorders and suicidal acts, the presence of a disorder does not explain why people attempt suicide, as the majority of individuals with psychiatric disturbance do not engage in suicidal acts. In chapter 3, we explain the manner in which cognitive distortions and emotional distress associated with psychiatric disturbance accumulate and increase the probability that cognitive structures specifically associated with suicidal acts are activated.

PSYCHIATRIC HISTORY VARIABLES

Perhaps the most potent predictor of suicide is the presence of a previous attempt (e.g., Beautrais, 2001; Blumenthal, Bell, Neumann, Schuttler, & Vogel, 1989; Oquendo et al., 2004; Suokas et al., 2001), especially in the 1st year following discharge from the hospital for that attempt (Nordström, Åsberg, Åberg-Wistedt, & Nordin, 1995). E. C. Harris and Barraclough (1997) estimated that individuals who have made a previous suicide attempt are 38 to 40 times more likely to eventually die by suicide than would be expected. Previous attempts predict suicide in a number of contexts, from suicide committed while on an inpatient unit (Krupinski et al., 1998) to years later after release from the hospital (e.g., Goldstein, Black, Nasrallah, & Winokur, 1991) or termination from outpatient treatment (e.g., G. K. Brown et al., 2000). Joiner, Conwell, et al. (2005) demonstrated that a history of a previous attempt remains significantly associated with suicide ideation even when a host of other well-established risk factors for suicidal acts are accounted for in analyses. Multiple suicide attempts, in particular, are associated with an increased risk for subsequent suicidal behavior (e.g., Oquendo et al., 2007). In fact, Carter, Reith, Whyte, and McPherson (2005) found that many individuals who make multiple attempts do so with increasing severity, and increasing severity of attempts is associated with higher rates of suicide deaths. Research by Rudd, Joiner, and Rajab (1996) raised the possibility that multiple attempters are at particular risk for committing suicide because they are characterized by more severe psychiatric disturbance than patients who have made a single attempt and those who report suicide ideation but who have never made an attempt.

Although not a psychiatric diagnosis, a history of childhood abuse is associated with increased levels of psychiatric disturbance and with an increased likelihood of engaging in suicidal acts. Many studies have found an association between childhood physical or sexual abuse and a history of suicide attempts (e.g., Anderson, Tiro, Price, Bender, & Kaslow, 2002; Glowinski et al., 2001; Joiner et al., 2007; McHolm, MacMillan, & Jamieson, 2003; Roy, 2003a, 2003b). Furthermore, some studies have shown that childhood physical and sexual abuse is more likely to be reported in patients who have made multiple suicide attempts than in those who have attempted only once

(J. Brown, Cohen, Johnson, & Smailes, 1999; Talbot, Duberstein, Cox, Denning & Conwell, 2004; Ystgaard, Hestetun, Loeb, & Mehlum, 2004). In a study using data from the National Comorbidity Survey, Joiner et al. (2007) concluded that childhood physical and violent sexual abuse should be seen as greater risk factors for future suicide attempts than other forms of abuse, such as molestation and verbal abuse. Together, these studies indicate that childhood physical and sexual abuse should be assessed when evaluating suicide risk.

Specific features of a patient's psychiatric and treatment history are also important in understanding suicidal acts. Goldstein et al. (1991) determined that chronicity of the index episode of the psychiatric diagnosis at the time of hospitalization was associated with increased risk for suicide many years later. Some studies have found that patients receiving psychiatric treatment who commit suicide are more likely than psychiatric patients who do not commit suicide to have had previous pharmacotherapy (e.g., G. K. Brown et al., 2000; Dahlsgaard, Beck, & Brown, 1998), previous psychotherapy (G. K. Brown et al., 2000), or previous psychiatric hospitalizations (e.g., Beautrais, 2001; G. K. Brown et al., 2000). These data suggest that long-standing psychiatric disturbance, as evidenced by a chronic psychiatric disorder or previous treatment, puts individuals at risk for engaging in suicidal acts. In addition, noncompliance with treatment may also be associated with suicide. Dahlsgaard et al. (1998) found that those who had died by suicide were more likely than other patients to have prematurely dropped out of psychotherapy, to have attended fewer sessions, and to have endorsed higher levels of hopelessness at the time of their final session. Conversely, Goldstein et al. (1991) found that a favorable response to treatment mitigated against eventual suicide, raising the possibility that patients' success in their current treatment regimen has lasting implications for their safety. Although the issue is not well researched, we propose that patients' negative expectations for psychiatric treatment—including their hopelessness and ambivalence about treatment—are likely to be related to treatment noncompliance and, ultimately, to suicidal acts. We revisit the clinical implications of this issue in chapter 6.

Finally, a family history of suicide is also associated with suicide attempts (Murphy & Wetzel, 1982; Sorenson & Rutter, 1991) and deaths (Cheng, Chen, Chen, & Jenkins, 2000). Furthermore, a family history of suicidal acts distinguishes between individuals who made single or multiple attempts, with those who made multiple attempts being more likely to have at least one family member who attempted or died by suicide (Forman, Berk, Henriques, Brown, & Beck, 2004). Relative to those without a family history of suicide, individuals who have attempted suicide and who have a family history of suicide attempts or deaths are characterized by elevated levels of depression and hopelessness (Jeglic, Sharp, Chapman, Brown, & Beck, 2005), which likely contributes further to the risk of engaging in suicidal acts.

How might these psychiatric history variables make a person vulnerable to engage in suicidal acts? As is described in chapter 3, the more severe a person's psychiatric disturbance, the more likely it is that he or she will experience negative cognitive distortions and information processing biases that exacerbate mood disturbance and functional impairment. A history of abuse further contributes to the development of maladaptive beliefs about the self, world, or future. According to cognitive theory, a history of psychiatric disturbance or negative childhood experiences increases the ease with which these negative cognitive patterns will be activated in the future. When a person has attempted suicide in the past, it increases the likelihood that cognitive patterns specifically related to suicide will be activated. A family psychiatric history certainly increases the probability that a person will also experience psychiatric disturbance, which is associated with the cognitive patterns described earlier. Furthermore, there is evidence for genetic transmission of increased risk of suicidal acts above and beyond genetic transmission of risk for psychiatric disturbance (see Brent & Mann, 2005, for a review), with approximately 43% of the variance in suicidal behavior explained by genetics (Bondy, Buettner, & Zill, 2006). In fact, genetic transmission of suicide attempts is particularly likely when there is a history of sexual abuse in both the proband and offspring (Brent et al., 2002). Thus, it is likely that these psychiatric history variables increase the risk of suicidal acts through psychological, environmental, and biological pathways.

PSYCHOLOGICAL VARIABLES

In contrast to demographic and psychiatric history variables, psychological variables (i.e., those that are cognitive, affective, or behavioral in nature) are indeed able to be modified through targeted psychotherapeutic interventions. We believe that many of these variables explain, at least in part, the association between demographic, diagnostic, and psychiatric history variables and suicide ideation and suicidal acts. That is, these variables have the potential to account for the mechanism by which suicidal acts are manifest in a particular person. Next we present five classes of psychological variables that have been considered at length in the literature: (a) hopelessness, (b) suicide-relevant cognitions, (c) heightened impulsivity, (d) problem solving deficits, and (e) perfectionism. Many of these variables are prominent in our cognitive model that we describe in chapter 3.

Hopelessness

Any thoughtful person, when asked to explain why someone attempted or died by suicide, would point his or her finger at depression. Indeed, as was demonstrated earlier in the chapter, depression is a significant predictor of suicide attempts and deaths. However, any theory that explains suicidal acts must take into account that the vast majority of depressed people do not attempt to take their own lives, even if they think about it from time to time. This realization led clinical researchers to consider whether there is a specific aspect of depression that is relevant to understanding the experience of the subset of depressed individuals who are suicidal. More than 30 years ago, Beck and his colleagues identified one such depressive feature—hopelessness.

As described in the Introduction, cross-sectional research by Beck and his research team determined that high levels of hopelessness, regardless of the level of depressive symptoms, were associated with high levels of suicidal intent (A. T. Beck, Kovacs, & Weissman, 1975; Kovacs, Beck, & Weissman, 1975; Minkoff, Bergman, Beck, & Beck, 1973). In addition, prospective research revealed that hopelessness predicted eventual suicide in inpatients hospitalized for suicide ideation (A. T. Beck, Steer, Kovacs, & Garrison, 1985) and outpatients (A. T. Beck, Brown, Berchick, Stewart, & Steer, 1990) up to 10 years later. A meta-analysis by McMillan, Gilbody, Beresford, and Neilly (2007) indicated that hopelessness increases the risk of eventual suicide at least threefold. Moreover, it appears that stable levels of hopelessness that persist over time are even stronger predictors of suicidal acts than hopelessness as measured on only one occasion (cf. Dahlsgaard et al., 1998; Young et al., 1996). In the next chapter, we propose a cognitive theory of suicidal acts that explains the manner in which stable, or traitlike, hopelessness makes a person vulnerable to engage in a suicidal act and the manner in which statelike hopelessness operates at the time of a suicidal crisis.

Suicide-Relevant Cognitions

As described in the previous chapter, suicide ideation is a central component of suicidal acts, and as would be expected, empirical research has demonstrated that suicide ideation is a robust predictor of suicide attempts and deaths. For example, suicide ideation at admission to the hospital predicted those who would later die by suicide while on an inpatient unit (e.g., Krupinski et al., 1998) and after being released from the hospital up to 13 years later (Goldstein et al., 1991). As noted earlier, suicide ideation is an especially potent predictor of eventual suicide when patients are asked to describe their ideation at its worst point in their lives, as compared to ideation or hopelessness at the time of the current assessment (A. T. Beck et al., 1999). In addition, in the previous chapter we indicated that suicidal intent is a crucial factor in classifying the nature of the self-injury behavior. Like suicide ideation, suicidal intent is fundamentally a cognitive variable, as it is characterized by mental acts associated with the motivation to commit suicide. Research has demonstrated that suicidal intent is positively associated with the demographic and clinical variables known to put individuals at risk for an attempt (Pallis & Sainsbury, 1976) and that suicidal intent associated with an index attempt predicts eventual suicide over approximately a 5-year period (Harriss & Hawton, 2005; Harriss, Hawton, & Zahl, 2005). Thus, not only are suicide ideation and suicide intent central characteristics of a patient's current suicidal crisis, they also are associated with the probability of eventually dying by suicide. In the next chapter, we explain the manner in which these suicide-relevant cognitions narrow the attention of suicidal patients on suicide as their only option during suicidal crises and the manner in which they contribute to the development of suicide-relevant cognitive structures over the long term.

Another cognitive variable related to suicide acts is the presence of homicidal ideation or intent because both are associated with aggression and violence. Surprisingly, only a few studies have examined the association between homicidal ideation and suicidal behavior. In one exception, Asnis, Kaplan, van Praag, and Sanderson (1994) indicated that psychiatric outpatients who made a past homicide attempt reported elevated rates of suicide ideation and suicide attempts. Despite the paucity of research on this topic, it is recommended that clinicians assess for homicidal ideation and behavior during a clinical interview when assessing for other suicide-relevant cognitions (e.g., R. I. Simon, 2004) because they have an ethical and legal responsibility to protect others' lives as well as their patients' (VandeCreek & Knapp, 2001).

Heightened Impulsivity

Impulsivity is perhaps the most widely studied individual difference variable in studies designed to identify factors that explain why people attempt suicide. Unfortunately, most research that has examined the association between impulsivity and suicidal acts has done so in the context of cross-sectional rather than prospective designs, and as a whole, this literature has yielded equivocal findings that are far from straightforward. One major problem that limits our understanding of impulsivity's relation to suicidal acts is the minimal agreement among researchers on the operational definition of impulsivity (Endicott & Ogloff, 2006). Some regard impulsivity as a personality trait characterized by an emphasis on the present, rapid decision making, the failure to consider the consequences of one's actions, disorganization, and/or the failure to plan ahead (e.g., Barratt, 1959). Others regard impulsivity as a behavioral style of responding in specific situations, such as the inability to inhibit responding (e.g., Dougherty et al., 2004; Swann et al., 2005). When both approaches to measuring impulsivity are examined in the same study, they are often not associated with one another (e.g., Swann et al., 2005), which raises the possibility that there are many facets of what is traditionally regarded as impulsivity.

The majority of empirical studies that have examined the association between impulsivity and suicidal acts regard impulsivity as a personality trait and measure it using a self-report inventory, the Barratt Impulsiveness Scale (BIS; Barratt, 1959; Patton, Stanford, & Barratt, 1995). Individuals who complete the BIS are asked to rate items such as "I am more interested in the present than I am in the future," "I am a careful thinker," and "I don't pay attention." If individuals who attempt suicide are characterized by heightened impulsivity and if impulsivity is considered a stable, traitlike characteristic, then one would expect that individuals with a history of suicide attempts would score higher on this measure than individuals who have never attempted suicide. Such findings would suggest that impulsivity is a correlate of suicidal acts.

Researchers who have conducted such studies sometimes find this association (e.g., Mann et al., 1999; Michaelis et al., 2004) and sometimes find no association (e.g., Roy, 2001). Baca-Garcia et al. (2005) divided their sample of suicide attempters into those who made impulsive attempts (defined as being characterized by a lack of premeditation) and those who did not make impulsive attempts. Contrary to expectation, groups did not differ in their BIS scores. We suggest two possibilities for these unexpected findings: (a) that suicidal patients in these studies lacked insight into their global behavioral tendencies, making their responses on inventories like these inaccurate (see Burdick, Endick, & Goldberg, 2005) or (b) that items on the BIS fail to assess impulsivity that is manifest specifically in times of emotional distress when a suicidal act would occur. The literature also points to a third option; there is evidence that BIS scores considered simultaneously with scores on measures assessing aggression and hostility distinguish attempters from nonattempters (Mann et al., 1999), raising the possibility that impulsivity is only one component of a larger *disinhibitory psychopathology* construct that better characterizes externalizing behavior in suicidal patients.

How does one make sense of the mixed results in this literature? We suspect that suicidal individuals are not uniformly impulsive, but that impulsivity characterizes a subset of suicidal patients and that it increases risk through indirect means, such as providing the context for more central risk factors to emerge when they otherwise would not (e.g., alcohol and drug use). In addition, it is likely that impulsivity works in conjunction with a number of other variables to increase the likelihood that a person will experience symptoms consistent with various types of psychiatric disturbance and that cognitive and behavioral tendencies associated with suicide ideation and suicidal acts will be activated. Thus, we regard impulsivity as one of many *dispositional vulnerability factors* that operate in some, but not all, suicidal patients and that exacerbate stress, general psychiatric disturbance, and cognitive process associated with suicide. This idea is elucidated to a greater degree in chapter 3.

Problem Solving Deficits

Problem solving deficits have long been investigated in relation to suicidal acts, as it is common to encounter suicidal patients who indicate that they made their attempt because they could see no way out of their life circumstances. In fact, our treatment package for suicidal patients described in Part II is based on the premise that a suicide attempt is, in part, a maladaptive approach to problem solving. A body of empirical research has suggested that problem solving deficits are indeed associated with suicide-relevant variables. However, nearly all of the studies examining the association between problem solving deficits and suicide-relevant constructs have focused only on suicide ideation, rather than suicide attempts and deaths, and, like impulsivity, problem solving deficits have been defined in many different ways.

A great deal of research has demonstrated that individuals who endorse suicide ideation are characterized by poorer problem solving skills than individuals who do not endorse suicide ideation. This finding emerges when problem solving is conceptualized as the inability to generate solutions to problems (e.g., Priester & Clum, 1993; Schotte & Clum, 1982, 1987), the focus on negative outcomes to proposed solutions (e.g., Schotte & Clum, 1987), avoidance of attempts to solve problems (e.g., Orbach, Bar-Joseph, & Dror, 1990), and low expectations of one's ability to solve problems (i.e., low problem-solving self-efficacy; Dixon, Heppner, & Anderson, 1991; Rudd, Rajab, & Dahm, 1994). Far fewer studies have examined the degree to which problem solving deficits predict suicide ideation at a later time. In one exception, Priester and Clum (1993) demonstrated that the ability to generate alternative solutions interacts with stress to predict suicide ideation in university students, such that students who were experiencing high stress and had trouble generating relevant alternate solutions to problems endorsed the highest level of suicide ideation.

Only a handful of studies have examined problem solving abilities in individuals who have made suicide attempts. Rudd et al. (1994) found that low problem solving self-efficacy predicted hopelessness and suicide ideation to a similar degree in individuals who have made suicide attempts as in those reporting only suicide ideation. Pollock and Williams (2004) reported that psychiatric patients who had attempted suicide generated fewer alternatives to problems than psychiatric patients who had not. Jeglic et al. (2005) found that a negative social problem solving orientation (i.e., having a pessimistic outlook that one can solve difficult problems) mediated the relation between a family history of attempts and attempt status, raising the possibility that individuals who make suicide attempts are reared in environments in which they learn that suicide is an acceptable solution to one's problems. Thus, the association between problem solving deficits and suicidality in suicide ideators has indeed been replicated in samples of people who have attempted suicide.

In all, cross-sectional research has demonstrated that the inability to generate solutions and negative attitudes toward one's ability to solve problems are characteristic of both those who report suicide ideation and those who have made suicide attempts. Because this construct is rarely included in prospective research designs, there is no evidence at this time to conclude that problem solving deficits are predictive of future suicidal acts. As is described in greater detail in the next chapter, we speculate that problem solving deficits constitute a dispositional vulnerability factor for some suicidal acts, in that they are associated with psychiatric and emotional disturbance and create life stress, much in the same manner as an impulsive personality style. In addition, it is also possible that poor problem solving plays a role during suicidal crises, such that ideation and hopelessness are exacerbated as the suicidal individual encounters difficulty identifying ways to address and cope with adversity in his or her life. Unfortunately, it is difficult for researchers to test this latter hypothesis, as problem solving is generally assessed in a neutral setting (e.g., a hospital or a research laboratory) and related retrospectively to past suicidal acts or current suicide ideation. In the next chapter, we propose a cognitive model that has the potential to explain the manner in which effective problem solving is thwarted in the midst of a suicidal crisis.

Perfectionism

Although empirical research has identified many facets of perfectionism, the one that is most associated with hopelessness and suicide ideation is *socially prescribed perfectionism*, defined as "an interpersonal dimension involving perceptions of one's need and ability to meet the standards and expectations imposed by others" (Hewitt, Flett, Sherry, & Caelian, 2006, p. 216; see also Hewitt & Flett, 1991). Results from many studies have suggested that socially prescribed perfectionism predicts suicide ideation above and beyond depression and hopelessness (Dean, Range, & Goggin, 1996; Hewitt, Flett, & Turnbull-Donovan, 1992; O'Connor et al., 2007; see O'Connor, 2007, for a comprehensive review). In some instances, another dimension of perfectionism—*self-oriented perfectionism* (i.e., "strong motivations for oneself to be perfect, holding unrealistic self-expectations, all or none thinking, and focusing on one's own flaws"; Hewitt et al., 2006, p. 216)— also differentiates people with and without suicide ideation above and beyond depression and hopelessness (e.g., Hewitt, Flett, & Weber, 1994). There are many ways in which perfectionism might put people at risk for suicide ideation, such as by creating life stress, by accentuating the aversiveness of stress or threat, or by focusing their attention on flaws or failures rather than on strengths or successes (cf. Hewitt et al., 2006).

In contrast to the research examining many other correlates of and risk factors for suicidal acts, far fewer studies have investigated the degree to which perfectionism is associated with attempts. Using a cross-sectional design, Hewitt, Norton, Flett, Callender, and Cowan (1998) found that alcoholic inpatients who had made a serious suicide attempt scored higher on socially prescribed perfectionism than did alcoholic inpatients who had not made a suicide attempt. Hunter and O'Connor (2003) reported that socially prescribed perfectionism discriminated between parasuicidal (i.e., those who engaged in self-injury behavior regardless of intent) and nonparasuicidal hospital control participants above and beyond depression and hopelessness. Moreover, socially prescribed perfectionism is elevated in adolescents whose attempts are characterized by a high level of intent to die (Boergers, Spirito, & Donaldson, 1998), a finding that will be important to replicate in an adult sample.

Thus, trait perfectionism, particularly the dimension of socially prescribed perfectionism, appears to be a dispositional vulnerability factor for suicide ideation and is a correlate of suicide attempts. It is likely that perfectionism is associated with suicidal acts through the activation of suicidal thoughts, or suicide ideation, although empirical research has not yet tested this sort of mediational model. Perfectionism is inherently a set of distorted cognitions about others' expectations and the consequences of not meeting those standards. Thus, it is logical that cognitive therapy strategies designed to modify cognitive distortions (see chap. 5) would be effective in reducing perfectionistic thoughts, which in turn has the potential to reduce suicide ideation.

PROXIMAL RISK FACTORS

The risk factors discussed to this point in the chapter are generally regarded as distal risk factors, or variables that "form the foundation for attempted and completed suicides" and that "may not obviously occur immediately antecedent to the suicidal event itself" (Mościcki, 1999, p. 44). Proximal factors, in contrast, are "closely associated with the suicidal event and can be thought of as precipitants or 'triggers' for suicidal behavior" (p. 44). As is seen in Part II of this volume, we encourage clinicians to identify the proximal risk factors associated with patients' suicidal crisis to develop strategies to manage similar problems in the future.

According to Mościcki (1999), proximal risk factors work in conjunction with distal risk factors to create an environment that is ripe for a suicidal act. Perhaps the most potent proximal risk factor is the presence of a firearm in the home (Kellerman & Reay, 1986). Other proximal risk factors include the presence of potential lethal prescription medications (Mościcki, 1995), life stressors (Rich, Warstadt, Nemiroff, Fowler, & Young, 1991), and, for youths, exposure to the suicidal acts of others (i.e., contagion; Gould & Shaffer, 1986). Mościcki (1999) regarded medical illness as a proximal risk factor, although we suggest that whether medical illness serves as either a proximal or a distal risk factor depends on the chronicity of and prognosis for the condition, such that chronic illnesses associated with little hope of recovery act as distal risk factors, whereas illnesses associated with acute pain, discomfort, or disability act as proximal risk factors. Levenson and Bostwick (2005) noted that medically ill patients are at greatest risk for engaging in suicidal acts around the time they first learn of their diagnosis, which suggests that the time at which one first receives the news of having a substantial medical problem could serve as a proximal risk factor for suicidal acts.

There are many negative life events that may activate a suicidal crisis and that can be regarded as proximal risk factors. In a large nationwide study of suicide in Finland, recent life events in the past 3 months were reported in 80% of the people who committed suicide (Heikkinen, Aro, & Lönnqvist, 1994). The most common life events reported in this study included job-related problems (28%), family conflict (23%), physical illness (22%), financial difficulties (18%), unemployment (16%), separation (14%), death of a close other (13%), and illness in the family (12%). Other types of stressful life events associated with suicide ideation and suicidal acts include recent incarceration (Hayes, 1995), a recent release from prison (Pratt, Piper, Appleby, Webb, & Shaw, 2006), and homelessness (e.g., Eynan et al., 2002). Taken together, these studies suggest that any type of loss (e.g., interpersonal, health, financial) that is perceived to be significant or highly valued by the individual may be associated with increased suicide risk. However, life events that are associated with significant loss may only be proximal risk factors for suicidal crises or acts in the presence of other risk factors, such as diagnostic or psychological risk factors.

A construct that is closely related to that of proximal risk factors is the notion of a warning sign, which is defined as "the earliest detectable sign that indicates heightened risk for suicide in the near-term (i.e., within minutes, hours, or days)" and "refers to some feature of the developing outcome (suicide) rather than to a distinct construct (e.g., risk factor) that predicts or may be causally related to suicide" (Rudd, Berman, et al., 2006, p. 258). Recently, an expert working group from the American Association for Suicidology identified three warning signs that signal immediate intervention: (a) threatening to hurt or kill him- or herself; (b) looking for ways to kill him- or herself, such as seeking access to pills, weapons, or other means; and (c) talking or writing about death, dying, or suicide (Rudd, Berman, et al., 2006, p. 259). In contrast, warning signs that an individual requires mental health treatment (not necessarily immediate) to prevent a suicidal act include (a) hopelessness; (b) rage, anger, or seeking revenge; (c) acting reckless or engaging in risky activities, seemingly without thinking; (d) feeling trapped; (e) increasing alcohol or drug use; (f) withdrawing from friends, family, or society; (g) anxiety, agitation, inability to sleep, or sleeping all the time; (h) dramatic changes in mood; and (i) no reason for living or no sense of purpose in life (Rudd, Berman, et al., 2006, p. 259). These warning signs were developed for the benefit of the general public, so that people would know when to get help for a loved one who is exhibiting these symptoms. Nevertheless, it is also useful for clinicians to keep these warning signs in mind when they are working with high-risk patients, with the understanding that a broader familiarity with the empirical literature, such as that described in this chapter, will supplement this list of warning signs in determining risk for individual patients. As is seen in Part II, many of the strategies in cognitive therapy for suicidal patients are designed to modify these acute warning signs.

PROTECTIVE FACTORS

In contrast to the vast literature on risk factors for suicidal acts, far fewer studies have identified *protective factors*, or factors that are associated with particularly low rates of suicidal acts. Some of the most consistent findings in the literature point to a supportive social network or family as a protective factor. Specifically, being married (e.g., Heikkinen, Isometsä, Marttunen, Aro, & Lönnqvist, 1995) and being a parent, particularly being a mother (e.g., Hoyer & Lund, 1993; Qin, Agerbo, Westergård-Nielsen, Eriksson, & Mortensen, 2000), are associated with decreased suicide risk.

One psychological variable that has received more attention in the suicide literature than other potential protective factors is the degree to which an individual can identify specific reasons for living. It is assumed that the more (or stronger) reasons a person has to live, the lower his or her risk for attempting suicide will be. Linehan, Goodstein, Nielsen, and Chiles (1983) developed the Reasons for Living Inventory, a 48-item self-report measure that assesses the beliefs and expectations for not committing suicide. They found that four of the subscales of the Reasons for Living Inventory—Survival and Coping, Responsibility to Family, Child-Related Concerns, and Moral Objections—correlated negatively with measures of suicide ideation and suicide probability in both community volunteers and psychiatric patients. Moreover, in a sample of hospitalized self-injury patients, the Survival and Coping subscale (i.e., positive expectations about the future and beliefs about one's ability to cope with whatever life has to offer) correlated negatively with suicidal intent (Strosahl, Chiles, & Linehan, 1992). The Reasons for Living Inventory also distinguishes patients who have attempted suicide from psychiatric control patients (Malone et al., 2000; Osman et al., 1999). In another approach to examining reasons for living, Jobes and Mann (1999) asked suicidal college students to list reasons for living and reasons for dying and found that the most frequently endorsed reasons for living included family and future plans. Although reasons for living have yet to be established as a protective factor against suicide deaths rather than suicidal behavior in general, we regard helping patients to identify and recall their reasons for living during a suicidal crisis as an important component of our treatment.

Small lines of research have been developed to identify protective factors at work in certain subgroups of the population characterized by particularly low rates of suicide. For example, many scholars have found that participation in religious activities decreases the probability that African American individuals, particularly African American women, will engage in a suicidal act (see Griffin-Fennell & Williams, 2006; Joe & Kaplan, 2001, for reviews). Griffin-Fennell and Williams (2006) speculated that participation in religious services fosters a sense of community and support and reinforces the notion that suicide is a sin, and J. B. Ellis and Smith (1991) reported a strong positive relation between an individual's religious well-being (faith in God) and moral objections to suicide. In their examination of the low rates of suicide in Hispanic individuals, Oquendo et al. (2005) found that Latino patients are particularly likely to report many reasons for living and that like African American individuals, they are more likely to be devoutly religious and attend church frequently.

Kraemer et al. (1997) regarded a protective factor as a characteristic that predicts "welcome outcomes." However, research studies are designed to identify instances of suicide attempts and deaths and compare them to a rather neutral outcome (i.e., no instance of a suicide attempt or death); thus, we simply are not privy to favorable outcomes in this population (cf. Murphy, 1984). We refer to many protective factors, not only reasons for living, in chapter 6, in which we present an approach for conducting risk assessments with suicidal patients and encourage clinicians to attend to factors that might deter a patient from engaging in a suicidal act. We acknowledge that this notion of a protective factor is a clinical heuristic to guide risk assessments that has less systematic scientific support than there is for the many correlates of and risk factors for suicidal acts. However, the clinician will find that protective factors are useful in balancing the many presenting characteristics that must be considered as a whole in determining suicide risk for an individual patient.

SUMMARY AND INTEGRATION

It is clear from this chapter that there are many variables associated with suicidal acts that can be assessed by clinicians and used in forming a comprehensive understanding of patients' current level of suicide risk. Some of these factors provide background information that the clinician uses in determining risk but that will not necessarily be targeted in treatment (e.g., demographics, psychiatric history). Others, such as psychiatric diagnoses and psychological variables, are not only targeted in treatment but also provide clues about the mechanism by which suicidal crises are activated in a particular person. There is a great deal of evidence that cognitive therapy is effective in reducing symptoms associated with many types of psychiatric disturbance (see Hollon, Stewart, & Strunk, 2006, for a review). Psychiatric disturbance provides a context for the suicidal acts to emerge, and treatment for psychiatric disturbance can decrease suicide ideation and risk factors indirectly by reducing depression, hopelessness, and other problematic behaviors. However, as is seen in the remainder of this book, we believe that treating the suicide-relevant psychological symptoms, such as those described in this chapter, is a more targeted approach to reducing suicide ideation and the likelihood of suicidal acts than treating the associated psychiatric disturbance. These psychological processes, identified largely from the literature on correlates of and risk factors for suicidal acts, are of central importance in the cognitive model that we describe in the next chapter.

Although the literature on correlates of and risk factors for suicidal acts is vast, surprisingly, many basic issues remain to be investigated adequately in the prediction of suicidal acts. As Pokorny (1983) aptly noted, most studies on risk factors follow patients over the course of several months or years, whereas clinicians must make decisions about a patient's risk in the subsequent minutes, hours, or days. Moreover, even when researchers make complex equations to predict suicides that are based on risk factors that emerge as significant in well-designed prospective studies, they fail to predict even one actual suicide (e.g., Goldstein et al., 1991) because of its low base rate. Thus, a clinician who has a perfect understanding of the literature might not be able to predict a suicidal act committed by an individual patient. We believe that the field is in great need of research on the proximal risk factors and specific triggers for suicidal acts to supplement our knowledge of distal risk factors.

One other limitation of the present review is that most of the published studies have focused on adult, nonminority populations, and caution should be taken when generalizing the results of these studies to specific age groups and to other racial and ethnic groups. We provide a brief review of studies on correlates of and risk factors for suicidal acts in adolescents in chapter 11 and for suicidal acts in older adults in chapter 12. Regardless of the age group that is the subject of study, however, there is a paucity of studies that have examined the risk factors for suicide among specific racial and ethnic groups, and further research with these populations is especially warranted. As mentioned previously, the scant research that has been conducted suggests that there might be clinically significant protective factors that are unique to some racial or ethnic groups, which suggests that in-depth study of suicidal behavior in these groups would be of great benefit.

Finally, we would be remiss not to acknowledge the burgeoning literature on the neurobiology of suicidal acts. Most of the research in this area is cross-sectional, which limits the degree to which we can regard biological variables as risk factors for suicide. Nevertheless, as stated earlier in the chapter, it is clear that there is a substantial genetic component to suicide that is independent of the genetic transmission of psychiatric disturbance such as depression (Brent & Mann, 2005). It is likely that the specific biological basis of suicidal behavior lies in a deficient serotonergic system, particularly in the prefrontal cortex (Mann, 2003). Postmortem research examining the brains of suicide victims has identified two candidate genes involved in the biological mechanisms underlying suicide—one that codes for tryptophan hydroxylase 1, an enzyme that determines the amount of serotonin in the synaptic cleft, and the other that codes for the serotonin transporter gene, which determines the rate of reuptake of serotonin from the synaptic cleft (Bondy et al., 2006). These scientific advances remind us of the interplay between biological and psychological factors in determining a complex behavior such as a suicidal act. The cognitive therapy protocol described in this volume is devoted to modifying the psychological characteristics of suicide ideation and suicide attempts, and we await future research to determine the degree to which such a therapeutic approach in turn modifies these biological correlates.

In sum, although there are many limitations to the manner in which the risk factors literature applies to individual suicidal patients, it provides a starting point for us to understand the underlying mechanism associated with suicidal acts, assess for relevant background factors and immediate precursors to suicidal acts, and intervene at points that are most likely to reduce future suicidal acts. In chapter 3, we incorporate many of these correlates and risk factors into a cognitive model of suicidal acts. In Part II, we describe the manner in which these factors are assessed, incorporated into a conceptualization of the patient, and modified during the course of cognitive therapy.

3

A COGNITIVE MODEL OF SUICIDAL ACTS

Cognitive therapy for suicidal patients is based on a framework that incorporates general cognitive theory, cognitive theory that is specific to suicidal acts, and results from empirical studies designed to identify important cognitive processes associated with suicidal acts. In this chapter, we bring these elements together into a coherent but flexible model, such that constructs can have more or less relevance for a particular person. We recognize that the category of "suicidal patients" is not homogeneous and that there are many different phenotypes of patients who have engaged in suicidal acts. Some suicidologists, for example, have argued that there are (at least) two classes of suicidal patients—those who are characterized by a pervasive sense of hopelessness and a strong intent to die and those for whom hopelessness and intent to die are not salient features but who have difficulties regulating affect and impulsive behavior or who make their attempt to communicate something to others (e.g., Apter et al., 1995; Kashden, Fremouw, Callahan, & Franzen, 1993; Nock & Kessler, 2006). As is seen later in this chapter, we propose that different suicide-relevant suicide schemas correspond to these different phenotypic presentations, but that (a) the likelihood that these schemas are activated depends on the loading of dispositional vulnerability factors, the degree of psychiatric disturbance, and life stress and (b) once activated, these schemas are associated with similar cognitive processes that are observed in suicidal crises.

Understanding this cognitive model of suicidal acts will inform clinical practice with suicidal patients. We argue that this model is central for conceptualizing individual patients' clinical presentations and selecting particular intervention strategies, a process we consider in more detail in chapter 7. Moreover, we believe that this model will help to demystify suicidal acts for the practicing clinician, such that there is a systematic framework to explain this behavior. We begin the chapter with a description of the general cognitive model and explain its relevance to suicidal individuals. Next, we turn to a discussion of suicide-relevant psychological constructs that have received attention in the empirical literature. Finally, we integrate this material into a cognitive model of suicidal acts that includes dispositional vulnerability factors, general cognitive processes associated with psychiatric disturbance, and suicide-specific cognitive processes.

GENERAL COGNITIVE THEORY

General cognitive theory, as applied to many different types of psychiatric disorders, emotional disturbances, and problematic behaviors, has been described in detail in nearly every book on cognitive therapy. We briefly review it here to orient the reader to cognitive theory and to use it as a springboard for describing specific processes at work in suicidal patients. Figure 3.1 illustrates the main concepts in the general cognitive model.

The central premise of cognitive theory is that the meaning people assign to particular environmental stimuli plays a significant role in shaping their subsequent affect, which is in turn associated with their behavioral responses (e.g., A. T. Beck, 1967). According to this theory, adverse events, such as the loss of a job, do not directly cause negative emotional experiences such as depression, anxiety, and anger. Instead, people's emotional experiences are determined, in large part, by the manner in which they perceive, interpret, and judge the implications of those situations. These emotional reactions, in turn, are distressing in and of themselves and feed back into additional thoughts people have about the situation and its aftermath, which have the potential to further exacerbate negative mood and maladaptive behavior. In other words, there is a feedback loop between cognitions and emotions, such that there is a potential for them to become increasingly negative, or maladaptive.

Consider, for example, a woman who recently learned that her husband is having an affair and is leaving her for his mistress. If she perceives the situation as meaning that she will be alone for the remainder of her life, she will likely experience depression. If she perceives the situation as meaning

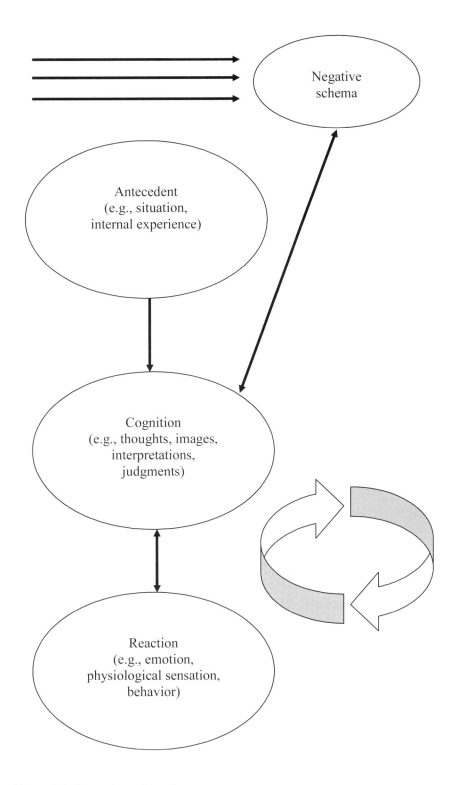

Figure 3.1. General cognitive theory.

that her husband has humiliated her in front of their community, she will likely experience anger. In contrast, if she perceives the situation as meaning that her quality of life will improve because she would be better off without him, she will likely not experience such extreme, and negative, emotional reactions. As is seen in chapter 5, one major activity in cognitive therapy is to identify these meanings, perceptions, interpretations, and judgments and to evaluate systematically the degree to which they objectively characterize the nature of the situation. An assumption underlying this process is that objectively evaluating one's circumstances will reduce the extremity of the maladaptive cognitions, which will in turn reduce negative affect.

The antecedents of these cognitive, emotional, and behavioral reactions need not always be situations encountered in one's daily life; they can also be internal experiences. For example, the woman described earlier might experience an increase in negative affect when her husband first tells her of the affair (i.e., antecedent = an event), when she remembers times in which her husband did not come home until late at night (i.e., antecedent = a memory), or when she has the idea that a divorce will ruin her children's lives (i.e., antecedent = a thought). The cognitions elicited from particular antecedents need not always be represented verbally in terms of thoughts, interpretations, or judgments; many individuals instead report vivid images such as a past trauma or worst-case scenarios in the future. Moreover, reactions need not always be restricted to emotions because they can encompass physiological responses and subsequent behaviors. In this scenario, the woman who has the idea that she will be alone for the rest of her life might feel as though she has a lump in the pit of her stomach and seek excessive reassurance from others about her worthiness. The woman who has the idea that her husband has humiliated her in front of their community might experience a racing heart and shallow breathing, and she might retaliate against her husband by spreading vicious rumors about him. The woman who has the idea that she would be better off without him might feel surprisingly light and go about making some adaptive changes in her life, such as opening up her own checking account. In other words, different interpretations of the same situation can facilitate very different emotional, physiological, and behavioral responses.

The cognitions people experience in particular situations are not random; instead, they are determined, in part, by people's previous experiences, whether they are experiencing symptoms of psychiatric disturbance, and whether they are experiencing significant stress in their lives. In the top right corner of Figure 3.1, we include the construct of a negative schema. According to D. A. Clark and Beck (1999), schemas are "relatively enduring internal structures of stored generic or prototypical features of stimuli, ideas, or experience that are used to organize new information in a meaningful way thereby determining how phenomena are perceived and conceptualized" (p. 79). That is, schemas are hypothetical cognitive structures that influence information processing or that guide the direction in which people allocate their attention and encode, organize, store, and retrieve information. When people encounter new information in their everyday lives, their schemas help to organize and make sense of it. Thus, schemas serve as the lenses through which people view the world. These lenses are not translucent; instead, people's previous experiences determine each lens's particular shade. This means that people do not view the world in an entirely objective manner, but rather that they assign meaning to incoming stimuli as a function of the lens, or the schema, that is operative at that time.

Schemas do not always distort reality in a problematic manner, and in fact, they are usually adaptive in helping people to process large amounts of information in a short period of time and to decide on the most appropriate course of action based on that information. However, negative schemas are those that are related to psychiatric disturbance and result in biased information processing, such that concerns associated with the domain of psychiatric disturbance are given preference. For example, depressive schemas contain negative attitudes about loss and failure and influence depressed individuals to place greater importance on processing negative information than positive information (A. T. Beck, 1967). Danger schemas contain exaggerated beliefs about harm or suffering and one's ability to cope with it, which influence anxious individuals to place greater importance on processing indications of threat than indications of neutrality or safety (A. T. Beck & Emery, 1985). Thus, schemas are associated with specific content (e.g., beliefs or attitudes) and patterns of information processing (cf. Ingram & Kendall, 1986). Suicidal individuals are often characterized by negative schemas associated with a number of types of psychiatric disturbance (e.g., depression, anxiety, substance abuse), which in turn exacerbate faulty information processing, negative mood, and subsequent maladaptive behavior. However, we propose that suicidal individuals are also characterized by suicide schemas that cut across many types of psychiatric disturbance and that are specific to suicidal acts. We return to this concept of suicide schemas later in the chapter.

According to cognitive theory, negative schemas are not perpetually active. These cognitive structures form from early experiences, often during childhood, but lie dormant until the person experiences significant stress. The stressor might take the form of one adverse event, such as the breakup of a relationship, or it may be the accumulation of many hassles that wear down the individual over time. As the characteristics of the stressor more closely match the nature of the negative schema, the probability that the negative schema is activated increases (cf. D. A. Clark & Beck, 1999). Once the negative schema is activated, incoming information is molded to fit the schema, inconsistent information is ignored, and the schema gains strength by becoming associated with more and more information. We view cognitive therapy as an approach that helps patients develop strategies for evaluating incoming information before it is integrated with negative schemas, which in turn will decrease the strength of these cognitive structures and assist patients in developing new, more adaptive cognitive structures.

This general cognitive model is useful in characterizing the myriad difficulties experienced by suicidal individuals. As we described in chapter 2, most suicidal individuals are diagnosed with one or more psychiatric disorders, which are in turn associated with the activation of a particular negative schema. Moreover, many suicidal individuals experience one or more major stressors, and negative schemas associated with a range of psychiatric disturbances are activated in the midst of this adversity. However, some suicidologists have argued that there is something fundamentally different about the cognitive processes of suicidal individuals, particularly when they are in the midst of a suicidal crisis, as compared to the cognitive processes of nonsuicidal individuals (e.g., Ellis, 2006). This means that we need to reach beyond the general cognitive model to capture the cognitive processes that are unique to suicidal individuals and that explain the specific cognitive processes at work in the time immediately preceding a suicidal crisis. Recently, two psychological theories, both with a cognitive behavioral basis, have been proposed to explain suicidal acts. These theories are reviewed in the next section.

COGNITIVE THEORIES OF SUICIDAL ACTS

One framework that expands on the general cognitive model is that of the *suicidal mode*. According to A. T. Beck (1996), modes "are specific suborganizations within the personality organization and incorporate the relevant components of the basic systems of personality: cognitive (or information processing), affective, behavioral, and motivational" (p. 4). These components form an "integrated cognitive–affective–behavioral network" that is activated in response to a particular situation or when one is attempting to reach a goal. Thus, beliefs about the self, world, and future represent the cognitive component of the system, but other systems are activated in concert with the cognitive system to facilitate a coherent response. According to Beck, data are processed simultaneously through all of these systems, and the systems remain activated for some time after the circumstances that initiated the system have dissipated.

Rudd (2004, 2006; see also Rudd, Joiner, & Rajab, 2001) applied the theory of modes to suicidal acts. His model is intricately related to the literature on risk factors described in chapter 2 (this volume); according to Rudd, the more risk factors a person has, the more likely it is that the suicidal mode will be activated. Individuals at high baseline risk for suicidal acts are those with pervasive suicide-relevant beliefs, affective instability, and a lack of behavioral coping skills. Rudd suggested that suicidal crises are time limited and require heightened levels of activation in all four systems (i.e., cognitive, affective, behavioral, motivational), which is prompted by some sort of aggravation. The severity of the suicidal act is a function of the person's level of vulnerability, or baseline risk, and the severity of the aggravating factor. Because a negative valence is attached to the aggravating event, there is an increased likelihood that the suicidal mode will be activated again in the future in the context of a similar event.

A second psychological theory of suicidal acts was developed by Joiner (2005) and consists of three main constructs, all of which need to be in place for an individual to engage in a suicidal act. First, the person must have acquired the ability to enact lethal self-harm. Most people are deterred from attempting suicide because they fear pain and death. However, people who have had "practice" with pain through experiences such as injuries, nonsuicidal self-injury behavior, or even tattooing and piercing habituate to, or get used to, pain. That is, as people obtain more experience with bodily harm, their threshold for pain tolerance increases, they find pain less aversive, and they might even get a sense of pleasure or relief from it. Joiner, like Rudd, suggested that future suicidal crises are reached more easily after a person has made a previous attempt, but different mechanisms account for this phenomenon—for Joiner, it is because the person has acquired a learned behavior; for Rudd, it is because suicidal cognitions have strengthened their association with other risk factors so that an increasingly large number of things trigger suicidal cognitions. In addition, Joiner's theory suggests that the person must be characterized by two psychological factors associated with the desire for death—failed belongingness and perceived burdensomeness. In all, his theory indicates that the ability to enact lethal self-injury (i.e., a learned behavior) combined with the desire for death in two major domains (i.e., cognitive factors) explains suicide attempts and deaths.

Both of these theories have a sound scientific basis and are compatible with our own. The construct of the suicidal mode is useful in describing the diverse array of processes at work in suicidal individuals (i.e., cognitive, affective, behavioral, motivational) and in specifying the manner in which risk factors translate to suicidal individuals' likelihood of engaging in various degrees of suicidal behavior (e.g., mild vs. severe attempt, single vs. multiple attempts). Thus, it can guide clinicians in conducting comprehensive suicide risk assessments (see chap. 6) and in selecting particular interventions to reduce the likelihood that the suicidal mode will be activated in the future. Joiner's (2005) theory is a parsimonious but elegant template for clinicians to keep in mind, particularly when they have a limited amount of time to make a clinical judgment. For example, a clinician would judge that a patient characterized by failed belongingness and perceived burdensomeness but who has not acquired the ability to enact lethal self-harm is at lower risk for making an attempt than a patient who has both of these elements of the desire to die in conjunction with a history of previous attempts and self-injury behavior.

Our cognitive model expands on these models in four ways. First, it integrates A. T. Beck's general cognitive model with suicide-specific cognitive processes, demonstrating the manner in which cognitive processes associated with general psychiatric disturbance become exacerbated and activate suicidal cognitions. Second, it speaks to the manner in which risk factors work in conjunction to bring about general psychiatric disturbance, activate suicide schemas, and exacerbate distress in times of suicidal crises. That is, it does not merely suggest that the accumulation of risk factors increases the likelihood that an individual will engage in a suicidal act, but it specifies multiple pathways by which they exert their effects. Third, it integrates other suicide-relevant constructs that have scientific bases in the empirical literature, such as impulsivity and problem solving deficits. Finally, it provides insight into the specific unfolding of events that occurs when a suicidal crisis develops. We believe that it is important to specify these mechanisms in a cognitive model of suicidal acts to capture the subjective, phenomenological experience of the suicidal patient, which can strengthen the clinician's conceptualization of the patient's clinical presentation and illustrate multiple points of intervention. Next, we describe empirically supported suicide-relevant cognitive constructs and processes and describe their place in our cognitive model of suicide.

EMPIRICALLY BASED SUICIDE-RELEVANT COGNITIVE CONSTRUCTS

As highlighted in chapter 2, there are several psychological constructs that empirical research has shown to be more characteristic of suicidal individuals than nonsuicidal individuals. In this section, we describe the manner in which these psychological constructs can explain how suicidal crises unfold.

Hopelessness

In chapter 2, we reviewed studies suggesting that hopelessness is uniquely associated with suicidal intent and that it has the potential to predict completed suicides years later. Because of this strong link between hopelessness and suicidal acts, it is incumbent on us to incorporate it into our overall understanding of suicide. At its most fundamental level, hopelessness is a cognition; it is a belief that the future is bleak, that one's problems will never be solved. As stated in the previous section, distorted cognitive content is an important part of negative schemas. From this perspective, hopelessness can be viewed as a belief associated with a suicide schema that, once activated, biases people to allocate cognitive resources toward processing cues that reinforce this schema.

In addition, some scholars have distinguished between state and trait hopelessness. State hopelessness is the degree of hopelessness that is activated at any one moment (e.g., immediately before a suicide attempt), whereas trait hopelessness is the degree to which an individual has stable, negative expectancies for the future (A. T. Beck, 1986). According to A. T. Beck (1986), the stronger one's trait hopelessness, the less adversity it will take to trigger a suicidal crisis and the experience of state hopelessness. That is, when trait hopelessness is activated, it interacts with environmental stressors to escalate state hopelessness. In our model, higher levels of state hopelessness are associated with increasingly acute suicide ideation.

Although results from empirical studies have suggested that hopelessness is a central construct in understanding suicidal acts, it is important to acknowledge that it does not characterize all suicidal patients. For example, hopelessness appears to play very little role in attempts made with a low intent to die, a lack of premeditation, and/or with the intent of getting the attention of or communicating something to others (Skogman & Öjehagen, 2003). In these instances, it is likely that life stressors accumulate to a point at which the person perceives that they are unbearable and cannot tolerate the associated distress, thereby increasing state hopelessness. Thus, in our cognitive model there are (at least) two types of suicide schemas—a schema characterized by trait hopelessness and a schema characterized by perceptions of unbearability (cf. Joiner, Brown, & Wingate, 2005; Rudd, 2004). This idea is similar to that proposed by Fawcett, Busch, Jacobs, Kravitz, and Fogg (1997), who speculated that there are multiple pathways to suicidal acts, only one of which implicates hopelessness. A person's previous experiences determine whether he or she is characterized by a particular type of suicide schema.

Regardless of which suicide schema is salient, we suggest that once it is activated, there is an increasingly large likelihood that the person will experience state hopelessness in times of continued stress and adversity (see Figure 3.2). That is, state hopelessness is an outcome associated with the activation of any suicide schema, not just a suicide schema characterized by trait hopelessness. State hopelessness may consist of ideas that one's future will not improve (e.g., "Things will never get better"), which is indicative of trait hopelessness, or instead it may consist of ideas such as "I can't take this anymore," which is indicative of unbearability. As the level of state hopelessness increases, so too does the probability that the individual will experience acute suicide ideation.

Suicide-Relevant Cognitions

In chapter 2, we identified many suicide-relevant cognitions that predict future suicidal acts, such as suicide ideation and suicidal intent. Suicide-relevant cognitive content can be associated with any suicide schema, whether

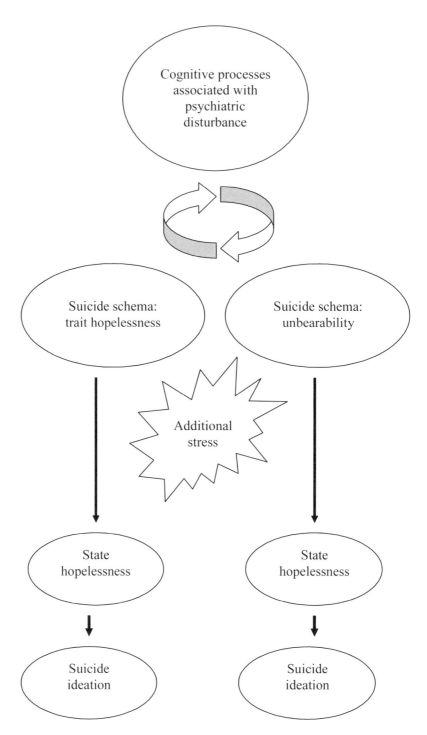

Figure 3.2. Suicide-relevant schemas, state hopelessness, and suicide ideation. From "A Cognitive Model of Suicidal Behavior: Theory and Treatment," by A. Wenzel and A. T. Beck, 2008, *Applied and Preventive Psychology, 12*, p. 194. Copyright 2008 by Elsevier. Adapted with permission.

it be hopelessness, unbearability, or another theme. In our model, the frequency, duration, and severity of these suicide-relevant cognitions accumulate to determine the probability that a person will engage in a suicidal act, such that the more frequently an individual experiences these cognitions, the longer these cognitions last, and the more severe these cognitions are, the greater the probability that the individual will attempt suicide. In our model, as well as in Rudd's and Joiner's models, it will take a smaller "dose" of suicide-relevant cognitions to trigger suicidal acts in individuals who have a history of suicide attempts because suicide schemas strengthen with each suicidal act. Figure 3.3 summarizes this influence of suicide-relevant cognitions on the likelihood that a person will make a suicide attempt, in the context of the person's history of previous suicide attempts.

Heightened Impulsivity

As seen in chapter 2 of this volume, impulsivity is an elusive concept. Some studies have found that individuals who have made suicide attempts are more impulsive than those who have not, whereas other studies have not found this. Joiner (2005) raised the possibility that this is so because impulsivity is a distal cause of suicidal acts, in that it increases a person's likelihood that he or she will experience harm or injury, which in turn increases the likelihood that he or she could tolerate a suicide attempt. In other words, Joiner suggested that impulsivity is only indirectly associated with suicidal acts, in that it exerts its effects through other mechanisms. Another reason why it has been so difficult to establish impulsivity's role in suicidal acts is that it has been defined and conceptualized in many different ways, such as a behavioral deficit (e.g., inability to inhibit responding), a cognitive problem (e.g., inability to plan ahead), and a personality trait (Endicott & Ogloff, 2006). A third reason why impulsivity is only sometimes related to suicidal behavior is the timing of the measurement. Typically, suicidal patients are administered measures of psychological symptoms, including impulsivity, after they have made an attempt. The measurement of impulsivity after the attempt, when in many instances the suicidal crisis has resolved, is likely very different than the impulsivity experienced when a person is acutely suicidal.

In our cognitive model of suicide, we view impulsivity as a dispositional vulnerability factor for suicidal acts. We use the term *dispositional* because we view this construct as a long-standing characteristic of the person, much like a personality trait. Moreover, we use the term *vulnerability factor* because, theoretically, we believe that the construct increases the likelihood of suicidal acts in some individuals, but that the term *risk factor* would be misleading because empirical research has not yet established with adequate methodology that this construct increases the risk of engaging in suicidal acts according to the definition we presented in chapter 2. Because instru-

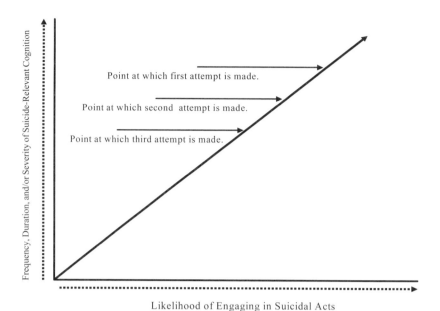

Figure 3.3. Suicide-relevant cognitions and the likelihood of engaging in suicidal acts.

ments that assess dispositional impulsivity typically assess several facets (e.g., nonplanning impulsivity, motor impulsivity, cognitive impulsivity, attentional impulsivity; see Barratt, 1985), we regard it as a broad, nonspecific construct.

We acknowledge that dispositional impulsivity is not a vulnerability factor for every suicidal patient, because some who attempt suicide are not particularly impulsive people and their suicidal act is carefully planned and executed. It is possible that dispositional impulsivity is most related to suicidal acts that are accompanied by the perception of unbearability or wanting to communicate something to others through the attempt rather than by hopelessness or a strong intent to die. That is, dispositional impulsivity might increase the likelihood of suicidal acts only when suicide schemas characterized by perceptions of the unbearability are activated. Indeed, results from empirical studies have suggested that impulsivity correlates negatively with hopelessness (Suominen, Isometsä, Henriksson, Ostamo, & Lönnqvist, 1997) and that those making impulsive attempts (i.e., attempts that were contemplated for fewer than 5 minutes) are less depressed than those making nonimpulsive attempts (T. R. Simon et al., 2001). These findings suggest that hopelessness is less important in explaining suicidal acts in impulsive individuals relative to nonimpulsive individuals.

It is also important to consider the phenomenon of impulsivity exhibited at the time of the attempt. Some suicide attempts are premeditated, whereas others seem to occur with little warning (e.g., T. R. Simon et al.,

2001), and dispositional measures of impulsivity do not always distinguish between individuals who make these very different kinds of attempts (e.g., Baca-Garcia et al., 2005). It is unclear whether the types of impulsivity manifested in the context of a suicide attempt are indicative of the impulsivity manifested at other times in the lives of individuals characterized by dispositional impulsivity. Instead, we view many indicators of impulsivity observed at the time of the attempt as occurring in the context of a unique kind of cognitive dysfunction experienced immediately preceding the attempt.

Clinically, we have observed that many patients describe a state of cognitive disorientation in the time immediately preceding their suicide attempt, and it appears that they are making an impulsive decision to attempt suicide and are impulsively engaging in reckless behavior to provide some relief from their emotional distress. They experience racing thoughts, often accompanied by acute restlessness and agitation. They experience "tunnel vision," focusing on suicide as the only answer to their problems at the expense of less harmful options. They are mentally consumed or preoccupied by the idea that there is no way out and would do anything possible to end the pain. They report that they are in a state of desperation. Others have observed similar phenomena; for example, Silverman (2006) noted that for many suicide attempters, their "cognitions were impaired and they were in such psychological pain that it was impossible to make rational choices or decisions about ending their lives" (p. 528). Baumeister (1990) theorized that suicidal people exhibit cognitive deconstruction, or a narrow focus on the present that precludes more sophisticated information processing and problem solving. Shneidman (1985) observed that suicidal patients are characterized by cognitive constriction, such that there is a "tunneling or focusing or narrowing of the range of options usually available to that individual's consciousness" (p. 138). We believe that these comments are indicative of a cognitive phenomenon called *attentional fixation*. Attentional fixation includes not only cognitive constriction but also a preoccupation with suicide as a solution to one's problems.

We first identified instances of attentional fixation in patients with panic disorder. A. T. Beck (1988) described this phenomenon as a "dissociation of the higher-level reflective processes from automatic cognitive processing" (p. 101), noting that patients with panic disorder lack the ability to reflect on what is happening and to distance themselves from their fears in the midst of an attack. When instructed to consider their internal state at the time of their most recent panic attack, patients with panic disorder assign high scores to items such as "All I can think about is how I feel" and "I imagine the worst," and they assign low scores to items such as "I remain coolheaded" and "I am able to apply logic to my problem" (Wenzel, Sharp, Sokol, & Beck, 2006). We believe the same sort of process is at work in suicidal patients in the time immediately preceding their attempt. There is some relevant empirical justification for this statement, as studies examining correlates of inpatient suicide have found that significant anxiety and/or agitation in the 7 days preceding the attempt is characteristic of the majority of inpatients who commit suicide (Busch, Clark, & Fawcett, 1993; Busch, Fawcett, & Jacobs, 2003; Sharma, Persad, & Kueneman, 1998). It is likely that anxiety and agitation are the emotional and behavioral expressions of attentional fixation.

In other words, we suggest that what seems like cognitive and behavioral impulsivity at the time of the attempt are actually manifestations of attentional fixation. Although it is conceivable that dispositional impulsivity increases the speed by which attentional fixation is activated and overcomes the person, we view the two constructs as largely separate. In addition, we propose that attentional fixation interacts with state hopelessness to create a downward cognitive–affective spiral, exacerbating suicide ideation and creating a context that is ripe for a suicide attempt. When suicidal individuals are in a hopeless state, they perceive that they have few options to solve their problems. Thus, we hypothesize that they are at increased risk of identifying suicide as an appropriate solution rather than systematically considering alternative means to solve their problems. The more they fixate on suicide as the only solution, the more hopeless they are about their life circumstances or the more likely they are to perceive their life circumstances as unbearable. Increased state hopelessness further overwhelms suicidal individuals, clouds their judgment, and increases the likelihood that they will conclude that there is no way out. State hopelessness increases attentional fixation, and the narrow focus on suicide as the only option increases state hopelessness.

Although we believe that this cognitive–affective–behavioral characterization of attentional fixation is relevant to many individuals who attempt suicide, it certainly does not pertain to all of these people. For example, some individuals characterized by high levels of trait hopelessness carefully plan their attempts over a long period of time and demonstrate relief rather than anxiety, agitation, or confusion. We still believe these individuals exhibit the cognitive aspects of attentional fixation in these instances, as they are convinced that suicide is the only solution and fail to entertain other alternatives. However, these individuals lack many of the affective and behavioral correlates indicative of the desperation associated with attentional fixation.

Information Processing Biases

A. T. Beck's cognitive theories of emotional and behavioral disturbances specify that not only do individuals experience distorted cognitive content (e.g., hopelessness) but that they also process information relevant to the current concerns in a biased manner. In other words, individuals' beliefs influence the manner in which they attend to information in their environment, interpret ambiguous information, and recall information from their past. These sorts of information processing biases make it likely that individuals will focus on negative, or maladaptive, information at the expense of positive, or adaptive, information, which further reinforces maladaptive beliefs. There are two domains of information processing biases that have been studied with suicidal patients—attentional biases and memory biases. These constructs were not covered in chapter 2 of this volume because they have received minimal attention in the empirical literature, and no studies have included such data in analyses that predict future suicidal acts. Nevertheless, they are included in our cognitive model of suicidal acts because information processing biases are central to general cognitive theory and because our patients have anecdotally described these phenomena as being important in understanding their suicidal acts.

Two groups of researchers have used the Emotional Stroop Task to examine attentional biases toward suicide-relevant stimuli in samples of suicide attempters. Participants who complete this task are presented with single words in various ink colors, and they are instructed to name the ink color as quickly as possible regardless of what the word means. In the Emotional Stroop Task with suicidal patients, participants are presented with words related to suicide (e.g., *suicide*), generally negative words (e.g., *lonely*), and neutral words (e.g., *statue*). An attentional bias is demonstrated when participants take longer to name the colors of a particular class of words, as it is assumed that the content of the word captures their attention and interferes with the color-naming task at hand. Empirical research has suggested that patients who have recently been hospitalized for an overdose (Williams & Broadbent, 1986b) and patients who have attempted suicide by one of several means in the previous year (Becker, Strohbach, & Rinck, 1999) demonstrate especially pronounced interference effects when naming colors for suicide-relevant words. Although some clinical scientists have questioned whether biased Stroop performance actually represents an attentional bias instead of other types of biases, such as a response bias (cf. MacLeod, Mathews, & Tata, 1986), the fact remains that these studies demonstrate that recent attempters process suicide-relevant information in a different manner than non–suicide-relevant information.

How are suicide-relevant attentional biases different from attentional fixation? We propose that attentional fixation is a *general* breakdown of cognitive processing, in which individuals are confused, unable to apply reason or good judgment to their circumstances, and ultimately fixate solely on suicide. Suicide-relevant attentional biases represent *selective* processing, such that suicidal individuals automatically allocate their attention toward suicide-relevant stimuli in the context of otherwise normative cognitive processing. Many scholars have viewed selective attention as the result of involuntary and unconscious processing (e.g., McNally, 1995). In contrast, attentional fixation is the disruption of conscious and reasoned processing.

We propose that suicide-relevant attentional biases narrow suicidal individuals' attention on suicide and away from indicators of other alternatives, safety, or reasons to live. We believe this happens regardless of whether suicidal individuals are in an acute state of hopelessness, as participants in the studies described earlier demonstrated these biases up to a year after their attempt, when, presumably, their suicidal crises had abated. However, when suicide-relevant stimuli are detected while suicide schemas are activated and individuals are experiencing state hopelessness, they will have difficulty disengaging from suicide-relevant stimuli, become overwhelmed by them (which further exacerbates state hopelessness and suicide ideation), and fixate on escape and suicide (see Figure 3.4). A threshold is reached when suicidal individuals decide that they cannot tolerate this experience and make the final choice to commit suicide. The threshold of tolerance represents the point in time at which they are no longer ambivalent about the intent to kill themselves and make a definite decision to end their lives. Thus, we propose that a suicide attempt will occur when the interplay between state hopelessness, attentional fixation, and suicide ideation spiral beyond a person's threshold of tolerance for distress, state hopelessness, and disorientation.

Selective attention, however, is only one domain of information processing bias associated with suicide attempts. An even greater body of work has accumulated to suggest that suicidal individuals are characterized by dysfunction in an aspect of their memory processes—an overgeneral memory style (Williams & Broadbent, 1986a; Williams & Dritschel, 1988; see Williams, Barnhoffer, Crane, & Duggan, 2006, for a review). That is, when given a cue that is supposed to prompt a personal memory from their past, individuals who have made a suicide attempt provide a vague response that seems to summarize a number of events (e.g., "when I went to the beach with my family every summer"). This response style persists even when these individuals are given instructions to articulate one specific memory and are given practice trials to learn how to do so. Williams et al. (2006) suggested that in instances in which suicidal individuals are characterized by a pervasive sense of hopelessness, overgeneral memory prevents them from accessing specific information that would assist in effective problem solving and in thinking in specific terms about the future.

It is likely that an overgeneral memory style exacerbates attentional fixation during suicidal crises, as suicidal individuals will have difficulty remembering specific reasons to live. Furthermore, it could also serve as a dispositional vulnerability factor for the activation of suicide schemas in three ways. First, suicidal individuals are unlikely to remember specific positive experiences from their past, which reinforces negative beliefs and has the potential to lead them to erroneously conclude that life is not worth living. This process, however, is not unique to suicidal individuals; a great deal of work has suggested that depressed patients are characterized by this process as well (see Williams, 1996, for a review). Second, as stated previously,

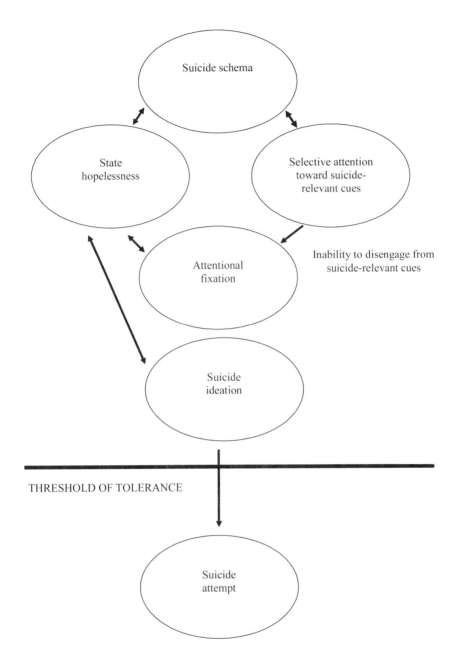

Figure 3.4. Proposed model of information processing in suicidal crises. From "A Cognitive Model of Suicidal Behavior: Theory and Treatment," by A. Wenzel and A. T. Beck, 2008, *Applied and Preventive Psychology, 12*, p. 195. Copyright 2008 by Elsevier. Adapted with permission.

overgeneral memory prevents suicidal individuals from accessing specific information that is necessary for effective problem solving, which could create additional life stress and adversity (Williams et al., 2006). Third, it promotes an overall overgeneral style of thinking, which affects the ability of suicidal individuals to think ahead to the future in specific terms (cf. Williams et al., 2006) and could strengthen a hopelessness-based suicide schema.

Thus, suicidal individuals are characterized by two types of information processing biases. They exhibit preferential processing of suicide-relevant cues in their environment, and they have difficulty retrieving specific personal memories. When the suicide schema is activated and patients are in a state of hopelessness, there is an increased likelihood that they will fixate on suicide-relevant cues once they are detected. Their overgeneral memory style will prevent them from identifying specific alternatives to self-injury. This focus on suicide at the expense of other alternatives further increases state hopelessness and a sense of desperation.

Problem Solving Deficits

Ineffective problem solving has already been mentioned in several of the previous sections, as it is a possible consequence of an overgeneral memory style, and it is manifested during suicidal crises in the context of attentional fixation. Cognitive models linking problem solving deficits with suicidal acts suggest that in times of life stress, suicidal individuals perceive their situation as intolerable and conclude that they do not have the ability to change it, which leads to an increase in hopelessness and then to suicide ideation (Reinecke, 2006). Empirical research has confirmed that relative to nonsuicidal individuals, suicidal individuals generate fewer solutions to problems (Pollock & Williams, 2004), are more likely to judge that their generated solutions will have negative consequences, are less likely to use the alternatives they generate (Schotte & Clum, 1987), and are more likely to use denial or avoidance strategies in dealing with their problems (D'Zurilla, Chang, Nottingham, & Faccini, 1998; Orbach, Bar-Joseph, & Dror, 1990).

As we saw with impulsivity, problem solving involves several components and processes (D'Zurilla, Nezu, & Maydeu-Olivares, 2004), and only a few have been examined systematically in suicidal individuals. When problem solving is conceptualized as the ability to generate solutions to problems, problem solving deficits are associated with life stress and suicide ideation, but not with hopelessness (Priester & Clum, 1993; Schotte & Clum, 1982, 1987). In contrast, when problem solving is conceptualized as problem solving self-efficacy, or the belief that one is able to influence the outcome of problems, then problem solving deficits are strongly related to hopelessness and modestly related to suicide ideation (Dixon, Heppner, & Anderson, 1991; Rudd, Rajab, & Dahm, 1994). Reinecke, DuBois, and Schultz (2001) found that depression and hopelessness mediate the relation between low problem solving self-efficacy and suicide ideation. Thus, the ability to generate solutions to problems interacts with life stress to prompt suicide ideation, although the mechanism for this is unclear because it does not seem to be associated with hopelessness. However, low problem solving self-efficacy is associated with hopelessness, which in turn makes individuals vulnerable to experiencing suicide ideation. It is possible that the interaction between the ability to generate solutions and life stress contributes to the activation of the suicide schema associated with unbearability, whereas low problem solving self-efficacy contributes to the activation of the suicide schema associated with hopelessness.

Although early theories linking problem solving with suicide ideation and suicidal acts regarded problem solving as a traitlike vulnerability factor (e.g., Schotte & Clum, 1982), results from one study suggested that at least to some degree, it is a statelike phenomenon that varies with mood and situational variables (Schotte, Cools, & Pavyar, 1990). Clum and Febbraro (2004) raised the possibility that problem solving deficits are a traitlike characteristic only in chronically suicidal individuals (e.g., those who have made multiple attempts). As Reinecke (2006) aptly noted, problem solving deficits are likely to be both proximal and distal risk factors for suicide, as they are risk factors for and concomitants of psychiatric disturbance as well as predictors of suicidal acts. We propose that problem solving impairment, like impulsivity, is a dispositional vulnerability factor for suicidal acts. The inability to generate solutions to problems likely puts individuals at risk for suicidal acts in the context of life stress, and in fact probably generates unnecessary life stress in and of itself and activates suicide schemas associated with unbearability. In contrast, low problem solving self-efficacy is associated with suicidal acts through its ability to activate suicide schemas characterized by hopelessness (cf. Rudd et al., 1994). However, we also suggest that problem solving ability and self-efficacy are further impaired during times of a suicidal crisis, which increases state hopelessness and attentional fixation on suicide as the only solution to one's problems. Thus, it is not surprising that cognitive behavioral treatments for suicidal acts place great emphasis on the development of problem solving skills, as it is assumed that these skills will generally reduce the amount of stress in a suicidal patient's life, as well as provide strategies for breaking out of attentional fixation in the midst of suicidal crises. As seen in subsequent chapters, a focus on problem solving is an important component of our cognitive intervention for suicidal patients.

Dysfunctional Attitudes

Any clinician who works with suicidal patients knows that they often express distorted beliefs about themselves, the world, and the future. Although these cognitive distortions are certainly not unique to suicidal patients, some empirical research has demonstrated that suicidal individuals endorse more dysfunctional attitudes than other psychiatric patients (T. E. Ellis & Ratliff, 1986), that endorsement of dysfunctional attitudes correlates with suicide ideation (Ranieri et al., 1987), and that a few domains of dysfunctional attitudes are particularly important in understanding the cognitive processes associated with suicide ideation and suicidal acts. For example, suicidal inpatients scored higher than nonsuicidal psychiatric inpatients on a measure of dysfunctional attitudes that assesses domains such as the demand for approval, sense of entitlement, and "emotional irresponsibility," or the lack of insight into the causes of one's emotional state (T. E. Ellis & Ratliff, 1986).

One particular type of dysfunctional attitude that has received much attention in the literature is trait perfectionism. As mentioned in chapter 2 of this volume, one facet of trait perfectionism, socially prescribed perfectionism, is associated with hopelessness (e.g., Dean, Range, & Goggin, 1996), suicide ideation (Hewitt, Flett, & Turnbull-Donovan, 1992), and suicide attempts (Hewitt, Norton, Flett, Callender, & Cowan, 1998). Perfectionistic individuals are vulnerable to perceive failure in all-or-nothing terms, ignoring the shades of gray. Moreover, recent research has raised the possibility that socially prescribed perfectionism is associated with suicide ideation through interpersonal mechanisms. For example, individuals who are high in socially prescribed perfectionism often display interpersonal hostility (Haring, Hewitt, & Flett, 2003), which has the potential to alienate them from others. In addition, individuals who are high in socially prescribed perfectionism report high levels of interpersonal sensitivity (Hewitt & Flett, 1991), which has the potential to facilitate faulty perceptions of social disconnection. Social disconnection, in turn, puts individuals at risk for suicidal behavior (Trout, 1980).

In many respects, the dysfunctional attitudes endorsed by suicidal patients reflect the activation of negative schemas, many of which are associated with psychiatric disturbance in general rather than being specific to suicide. However, T. E. Ellis and Ratliff's (1986) study suggested that dysfunctional attitudes are more characteristic of suicidal patients than of other nonsuicidal psychiatric patients, which raises the possibility that suicidal patients' negative schemas are stronger or are activated to a greater degree. As outlined in the next section, we propose that increased activation of one or more negative schemas associated with general psychiatric disturbance is associated with a greater likelihood of activation of suicide schemas. In addition, it is likely that dispositional perfectionism, as measured in studies by Hewitt, Flett, and their colleagues, is another dispositional vulnerability factor not only for the activation of negative schemas associated with psychiatric disturbance, but also for the activation of suicide schemas. As we saw with impulsivity and problem solving deficits, dispositional perfectionism likely characterizes only a subset of individuals. However, it is likely that (a) it works with other dispositional risk factors to increase vulnerability to psychiatric disturbance and suicidal acts, much in the way Rudd (2004, 2006) discussed in his theory of the suicidal mode, and (b) it increases the likelihood that a hopelessness schema will be activated in times in which the person experiences failure.

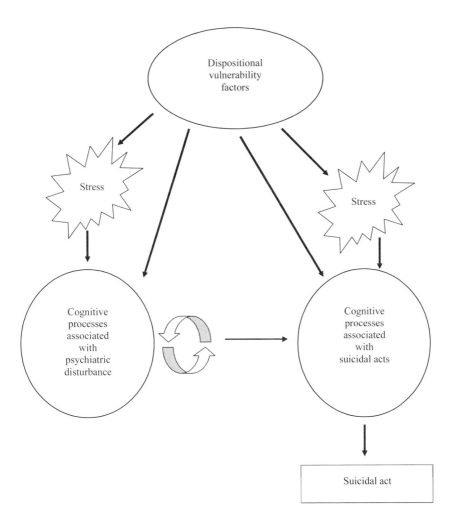

Figure 3.5. An integrative cognitive model of suicidal acts. From "A Cognitive Model of Suicidal Behavior: Theory and Treatment," by A. Wenzel and A. T. Beck, 2008, *Applied and Preventive Psychology, 12*, p. 191. Copyright 2008 by Elsevier. Adapted with permission.

A COGNITIVE MODEL OF SUICIDAL ACTS

A cognitive model of suicidal acts must be capable of incorporating general cognitive theory, suicide-relevant theoretical constructs, and empirically supported psychological constructs that have been shown to be related to suicidal acts. Figure 3.5 displays our comprehensive cognitive model of suicidal acts that was constructed to achieve this aim. Three main constructs are relevant to this model.

The top oval represents dispositional vulnerability factors, including impulsivity, problem solving deficits, perfectionism and other dysfunctional attitudes, and an overgeneral memory style. Although we highlight the psychological dispositional vulnerability factors in this chapter, in reality many of the risk factors described in chapter 2 can be included in this construct (e.g., low socioeconomic status, low educational attainment). These constructs, by themselves, they do not directly lead to psychiatric disturbance and suicidal acts. Rather, we propose that they are associated with suicidal acts in three ways. First, they have the potential to activate negative schemas related to psychiatric disturbance in times of life stress. It is likely that the specific contents of negative schemas emerge depending on the particular combination of dispositional vulnerability factors that an individual has. Second, these dispositional variables likely create stress in and of themselves, either in the context of stressors that exacerbate psychiatric disturbance or in the context of stressors that are more direct precursors to suicidal acts. For example, as discussed earlier, perfectionism is associated with interpersonal hostility, which has the potential to disrupt connections with others. Finally, these dispositional variables influence the course of cognitive processing during suicidal crises. As stated previously, an important feature of attentional fixation is that individuals are unable to apply reason to their problems and focus on suicide as the only way out. Thus, dispositional problem solving impairment is likely to increase the probability that the suicidal individual will (a) experience attentional fixation in times of state hopelessness and (b) make a suicide attempt rather than engage in more adaptive alternatives. A dispositional overgeneral memory style is likely to exacerbate attentional fixation because it reduces the probability that the suicidal individual will identify specific reasons to live. Moreover, dispositional impulsivity could influence the speed at which the suicidal individual spirals into a state of attentional fixation.

The left oval represents cognitive processes associated with general psychiatric disturbance, or the processes that are presented in more detail in Figure 3.1. As stated previously, negative schemas are activated in times of stress. Maladaptive thoughts, interpretations, judgments, and images, reminiscent of the content of these negative schemas, are prompted by external or internal antecedents, or both. The person, in turn, exhibits maladaptive emotional, physiological, and behavioral reactions that further strengthen the negative schema. However, the vast majority of individuals who experience this negative feedback cycle, or who are characterized by the dispositional vulnerability factors, do not subsequently attempt suicide. Thus, a cognitive model of suicidal behavior must explain the mechanism by which these variables escalate suicidal thoughts and behavior in only a subset of people.

We propose that in suicidal individuals, the negative feedback cycle between maladaptive cognitions and emotional, physiological, and behavioral reactions escalates, such that the negative schema assumes great strength (e.g., that which would be associated with a severe Axis I disorder) or additional negative schemas are activated (e.g., that which would be associated with comorbid Axis I disorders). This feedback cycle is represented by the arrows to the right of this oval. As negative schemas gain strength, and as additional negative schemas are activated, there is an increased likelihood that a suicide schema will be activated, especially when the person is also characterized by dispositional vulnerability factors. In other words, the consequences of the operations of negative schemas accumulate to a point at which the individual experiences hopelessness about the future, perceives that his or her situation is unbearable, or both. We believe this characterizes the majority of individuals who attempt suicide, as most are diagnosed with at least one psychiatric disturbance. It is likely that those individuals who attempt suicide but are not diagnosed with psychiatric disturbance have a particularly high loading on dispositional vulnerability factors or are experiencing a particularly high level of environmental stress.

The right oval represents the cognitive processes that are specific to suicidal acts, as is depicted in greater detail in Figures 3.2 and 3.4. When a suicide schema is activated, and when the person is experiencing life stress, it is likely that he or she will experience state hopelessness. When the person detects suicide-relevant cues and is concurrently in a state of hopelessness, there is an increased probability that he or she will have difficulty disengaging from suicide-relevant information, which serves to narrow attentional focus, limit his or her ability to engage in effective problem solving, exacerbate his or her sense of desperation, and increase suicide ideation. A suicide attempt occurs when this confluence of state hopelessness, suicide ideation, and attentional fixation passes a critical threshold, represented in the rectangle at the bottom of the figure. This threshold of tolerance is different for each individual and is likely determined by previous experiences with tolerating distress, previous experiences with pain and injury (cf. Joiner, 2005), and dispositional variables such as resiliency (or the lack thereof). For example, because a history of attempts is such a strong predictor of future attempts, it is possible that a previous attempt lowers one's threshold of tolerance.

An important point that has been stressed throughout this chapter is that this model is dimensional. In other words, the presence of any one of these constructs does not guarantee that an individual will engage in a suicidal act. Rather, dispositional vulnerability factors, negative schemas, and life stress interact and increase the probability that suicide schemas will be activated. If a person is characterized by few dispositional vulnerability factors and/or mild psychiatric disturbance, a great deal of life stress is needed to activate suicide schemas. However, if a person is characterized by many dispositional vulnerability factors and/or severe psychiatric disturbance, then much less life stress is required to activate suicide schemas. In addition, the activation of a suicide schema does not ensure that the person will engage in a suicidal act; rather, it is the interaction of suicide-relevant cognitions (e.g., state hopelessness, suicide ideation) and suicide-relevant cognitive processes (e.g., attentional biases toward suicide-relevant cues, attentional fixation) that increases the likelihood that a person will engage in a suicidal act. Moreover, there are differences in the manner in which these cognitive processes unfold within the same person, as the likelihood of engaging in suicidal acts will vary depending on whether this is the first or a repeat attempt (cf. Joiner & Rudd, 2000) and whether the individual has developed strategies for coping successfully with suicidal crises. We view our cognitive intervention described in Part II as providing patients with the requisite tools for modifying suicide schemas, coping with state hopelessness and suicide ideation, and disengaging from suicide-relevant cues.

We believe that this cognitive model of suicidal acts is compatible with existing theoretical perspectives on psychiatric disturbance and suicidal behavior; rather than contradicting them, it specifies more precisely the mechanism by which (a) dispositional vulnerability factors put individuals at risk for suicidal acts, (b) cognitive processes associated with psychiatric disturbance build to activate cognitive processes relevant to suicidal acts, and (c) psychological events unfold once a suicidal crisis is in motion. We agree with Rudd (2004) that a person's loading on risk factors, such as the dispositional variables presented in our model, increases the likelihood that the suicidal mode will be activated. As Rudd suggested, there are cognitive (e.g., hopelessness), affective (e.g., a state of desperation), motivational (e.g., the desire to end one's life), and behavioral (e.g., suicide attempt) features of suicidal crises, and we suspect that many of those are experienced as the suicide schema is activated and then become the primary focus in the context of attentional fixation. In fact, one could argue that the constructs presented in Figure 3.5 are a more precise representation of the cognitive components of the suicidal mode.

In addition, we agree with Joiner (2005) that cognitions about failures in life, such as failed belongingness or burdensomeness, are necessary for suicidal crises to develop. These perceptions of failure feed into suicide schemas, particularly the hopelessness-based schema. Although we do not explicitly include the acquired ability to enact lethal self-injury into our model, it could be argued that this is another dispositional vulnerability factor. As one's acquired ability to enact lethal self-harm increases, it is more likely that the direct path from dispositional vulnerability factors to cognitive processes associated with suicidal acts would be activated and that this construct would assume central importance relative to the other dispositional vulnerability factors.

SUMMARY AND INTEGRATION

In this chapter, we described a cognitive model of suicidal acts that incorporates general cognitive theory, psychological risk factors that have been identified in the empirical literature, and additional theoretical constructs that we believe are unique to suicidal acts. The cognitive model of suicidal acts that we describe here is far from complete; there is a large base of empirical literature that supports the role of some constructs, such as hopelessness and impaired problem solving, in explaining suicidal acts, but there are other constructs, such as information processing biases, that are just now beginning to receive attention from researchers. Parts of our model were derived from patients' reports of their experience in the time immediately preceding their attempt, and we face the challenge of designing innovative research methodologies to prospectively investigate these processes. Moreover, the model, as a whole, must be subjected to empirical scrutiny because there is a possibility that some constructs, such as perfectionism, could be explained by other, more general factors, such as the tendency to respond to adversity with dysfunctional attitudes. We also suspect that there are many other dispositional psychological variables that put individuals at risk for the activation of negative schemas associated with psychiatric disturbance and suicidal acts. We eagerly await future research to provide an empirical basis for refining this model to better understand suicidal acts.

How does this model help the clinician who has a suicidal patient in his or her office? First, we believe that this model provides a logical framework for understanding the reasons why a suicide schema has been activated and for anticipating circumstances that would increase the likelihood of engaging in suicidal acts (e.g., being in an environment in which there are many suicide-relevant cues). This knowledge has the potential to ground the clinician in the midst of a session that is likely characterized by intense affect or acting-out behavior. Moreover, as is discussed at length in chapter 7, the cognitive case conceptualization of a patient's clinical presentation stems from relevant theory, and the clinician will be able to identify interventions associated with the greatest likelihood of success by understanding the factors that are most relevant to the patient's suicide ideation and suicidal act. For example, a clinician will choose very different strategies for a patient with vague suicide ideation but who has several dispositional vulnerabilities than for a patient who is in an acute state of hopelessness. In Part II, we expand on strategies to intervene at the levels of the dispositional vulnerability factors, maladaptive cognitions associated with general emotional disturbance, and suicide-relevant cognitive processes that are evident in suicidal crises.

4

EVIDENCE-BASED TREATMENTS FOR THE PREVENTION OF SUICIDAL ACTS

Before we present our protocol based on the cognitive model of suicidal acts, we first describe existing treatments that have been designed with the intention of preventing suicidal and self-injury behavior to inform the reader of the scope of available interventions. There are diverse opinions about whether psychiatric treatments, including pharmacotherapy and psychosocial interventions, can prevent suicide. Some experts believe that suicide is preventable if individuals with psychiatric disturbance obtain and adhere to the recommended treatment for a specific disorder (e.g., Lönnqvist et al., 1995; Mann et al., 2005), whereas others have concluded that suicide is not preventable (e.g., Gunnell & Frankel, 1994; Wilkinson, 1994). One reason for the diversity of opinions among health care professionals is that very few empirical studies have been conducted explicitly to test the notion that suicide is a preventable behavior. Without definitive, empirically supported treatments for preventing suicide, clinicians and researchers draw their own conclusions based on their clinical experience or according to the manner in which they extrapolate from evidence-based treatments that have been found to reduce risk factors associated with suicide.

There are many clinical epidemiological studies using prospective and retrospective designs that support the conclusion that individuals who receive psychiatric treatment are less likely to die by suicide than individuals who do not receive psychiatric treatment (see Mann et al., 2005, for a review). However, the most scientifically rigorous study design for evaluating the efficacy or effectiveness of a treatment is the randomized controlled trial (RCT). Randomly assigning patients to either an intervention condition or a control condition and prospectively following them to determine the rates of suicide in both groups is the most stringent scientific method for determining whether an intervention prevents suicide.

Unfortunately, very few RCTs have examined whether psychiatric treatments reduce suicide to a greater extent than a control condition. RCTs can address this issue in two ways. *Efficacy* studies are designed to evaluate the effects of an intervention under optimal circumstances in which a number of confounding variables can be controlled. In contrast, *effectiveness* studies are conducted in "real-world" settings, wherein it is much more difficult to control for confounding variables. Throughout the remainder of this chapter, we use the terms *efficacy* or *efficacious* to describe results associated with the former type of study and *effectiveness* or *effective* to describe results associated with the latter type of study. In many of the studies reviewed in this chapter, the control condition is *usual care*, or the treatment that patients would usually receive in the community. There are two important advantages of using usual care control conditions: (a) The treatment of interest is compared to the standard of care in the community, which means that the treatment will be identified as efficacious or effective only if its benefits surpass those associated with the treatments patients typically receive, and (b) All patients in the study are receiving at least the standard of care in the community, so that no patient is required to wait a period of time for treatment or be subjected to a treatment that is inert.

To our knowledge, Motto and Bostrom (2001; Motto, 1976) conducted the only RCT demonstrating that an intervention can prevent suicide. In this effectiveness study, 3,005 patients who were hospitalized as a result of depression or a "suicidal state" were contacted 30 days after they were discharged to determine whether they had participated in outpatient therapy as recommended. Those patients who either refused or discontinued therapy by the 1-month follow-up (n = 843) were randomized to an experimental intervention or a control condition. The intervention consisted of a brief letter that was sent to patients by the research staff member who had interviewed them while they were hospitalized. The intent of the letter was simply to let patients know that the research staff was aware of their existence and maintained a positive attitude toward them. It made no demands for patients to take any action and did not request any specific information from them. An example of this type of letter is "Dear ____: It has been some time since you were here at the hospital, and we hope things are going well for you. If you wish to drop us a note we would be glad to hear from you" (Motto & Bostrom, 2001, p. 829). Each mailing also included a self-addressed, unstamped envelope so that patients could respond if they desired to do so, and patients who indeed responded received additional letters. Patients in the intervention condition received these letters monthly for 4 months, then every 2 months for 8 months, and then every 3 months for 4 years. In contrast, patients in the control condition did not receive any letters.

Suicide was determined by state records, clinical sources, and reports from family members. Results from this study indicated that the rate of suicide for patients in the intervention condition was significantly lower than the rate of suicide for patients in the control condition for the first 2 years of follow-up. However, there were no significant differences in the suicide rate between groups over the entire 5-year follow-up period, and the significant findings for the first 2 years of follow-up have not been replicated. Nonetheless, the Motto and Bostrom (2001) study is the only study of which we are aware that showed a significant effect for an intervention on death by suicide, at least across a 2-year period. The clinical implication of this finding is that clinicians who reach out to patients using letters that express concern and support, especially to those patients who are not engaged in treatment, may help to reduce the risk of suicide over the first 2 years following discharge.

Why have there been so few RCTs conducted to investigate the effects of interventions for suicide? A major methodological difficulty associated with conducting these studies is that suicide is a rare event (Hawton et al., 1998). In general, the lower the base rate and the greater the need to detect small treatment effects, the larger the sample size that is necessary to show statistically significant differences between an intervention and a control condition. Some researchers have estimated that to determine the overall incidence of suicide in the general population within plus or minus 5 individuals per 100,000 with a 90% confidence interval, a very large study sample of about 100,000 people would be required (Goldsmith, Pellman, Kleinman, & Bunney, 2002). Studies that include large sample sizes may be feasible for an intervention such as that described in Motto and Bostrom (2001), which poses minimal economic costs. However, the financial costs associated with conducting a large, multisite RCT of a psychiatric treatment, such as a 16-week pharmacotherapy or psychotherapy intervention, with adequate power to detect a possible intervention effect would be exorbitant.

An alternative and less expensive strategy for studying intervention effects on suicide is to select an outcome measure that is highly associated with suicide. As described in chapter 2, attempted suicide constitutes one of the strongest risk factors for suicide; thus, one possible proxy measure of suicide is the occurrence of a suicide attempt. The occurrence of suicide attempts is a more viable outcome measure than death by suicide because suicide attempts occur more often, especially in people who are at risk to engage in this behavior. RCTs may then be designed so that they have the potential to detect an intervention effect if they include individuals who are likely to attempt suicide during a limited follow-up period. Such studies typically recruit people who have recently attempted suicide or who have made multiple suicide attempts because they are particularly likely to make a repeat suicide attempt during the study follow-up period.

EVIDENCE-BASED TREATMENTS FOR THE PREVENTION OF SUICIDE ATTEMPTS

Despite the public health value of evaluating treatments for decreasing the rates of suicide attempts, there is a paucity of clinical trials that have developed and evaluated new treatments or have evaluated existing treatments for this problem. Several literature reviews (Comtois & Linehan, 2006; Gunnell & Frankel, 1994; Hepp, Wittmann, Schnyder, & Michel, 2004; Linehan, 1997) and meta-analyses (Arensman et al., 2001; Hawton et al., 1998; Hawton, Townsend, et al., 2005; Van der Sande et al., 1997) of RCTs evaluating pharmacological and psychosocial interventions have focused on the prevention of suicide attempts or self-injury behavior. The results of the RCTs have been mixed, with some studies reporting an effect of a specific intervention in reducing suicide attempts and self-injury behavior, and other studies finding no evidence for an effect. Meta-analyses of these studies are problematic because they have grouped studies together with different treatment approaches, different study designs, different outcome measures, and different study inclusion criteria. Hence, the conclusions of these meta-analyses have varied according to how these studies were categorized (Comtois & Linehan, 2006). For example, one meta-analysis found that cognitive behavior therapy (CBT) was effective in reducing suicidal behavior (Van der Sande et al., 1997), whereas another meta-analysis found that CBT was ineffective in reducing suicidal behavior (Hawton et al., 1998). Because results from meta-analyses on this topic have been mixed, and in fact have sometimes contradicted each other, we review individually the design of and results from each RCT.

We identified studies that aimed to investigate the efficacy or effectiveness of a pharmacological or psychosocial intervention for preventing suicide attempts or self-injury behavior. We included studies that focused on self-injury behavior along with studies that focused on suicide attempts as outcome variables because many did not differentiate between these two types of behaviors (e.g., Linehan, Armstrong, Suarez, Allmon, & Heard, 1991). All clinical trials that we included in this review were required to have the following characteristics: (a) to have been published in a peer-reviewed journal, (b) to have included participants who had attempted suicide or engaged in a self-injury behavior before entering the study, (c) to have randomly assigned participants to an intervention versus a control condition, and (d) to have included suicide attempts or self-injury behavior as a main outcome variable. We identified the RCTs through previous reviews and meta-analyses; through searches on MEDLINE, the Cochrane Library, and PsycINFO electronic databases; through references of published articles; and through personal communication. We review the following groups of studies: (a) pharmacotherapy, (b) intensive follow-up and case management, (c) inpatient treatment, (d) primary care treatment, (e) adolescent treatments, (f) psychodynamic therapy, (g) dialectical behavior therapy (DBT), (h) problem solving therapy (PST), and (i) cognitive therapy. Following this review, we provide a discussion of the implications for future research. Although this review focuses solely on the efficacy and effectiveness of interventions for preventing suicide attempts or self-injury behavior, we recognize that many other studies have reported significant findings on other associated risk factors (e.g., depression) or other related variables (e.g., treatment adherence).

Pharmacotherapy

Few pharmacotherapy studies have identified suicide attempts or self-injury behavior as a target for treatment or systematically assessed these behaviors during follow-up. Although depression has commonly been observed among individuals who have attempted suicide, it is often untreated or inadequately treated even after individuals attempt suicide (Oquendo et al., 2002). Meta-analyses examining studies of antidepressant medication for mood disorders have found that this intervention approach is generally ineffective in preventing suicide (Agency for Health Care Policy & Research, 1999). The few RCTs that have examined antidepressants' effects specifically on suicidal behavior found that these medications were not efficacious in preventing suicide attempts or intentional self-injury behavior (D. B. Montgomery et al., 1994; S. A. Montgomery, Roy, & Montgomery, 1983; Verkes et al., 1998). However, Verkes et al. (1998) reported that paroxetine (Paxil), a selective serotonin reuptake inhibitor, was more efficacious than placebo in preventing subsequent suicide attempts, but only for those patients who had attempted suicide fewer than five times before entry into the study. The findings of this secondary analysis have yet to be replicated.

More promising results for preventing suicide attempts have been reported for patients with major affective disorder treated with lithium and for patients with schizophrenia treated with clozapine (Leponex). Thies-Flechtner, Müller-Oerlinghausen, Seibert, Walther, and Greil (1996) compared the efficacy of lithium versus carbamazepine (Tegretol) and amitriptyline (Elavil). Of the nine suicides and five attempted suicides that occurred during follow-up, none took place during lithium treatment. In a multisite RCT, Meltzer et al. (2003) compared the efficacy of clozapine versus olanzapine (Zyprexa) in patients diagnosed with schizophrenia or schizoaffective disorder. Results indicated that significantly fewer clozapine-treated patients attempted suicide during a 2-year follow-up period than did olanzepine-treated patients. Subsequent analyses supported this finding when the potential effects of additional (or concomitant) psychotropic medications were considered (Glick et al., 2004). From this brief review, we can conclude that antidepressants are generally not efficacious in reducing the rate of suicide attempts but that lithium and clozapine show some promise.

Intensive Follow-Up and Case Management

Several studies have examined the efficacy or effectiveness of clinical case management or intensive follow-up approaches involving outreach services in reducing the likelihood of reattempts or additional self-injury behavior. Many of these studies failed to report a significant effect of these interventions on reducing these behaviors during follow-up (Allard, Marshall, & Plante, 1992; Cedereke, Monti, & Ojehagen, 2002; Chowdhury, Hicks, & Kreitman, 1973; Hawton et al., 1981; Van der Sande et al., 1997; Van Heeringen et al., 1995). In one exception, Welu (1977) found that a comprehensive follow-up intervention reduced repeat suicide attempts, relative to usual care. The study intervention included psychotherapy, crisis intervention, family therapy, and pharmacotherapy interventions according to the clinical evaluation of the patient's needs. Patients assigned to the intervention condition were contacted by a mental health clinician as soon as possible after discharge. Follow-up contacts usually included a home visit, and weekly or biweekly contact occurred over a 4-month follow-up period. Unlike the other studies that failed to find a significant treatment effect, the intervention in the Welu (1977) study provided evidence demonstrating that outreach programs that provide comprehensive mental health treatment and emphasize follow-up and continuity of care after discharge from the hospital prevent repeat suicide attempts.

Three other studies have found encouraging results depending on the type and frequency of follow-up contact. First, Termansen and Bywater (1975) conducted an RCT that compared in-person follow-up, telephone follow-up, and no follow-up after discharge from a hospital after attempting suicide. The study found a significant reduction in repeat suicide attempts for the in-person follow-up condition relative to the no follow-up condition. In addition, Vaiva et al. (2006) found that patients who intentionally overdosed and received a 1-month follow-up call from a psychiatrist were less likely to make a subsequent suicide attempt than patients who received usual care (i.e., no telephone contact). However, there were no significant differences between patients who received calls and patients in the usual care group at the 3-month follow-up assessment.

In a partial replication of the Motto and Bostrom (2001) study, Carter, Clover, Whyte, Dawson, and D'Este (2005) recruited patients from a regional toxicology unit who had presented to emergency departments in New South Wales, Australia. All patients had sought an evaluation after an intentional self-poisoning (e.g., pharmaceuticals, illicit drugs, carbon monoxide, herbicide or rodenticide, insulin, other unknown substance). They randomly assigned 772 patients to an intervention or control group. The intervention was very similar to the Motto and Bostrom (2001) study, which involved sending eight nondemanding postcards to patients (in sealed envelopes) over a 12-month period after discharge. This study found no significant differences between groups in the *proportion of participants* who made a repeat overdose during the 1-year follow-up period. However, when multiple attempts made by the same patient in the follow-up period were considered, the individuals who were sent the postcards made approximately half the *total number* of repeat attempts than did individuals in the control condition. Subgroup analyses showed that the intervention predominantly reduced the number of attempts made by women.

Several studies have examined the coordination of care after discharge from the hospital (Moller, 1989; Torhorst et al., 1987). Moller (1989) reported that continuation of treatment after discharge with the same clinician who provided inpatient treatment was no more effective in preventing suicide attempts or self-injury behavior compared to treatment provided by a different clinician. However, Torhorst et al. (1987) reported that the rate of suicide attempts and self-injury behavior in the group of patients who saw the same person for treatment after discharge from the hospital was significantly lower that that of patients who had a change of clinicians postdischarge.

In all, we have reason to be cautiously optimistic about the effectiveness of intensive follow-up and case management in reducing suicide attempts and self-injury behavior. Although not all studies examining this issue found that the intervention condition reduced these behaviors to a greater degree than a control condition, there is at least some evidence that in-person, telephone, and mail contact after discharge from the hospital is beneficial to suicidal patients.

Inpatient Treatment

Several RCTs have been conducted with patients who had been admitted to inpatient units. However, these studies failed to find a significant treatment effect on suicide attempts or self-injury behavior in comparing (a) behavior therapy and insight-oriented therapy (i.e., the control condition; Liberman & Eckman, 1981); (b) cognitive therapy, PST, and nondirective therapy (i.e., the control condition; Patsiokas & Clum, 1985); and (c) general hospital admission and discharge for patients with no immediate medical or psychiatric needs (i.e., the control condition; Waterhouse & Platt, 1990). Other inpatient studies have examined whether giving patients a "green card" is beneficial in reducing suicide attempts and/or self-injury behavior.

The green card functions as a passport to guarantee readmission to the hospital or to an on-call psychiatrist. However, these studies found that access to inpatient admission or an on-call psychiatrist was no more effective in preventing suicide attempts or self-injury behavior than usual care for adolescents (Cotgrove, Zirinsky, Black, & Weston, 1995) or for adults (J. Evans, Evans, Morgan, Hayward, & Gunnell, 2005; Morgan, Jones, & Owen, 1993). Thus, researchers have not been successful in identifying an inpatient treatment that reduces the frequency of suicidal or self-injury behavior beyond that achieved through usual care.

Primary Care Treatment

Primary care treatment has the potential to be critical for the management of patients who attempt suicide or engage in intentional self-injury behavior because these patients typically have poor compliance with outpatient psychiatric treatment and might be more likely to be seen by a primary care physician (Kreitman, 1979; Morgan, Burns-Cox, Pocock, & Pottle, 1975; O'Brien, Holton, Hurren, & Watt, 1987). In one of the few studies conducted in a primary care setting, Bennewith et al. (2002) evaluated the effects of an intervention on the incidence of repeat episodes of self-injury behavior. Physicians' practices, rather than patients themselves, were randomized to test an intervention versus usual care. General practitioners whose practices were assigned to the intervention condition received letters informing them of instances in which one of their patients had engaged in self-injury behavior, as determined by the research team that was tracking this behavior, and consensus guidelines for the clinical management of self-injury behavior. The mailing also included another letter to send to patients, inviting them to make an appointment for consultation. Results indicated that the intervention was not effective in reducing the incidence of repeat episodes of self-injury behavior in the total sample, relative to usual care. However, subgroup analyses indicated a beneficial effect in patients with a history of repeated intentional self-injury behavior but a harmful effect in those without a history of self-injury behavior. That is, for patients with no history of self-injury behavior, those in the intervention condition were significantly more likely to engage in subsequent self-injury behavior than were those in the usual care condition. Thus, there is no evidence that tracking self-injury behavior in primary care settings is effective in reducing this behavior, and in fact, it may actually have the opposite effect.

Psychosocial Treatments for Adolescents

Many psychosocial treatments for adolescents who engage in suicidal or self-injury behavior incorporate elements from several theoretical approaches. For example, Wood, Trainor, Rothwell, Moore, and Harrington

(2001) evaluated the efficacy of developmental group therapy for adolescents with self-injury behavior, which consisted of strategies from problem solving and CBT, DBT, and psychodynamic group psychotherapy. Patients attended six "acute" group sessions that were organized around specific themes (i.e., relationships, school problems and peer relationships, family problems, anger management, depression and self-harm, hopelessness and feelings about the future), followed by weekly group therapy. Results indicated that the adolescents who had received group therapy were less likely to have engaged in subsequent, intentional self-injury behavior on two or more occasions than were adolescents who received usual care only.

Two studies, yielding mixed results, investigated the efficacy of family therapy on suicide attempts in youths. In the first study, Huey et al. (2004) evaluated the effectiveness of multisystemic therapy (MST), relative to usual psychiatric hospitalization, in reducing attempted suicide among predominately African American youths (ages 10–17) who were referred for emergency psychiatric hospitalization. MST is a home-based intervention that focuses primarily on the family by (a) empowering caregivers with the skills and resources they need to communicate with, monitor, and discipline their children effectively; (b) assisting caregivers in engaging their children in prosocial activities while disengaging the youths from deviant peers; and (c) addressing individual and systemic barriers to effective parenting. In addition, MST requires family members to remove or secure any potentially lethal methods in the home. The results of this study indicated that MST was significantly more effective than psychiatric hospitalization in reducing attempted suicide over a 16-month follow-up period. However, a limitation of this study was that the youths who were assigned to the MST condition had significantly higher rates of previous suicide attempts than did the youths who were assigned to the hospitalization condition. Thus, treatment findings might be explained by regression to the mean, or the statistical fact that groups who demonstrate extreme behavior on one occasion tend to exhibit less extreme behavior when tested on a subsequent occasion.

In the second study, Harrington et al. (1998) investigated whether an intervention given by child psychiatric social workers to the families of children and adolescents who had intentionally injured themselves by taking an overdose reduced subsequent intentional self-injury more than did usual care. The intervention consisted of an assessment session and four home visits that focused on family problem solving. The study found no significant differences between groups on episodes of intentional self-injury during the follow-up period. However, the authors raised the possibility that because it was necessary for the research social workers to have some contact with the patients assigned to the usual care condition, some aspects of the intervention became incorporated into usual care.

King et al. (2006) investigated the efficacy of the Youth-Nominated Support Team—Version 1 with suicidal, psychiatrically hospitalized adolescents. This innovative intervention consisted of asking adolescents to identify caring individuals from all of the domains of their lives, including school, neighborhood and community, and family. With parent or guardian permission, the support persons participated in psychoeducation sessions that were designed to help them understand the youth's psychiatric disorder(s) and treatment plan, suicide risk factors, strategies for communicating with adolescents, and emergency contact information. Support persons were encouraged to have weekly contact with the adolescents. The results of this study, however, showed no beneficial effect of this treatment on reducing suicide attempts compared to usual care. Thus, researchers have designed some innovative and comprehensive psychosocial treatments for suicidal adolescents, but more work is needed to ensure that they translate to meaningful reductions in suicidal and self-injury behaviors.

Psychodynamic Psychotherapy

Guthrie et al. (2001) sought to determine the effects of a brief psychodynamic interpersonal psychotherapy for patients who intentionally poisoned themselves. This treatment focused on identifying and helping to resolve interpersonal difficulties that contributed to psychological distress and was based on a "conversational model" of psychotherapy developed by Hobson (1985). Patients were randomly assigned to four sessions of therapy delivered in patients' homes by a nurse therapist or to a usual care condition that did not include interpersonal psychotherapy. Patients who received the study intervention were significantly less likely to intentionally harm themselves than patients in the control condition during the 6-month follow-up period.

Bateman and Fonagy (1999) compared the effectiveness of psychoanalytically oriented partial hospitalization to usual psychiatric care for patients with borderline personality disorder (BPD). Treatment consisted of individual therapy (weekly), psychoanalytic group psychotherapy (three times a week), expressive therapy oriented toward psychodrama techniques (weekly), community meetings (weekly), meetings with a case administrator (weekly), and medication management (weekly). Therapy was provided by psychoanalytically trained nurses. If patients missed sessions, they received a telephone call, a letter, or a home visit if needed. The results revealed a significant reduction in self-injury behavior and in suicide attempts over an 18-month follow-up period. Although both studies reviewed in this section used a psychodynamic approach to treatment and incorporated home visits into their protocol, they differed in the type of treatment (interpersonal psychotherapy, psychoanalytic psychotherapy) and in the intensity of treatment. Nevertheless, these studies raise the possibility that a comprehensive approach to treatment that incorporates a psychodynamic focus reduces self-injury behavior.

Dialectical Behavior Therapy

DBT is a cognitive behavioral intervention that was developed by Linehan (1993a, 1993b) to treat suicidal patients who meet criteria for BPD. DBT targets three types of behaviors in the following order of priority: (a) life-interfering behaviors (e.g., suicide attempts, self-injury behavior), (b) therapy-interfering behaviors, and (c) behaviors that interfere with quality of life. According to Linehan et al. (2006, p. 759), DBT achieves the aims through five mechanisms:

> (1) increasing behavioral capabilities, (2) improving motivation for skillful behavior (through contingency management and reduction of interfering emotions and cognitions), (3) assuring generalization of gains to the natural environment, (4) structuring the treatment environment so that it reinforces functional rather than dysfunctional behaviors, (5) enhancing therapist capabilities and motivation to treat patients effectively.

DBT is provided through four modes of service delivery: (a) weekly individual psychotherapy, (b) weekly group skills training, (c) telephone consultation as needed, and (d) weekly therapist consultation team meetings.

Linehan et al. (1991) initially studied the efficacy of DBT in a sample of 44 women who had engaged in at least two self-injury behaviors, with or without suicidal intent, and who were diagnosed with BPD. Patients were randomized to either DBT or usual care as provided in the community. DBT was provided over a 1-year interval, and patients in both conditions were followed for 1 year thereafter. The proportion of patients assigned to the DBT condition who engaged in repeat self-injury behavior in the following year was significantly lower than the proportion of those who engaged in repeat self-injury behavior and who were assigned to the usual care condition. A replication trial was subsequently conducted to determine whether unique aspects of DBT were more efficacious than treatment offered by non–behavioral psychotherapy experts (Linehan et al., 2006). The study sample consisted of 101 women who engaged in recent suicide attempts or self-injury behavior and who were diagnosed with BPD. Participants were randomly assigned to DBT or community treatment by experts for a 1-year period, and follow-up assessments were conducted over a 2-year period. Results indicated that patients who were assigned to the DBT condition were approximately half as likely to make a subsequent suicide attempt than were patients assigned to the community-treatment-by-experts condition. Research is currently being conducted to clarify which components of DBT are essential and to what degree fidelity to the DBT manual is needed to achieve comparable results to this and other studies. DBT is one of the few interventions for suicidal patients for which multiple RCTs have been conducted that support the efficacy of the treatment.

Problem Solving Therapy

PST is a type of cognitive behavioral intervention in which the clinician and patient work together to address issues using problem solving strategies. Most studies investigating this approach to treatment have found that it is not efficacious in preventing subsequent self-injury behavior when compared to usual care (Gibbons, Butler, Urwin, & Gibbons, 1978; Hawton et al., 1987; Salkovskis, Atha, & Storer, 1990). In addition, McLeavey, Daly, Ludgate, and Murray (1994) found no differences between interpersonal problem solving skills training and a problem-oriented crisis approach for attempts made by self-poisoning. Furthermore, Donaldson, Spirito, and Esposito-Smythers (2005) found no significant differences between problem solving and affective skills management therapy when compared to a supportive relationship treatment for adolescents who had recently made a suicide attempt.

In addition to these studies, two other studies are worth noting because the investigators attempted to evaluate a treatment approach in two separate clinical trials and because one of these studies used a much larger sample size than most other efficacy studies reviewed in this chapter. These studies examined the efficacy of manual-assisted CBT for the treatment of suicidal and nonsuicidal self-injury behaviors. Manual-assisted CBT is an intervention that combines aspects of PST, cognitive restructuring, and alcohol and substance abuse reduction strategies as well as some strategies adapted from DBT. Patients are provided with a treatment manual and up to seven individual therapy sessions. Although this intervention consists of several different strategies, its core feature is geared toward helping patients to deal with specific problems that are identified as contributing to their self-injury behavior and that can be addressed using problem solving strategies. An initial pilot study found no treatment effect for manual-assisted CBT on reducing self-injury behavior when compared to a usual care condition (K. Evans et al., 1999). Subsequently, a large clinical trial ($n = 480$) also failed to find a significant effect of this intervention on reducing self-injury behavior relative to usual care (Tyrer et al., 2003).

In all, studies examining the efficacy of problem solving strategies in reducing suicidal and self-injury behavior have yielded disappointing results. However, we note that although Salkovskis et al. (1990) did not find an intervention effect for PST on repeat suicide attempts over a 1-year follow-up period, this study did identify a significant treatment effect at the 6-month follow-up assessment. These results are particularly impressive given that the sample consisted of only 20 patients, a small sample size that usually can only detect large treatment effects, and that treatment effects were also found for measures of depression and hopelessness. Thus, the results of the Salkovskis et al. study inspired us to further develop our cognitive intervention for suicidal patients, with a focus on problem solving and on developing cognitive and behavioral coping strategies, and to evaluate its efficacy.

Cognitive Therapy

In the mid-1990s, we began to explore the feasibility of cognitive therapy as a brief crisis intervention that could be used in the emergency department for patients who came to the hospital after a suicide attempt. At the time, our clinical inclination was that patients who recently attempted suicide would be receptive to a brief problem solving intervention because most of the suicide attempts that we had observed were triggered by a recent stressful life event that typically involved a loss of one type or another, such as a breakup of a relationship, physical illness, drug relapse, or unemployment. We observed that although some of these patients welcomed our offer to address their problems in the emergency department, others were reluctant or refused to speak with us. Some patients reported that they had "made a mistake," that the suicide attempt was "in the past," and that they would never make another attempt again. They perceived that they did not need psychiatric treatment for their suicidal behavior because they had made a definite commitment to live and, therefore, further treatment was unnecessary. Other patients, however, were too upset to talk about their problems in detail and believed that addressing their problems directly would result in continued emotional pain. Still other patients were unable to speak with us because they were physically incapacitated (e.g., semi-unconscious because of drug overdose), and some patients refused to give us any reason for declining our offer to discuss their problems.

We quickly realized that patients were more likely to be cooperative with us after they had been admitted to the hospital or discharged and became more emotionally stable; the time frame that we found most optimal for approaching patients about the possibility of participating in the study was approximately 24 to 72 hours following the initial hospital evaluation in the emergency department. Typically, we would conduct a psychological evaluation while the patient was hospitalized, and we would begin to identify the patient's motivation for the suicide attempt. Given that the length of hospitalization was usually brief, we offered outpatient sessions following discharge. Initially, we thought that a very brief course of cognitive therapy (approximately four or five sessions) would be sufficient for addressing the patient's most immediate difficulties, but then we realized that several sessions were required just to gain an understanding of the timeline of events that occurred before the attempt and to formulate a case conceptualization of the patient's clinical presentation (as described in chap. 7). In addition, we found that patients often required more time to build a trusting relationship with the clinician so that they could feel comfortable in addressing emotionally distressing issues and building a sense of hope.

Our preliminary clinical trial involved randomly assigning patients to receive approximately 10 sessions of cognitive therapy or to receive usual care. Patients in both groups were allowed to participate in any other treatment that was usually provided in the community. Patients received a baseline assessment shortly after they had been admitted or discharged from the hospital, and follow-up assessments were conducted at 1, 3, 6, and 12 months thereafter.

After we had conducted the study for about a year, we became concerned about our attrition rate. We noticed that the majority of patients were not attending the follow-up evaluation sessions. This finding alarmed us because there can be major differences between those who complete and those who do not complete a study. For example, improved clinical status can lead patients to conclude that a study is no longer beneficial to them and that there is no need to continue study participation. Conversely, patients who experience a worsening of symptoms might also conclude that the study is not beneficial to them and discontinue study participation before they receive a full "dose" of treatment. Regardless of the reasons for attrition, poor retention rates severely limit conclusions regarding efficacy and generalizability of the findings.

Given this major methodological problem, we were determined to improve our efforts in retaining participants in the study and in engaging them in treatment. We quickly realized that we needed to employ additional staff, whom we identified as study case managers (SCMs). The primary role of the SCM was to engage and to facilitate patients' ongoing participation in the study (Sosdjan, King, Brown, & Beck, 2002). The SCM usually established a relationship with patients during hospitalization while they were in the emergency department or on the inpatient unit. They assisted patients in staying engaged in the study and provided other referral services as needed. Our hope was that patients would come to identify the SCM as a valuable resource who was consistently available throughout the duration of the study.

Although a major task of the SCM was to provide written and/or verbal reminders of upcoming appointments, SCMs also provided regular and ongoing contact with the patient through phone calls or letters. In accordance with results from the Motto and Bostrom (2001) study, SCMs also sent other nondemanding cards and letters to the patients just to check in with them. Given the potential for high rates of attrition and noncompliance with treatment sessions, our team made it a priority to contact patients directly, rather than leaving messages for them, because our experience indicated that this practice made subsequent attendance at sessions more likely. During these check-ins, patients reported many roadblocks or barriers to attending study assessments and treatment, including transportation problems, child-care responsibilities, physical disabilities, lack of organizational skills, and forgetfulness. SCMs assisted patients in addressing and solving the problems that patients had in getting to therapy or evaluation appointments.

Despite many reminder calls and letters, patients still failed to attend assessment interviews and treatment sessions, regardless of whether they were in the cognitive therapy or the usual care condition. Patients often reported that they felt ambivalent about or reluctant to attend these appointments for a variety of reasons, including (a) being hopeless about treatment or perceiving that treatment was unhelpful, (b) experiencing anxiety about discussing personal problems, or (c) perceiving that the attempt was a mistake and that they no longer needed treatment (see chaps. 6 and 10 for strategies that address these challenges). SCMs were cognizant of these attitudes toward treatment and listened and empathized with patients' concerns. Once patients felt understood, SCMs assisted them in developing a more adaptive stance toward treatment or the study and in overcoming potential roadblocks. We soon saw that attendance in assessment and treatment sessions increased substantially.

Given the success of our study case management protocol in retaining patients in treatment and in the study, we proceeded with a larger clinical trial to evaluate the efficacy of cognitive therapy for the prevention of repeat suicide attempts, relative to usual care (G. K. Brown, Tenhave, et al., 2005). It is the cognitive therapy protocol evaluated in this study that is the subject of Part II of this volume. Although we included the case management approach in this study's research design, it is important to note that the primary focus of this study was still on the evaluation of the efficacy of cognitive therapy rather than on the effects of the study case management, as all patients who were assigned to either treatment condition received study case management. Next, we provide a brief description of the study's procedures and findings to provide a context to support the extensive discussion of the intervention in Part II of this book.

The sample consisted of 120 patients who attempted suicide and who received a medical or psychiatric evaluation within 48 hours of the attempt. Patients were recruited from medical or psychiatric emergency departments at the Hospital of the University of Pennsylvania. Potentially eligible participants were initially identified in the emergency department after a suicide attempt (e.g., overdose, laceration, gunshot wound). Other inclusion criteria included (a) being 16 years of age or older, (b) speaking English, (c) having the ability to complete a baseline assessment, (d) having the ability to provide at least two verifiable contacts to improve tracking for subsequent assessments, and (e) having the ability to understand and provide informed consent. Patients were excluded if they had a medical disorder that would prevent participation in an outpatient clinical trial.

Following a baseline assessment, patients were randomly assigned to one of two treatment conditions: cognitive therapy or no cognitive therapy. Patients in the cognitive therapy condition were scheduled to receive 10 individual therapy sessions according to a treatment manual (G. K. Brown, Henriques, Ratto, & Beck, 2002). Patients in both conditions received usual care in the community. We conducted follow-up assessments on all individuals over an 18-month period to determine whether they made another suicide attempt.

Patients' ages ranged from 18 to 66 years, and 61% were women. As assessed by patient self-report for the purpose of describing the racial characteristics of the sample, 60% were African American, 35% were Caucasian, and 5% were Hispanic, Native American, or unspecified. At baseline, 92% were diagnosed with major depressive disorder, and 68% were diagnosed with a substance use disorder. Specific substance use disorders included alcohol (30%), cocaine (23%), and heroin (17%) dependence. Most patients (85%) had more than one psychiatric diagnosis. The majority of patients (58%) attempted suicide by overdosing using prescription, over-the-counter, or illicit substances. Other methods were skin puncture or laceration (17%); jumping (7%); and hanging, shooting, or drowning (4%).

We found that 24% of the individuals who received cognitive therapy made another suicide attempt, whereas 42% of the individuals who received only usual care made another suicide attempt. The most important finding was that patients who received cognitive therapy were about 50% less likely to make a repeat suicide attempt during the follow-up period than those who did not receive cognitive therapy. We also found that patients who received cognitive therapy were significantly less depressed and hopeless than patients who received only usual care over the 18-month follow-up period. Post hoc analyses indicated that patients who received cognitive therapy had lower scores on the Beck Depression Inventory at the 6-, 12-, and 18-month follow-up period and significantly lower scores on the Beck Hopelessness Scale at the 6-month follow-up period than patients who received only usual care.[1]

We concluded that cognitive therapy was efficacious for preventing suicide attempts. This effect was above and beyond the case management provided by the SCMs, as patients in both the cognitive therapy and the usual care conditions received this service. We suspect that patients who learn more adaptive ways to handle acute distress are better equipped to avert a future suicidal crisis. Although the development of effective problem solving strategies is a vital focus of our intervention, there are several equally important components, including behavioral strategies focused on improving patients' social support network and increasing their compliance with adjunctive services, which in turn engage them in their community, and cognitive strategies focused on modifying maladaptive thoughts and beliefs that emerge in suicidal crises and reminding patients of reasons for living.

---

[1]As we were in the final stages of preparing this volume, we learned of another RCT that investigated the efficacy of a brief cognitive behavioral intervention on repeat episodes of self-injury behavior, with or without suicide intent, with adolescent and young adult patients (Slee, Garnefski, van der Leeden, Arensman, & Spinhoven, 2008). The results of the study found that the study intervention, which was mostly based on our cognitive therapy protocol (see Slee, Arensman, Garnefski, & Spinhoven, 2007), was efficacious in preventing self-injury.

The remainder of this book is devoted to describing the components and applications of this intervention.

IMPLICATIONS FOR FUTURE RESEARCH

In summary, only a few studies have examined the efficacy and effectiveness of treatments for the prevention of suicide. With the exception of one study that found an effect for sending nondemanding contact letters to patients who did not receive treatment following hospitalization (Motto & Bostrom, 2001), the efficacy–effectiveness literature on suicide prevention is practically nonexistent. However, there have been a modest number of RCTs supporting the efficacy of various treatment strategies for preventing suicide attempts and intentional self-injury behavior. Successful interventions for adults include intensive follow-up and case management (Termansen & Bywater, 1975; Vaiva et al., 2006; Welu, 1977), psychodynamic psychotherapy (Bateman & Fonagy, 1999; Guthrie et al., 2001), DBT for BPD (Linehan et al., 1991, 2006), cognitive therapy (G. K. Brown, Tenhave, et al., 2005), lithium for major affective disorders (Thies-Flechtner et al., 1996), and clozapine for schizophrenia (Meltzer et al., 2003). For adolescents, developmental group therapy (Wood et al., 2001) is an efficacious treatment, and MST (Huey et al., 2004) shows some promise. Despite these encouraging findings, there is insufficient evidence to make recommendations about the most effective type of treatment for patients who attempt suicide or engage in intentional self-injury behavior, as the effectiveness of these interventions has not been directly compared.

In this section, we make several observations about the state of this literature. Most of our comments have implications for understanding the strengths and limitations of the research designs that form the basis of the studies reviewed in this chapter. It will be important for researchers who evaluate treatments for suicidal patients to consider these suggestions as they design future studies. However, we also believe it is important for clinicians to understand these design issues so that they can be critical consumers of the research literature and evaluate the degree to which such research findings apply to their clinical practice.

One limitation of most of the studies cited in this review is the lack of standards in reporting the results of the trials. Inadequate reporting, specifically, makes the interpretation of results difficult, if not impossible, and it runs the risk that biased results will receive false credibility (Moher, Schulz, & Altman, 2001). To improve the quality of reports, an international group of clinical trial researchers, statisticians, epidemiologists, and biomedical editors published the Consolidated Standards of Reporting Trials (CONSORT) guidelines (Begg et al., 1996). The CONSORT guidelines encompass a checklist and flow diagram to help improve the quality of reports of

RCTs. The checklist includes items that should be addressed in the report; the flow diagram provides readers with a clear picture of the progress of all participants in the trial, from the time they are randomized until the end of their study involvement. The intent of these guidelines is to make the experimental process clearer, whether it is flawed or not, so that users of the data can more appropriately evaluate its validity for their purposes. For example, the guidelines require that RCTs report the methods used to generate the randomization sequence, the methods used to implement randomization including concealment, and an indication of the person(s) who generated the randomization sequence, who enrolled participants, and who assigned them to the groups. Many trials reported in this review failed to report important details of the randomization procedure that was used. The CONSORT guidelines have been endorsed by prominent medical and psychology journals such as *The Lancet*, the *Journal of the American Medical Association*, and the *Journal of Consulting and Clinical Psychology*. It is hoped that future clinical trials in suicide prevention will adopt more rigorous reporting standards.

The main methodological flaw in nearly all of these trials is that they included too few participants for a potential intervention effect to be detected (Arensman et al., 2001; Hawton et al., 1998). Very few clinical trials reported power analyses that were performed before the study, which would have increased the likelihood that a large enough sample size would have been recruited to detect significant differences between the intervention and control conditions (but see G. K. Brown, Tenhave, et al., 2005; Carter et al., 2005; and Linehan et al., 2006, for exceptions). Arensman et al. (2001) computed sample size estimates for the number of patients needed to detect statistically significant differences in repeat attempt rates and concluded that for most of the RCTs that they reviewed, there were considerable discrepancies between the actual number of patients included and the sample size required to detect an effect.

A related point is that many patients who were deemed to be at high risk for suicide (such as suicidal patients needing immediate hospitalization) were actually excluded from these studies despite the fact that they were evaluating the efficacy or effectiveness of treatments in reducing suicidal behavior! Researchers who have examined the efficacy of psychotropic medication have routinely excluded individuals who were at the highest risk for suicide. Perhaps researchers were concerned that these patients were too risky to be treated on an outpatient basis or that they were too difficult to retain in a clinical trial. Regardless, given this industry standard, investigators who have studied the effects of other treatments designed to reduce suicide risk have used a similar approach. For example, Linehan (1997) reviewed 13 outpatient RCTs that included six studies in which high-risk individuals were excluded (Allard et al., 1992; Chowdhury et al., 1973; Gibbons et al., 1978; Hawton et al., 1981; McLeavey et al., 1994; Waterhouse & Platt, 1990), and none of the studies that excluded high-risk patients found a significant treatment effect. The inclusion of high-risk patients may improve statistical power and increase the probability that the results of suicide prevention studies will be generalizable to high-risk individuals (Comtois & Linehan, 2006).

The generalizability of findings from RCTs is based on the assumption that research participants represent the population from which they are sampled. Biases from differential patterns of study enrollment among patient subgroups can lead to overestimates or underestimates of the effectiveness of an intervention. Research involving individuals being treated for a psychiatric problem may be particularly vulnerable to participation bias (Patten, 2000; Vanable, Carey, Carey, & Maisto, 2002) because symptom severity and social circumstances (e.g., homelessness, poverty) may lead to differential participation among patient subgroups. Specifically, individuals with greater severity of symptoms and fewer social resources may be more likely to enroll in mental health (Shadish, Matt, Navarro, & Phillips, 2000) and substance abuse treatment trials (Rychtarik, McGillicuddy, Connors, & Whitney, 1998; Strohmetz, Alterman, & Walter, 1990) relative to individuals with lower severity of symptoms and more social resources. Thus, the information obtained from clinical trials that have included participants with increased symptom severity, limited availability of social resources, and lower suicide risk is likely to limit the generalizability of these studies.

The nature and degree of participation bias among individuals who attempt suicide or who engage in self-injury behavior and who are recruited for clinical outcome studies is virtually unknown (Arensman et al., 2001). For example, among the RCTs cited in this review, only 11 studies reported the proportion of patients who refused to participate (Allard et al., 1992; G. K. Brown, Tenhave, et al., 2005; Carter et al., 2005; Evans et al., 1999; Guthrie et al., 2001; Hawton et al., 1981; Linehan et al., 2006; Verkes et al., 1998; Waterhouse & Platt, 1990; Welu, 1977). In these studies, the proportion of eligible patients who refused to participate in the clinical trials ranged from 0% (Waterhouse & Platt, 1990) to 49% (Allard et al., 1992). Moreover, only 2 studies examined the factors that were associated with participation bias. Welu (1977) found that there were no significant differences in demographic variables between the study participants and the study refusers. In our study, Caucasian individuals were approximately 2.6 times more likely than African American individuals to decline participation (G. K. Brown, Tenhave, et al., 2005). Further efforts are underway that examine the reasons for and implications of this potential bias.

Another problem with many of these studies is the use of an idiosyncratic, study-specific nomenclature for constructs of interest. Using a common nomenclature to describe suicide attempts and intentional self-injury behavior is essential for comparing the results across studies. Definitions of suicidal behavior, such as those described in chapter 1, are not often included in the reporting of these studies. The implication of not including definitions of suicidal behavior in reports of clinical trials is that it leaves out important details that are necessary for the potential replication of studies or for combining the results of studies using meta-analyses so that conclusions may be made about the effectiveness of a specific type of treatment.

A related concern is that there was a lack of consistency among the trials in the types of outcome measures that were used, and most studies did not describe the methods used to enhance the quality of the measurements (e.g., training of assessors). Even more problematic is that many studies failed to use standardized outcome measures altogether. As reviewed in chapter 1, there are many outcome measures of suicide attempts and other suicide-related variables that have adequate reliability and validity. Suicide attempts, especially those attempts that involve a lower level of lethality, are often difficult to assess reliably and require consensus among raters who are blind to the treatment condition. Moreover, very few studies described whether those assessing outcomes were blind to the treatment group assignment, and if so, how the success of the blind was evaluated. The inclusion of blind assessors is a critical design component to prevent assessors from consciously or unconsciously adjusting their ratings as a function of the treatment condition to which patients are assigned. We recognize, however, that conducting blinded assessments is particularly problematic when the patients being evaluated are experiencing a suicidal crisis and breaking the blind may be necessary to effectively manage a suicidal study participant.

Treatment integrity is another area of concern in which most intervention trials fall short. For intervention studies to be replicated, treatment manuals are required to prevent obfuscation of the treatment. Moreover, most RCTs failed to provide any description of how clinicians were trained in the intervention or to include measures of adherence or competency of therapeutic skills. For psychotherapy studies, sessions should be audio- or videotaped and rated using a competency measure with established reliability and validity. In our clinical trials, for example, we use the Cognitive Therapy Rating Scale (Young & Beck, 1980), supplemented by additional items for specific components of the intervention that are focused on suicide prevention. Treatment integrity may be enhanced further when sessions are rated by multiple independent raters.

We also have several recommendations for handling the data collected in the context of RCTs. All efficacy or effectiveness analyses should be conducted using an intent-to-treat principle, which includes all randomized patients in the treatment groups to which they were assigned, regardless of their protocol adherence, actual treatment received, or subsequent withdrawal from treatment or assessment. To account for dropouts, survival analyses may be used when the outcome is the occurrence of a suicide attempt or the time to a suicide attempt. Hierarchical linear (or logit) modeling can also be used for the estimation of changes in repeated measures without necessitating last observation carried forward or exclusion of participants with missing data.

The use of appropriate analytic strategies to address study attrition is critical for determining whether treatments are truly efficacious or effective. For example, if analyses that examine the efficacy of treatment include only those participants who actually complete the study, then it is possible that patients who dropped out of the study may have done so because they were clinically worse (or better). This strategy has the potential to lead to a biased conclusion about the efficacy of the intervention.

Finally, we note that this review includes studies that focused on the prevention of suicidal acts and does not include research studies that focused on decreasing suicide ideation. Several promising treatments are available for resolving suicide ideation. For example, the Collaborative Assessment and Management of Suicidality (Jobes, 2000, 2006) is a suicide-specific manualized assessment and treatment approach for the clinical care of patients with suicide ideation. Collaborative Assessment and Management of Suicidality is based on the Suicide Status Form (Jobes, Jacoby, Cimbolic, & Hustead, 1997), a measure that serves as a guide to the assessment of patients' suicidality and leads to the emergence of underlying constructs that can be used to inform and shape a treatment plan. There is preliminary support for the beneficial effects of this approach (Jobes, Wong, Conrad, Drozd, & Neal-Walden, 2005), and it is currently being evaluated in the context of an RCT.

SUMMARY AND INTEGRATION

The studies reviewed in this chapter support the view that suicidal acts are preventable. Despite the limited number of studies and the fact that many of these studies are characterized by methodological flaws, there are several evidence-based treatments, such as cognitive therapy, that have been shown to be efficacious in reducing the rate of suicide attempts. We highly recommend that clinicians who treat patients at risk for suicide become knowledgeable and skilled in evidence-based treatments. The application of evidence-based treatments is especially important for treating high-risk patients who may feel ambivalent or even hopeless about treatment, as clinicians can communicate to these patients specific information about the likelihood of treatment success.

It is important to acknowledge that there are several limitations to the generalizability of these findings to diverse high-risk populations. To date, most of the treatment trials that have been conducted have used adult samples, so caution is advised in generalizing the findings of these studies to other age groups. Although a few treatment trials have been conducted with adolescents, we could find no RCTs that focused on preventing suicidal acts with older adult populations or with college-age young adults. Furthermore, few intervention trials have been conducted with racial or ethnic minorities;

gay, lesbian, bisexual, or transgender minorities; and other vulnerable populations (e.g., prisoners). Additional innovative or culturally adapted interventions for these special populations need to be developed and tested. For current evidence-based interventions, additional studies are needed to test the effectiveness of these treatments in community settings, to understand the mechanisms of change associated with treatment response, and to evaluate the effectiveness of disseminating these treatments to the public.

We designed our RCT evaluating the efficacy of cognitive therapy versus usual care in reducing the reattempt rate in at-risk patients (G. K. Brown, Tenhave, et al., 2005) to (a) expand on the aspects of PST that showed promise and (b) implement a rigorous study on this topic that improved on many of the methodological limitations of other studies. From a treatment standpoint, our intervention included not only a focus on developing effective problem solving strategies but also a focus on developing other cognitive and behavioral strategies to manage future suicidal crises, develop reasons for living, improve social relationships, and increase compliance with other medical and psychiatric treatment. This intervention was derived from the general cognitive therapy principles that are described in the next chapter and emerged in the context of the research efforts described in chapters 1, 2, and 3. From a methodological standpoint, our RCT used an adequate sample size, maintained rigorous standards to ensure that assessments were reliable and that treatment was delivered with integrity, and adopted sophisticated statistical techniques to accurately characterize trends that emerged from the data set.

The result of our effort was that we identified a treatment that is efficacious, relative to usual care, in reducing the rate of reattempts. As described earlier in this chapter, we found that patients who received cognitive therapy and who received usual care in the community were approximately 50% less likely to make a repeat suicide attempt during the 18-month follow-up period than patients who received usual care alone. Relative to patients in the usual care condition, those in the cognitive therapy condition endorsed less depression and hopelessness, which are two variables that contribute to the risk of patients engaging in a suicidal act. Although we continue to evaluate the efficacy and effectiveness of this intervention (see chaps. 11–13 for innovative applications), there is solid empirical support to regard cognitive therapy as a treatment for adult suicidal patients. In the next section, we describe the specific manner in which this treatment is implemented. We provide a systematic guide for the reader to receive a brief orientation to cognitive therapy (chap. 5) and to gain an in-depth understanding of the goals and strategies associated with the major phases of cognitive therapy for suicidal patients (chaps. 6–9). Throughout these chapters, we illustrate the application of this protocol with a case example.

II

CLINICAL APPLICATIONS

5

COGNITIVE THERAPY: GENERAL PRINCIPLES

Cognitive therapy is based on a solid foundation of cognitive theory, a specified session structure, and an array of cognitive and behavioral strategies from which the clinician can choose on the basis of the patient's cognitive case conceptualization (i.e., the understanding of the patient's clinical presentation in light of cognitive theory). Cognitive therapy for suicidal patients shares many basic similarities with cognitive therapy for patients who struggle with other types of difficulties, such as cognitive therapy for depression (A. T. Beck, Rush, Shaw, & Emery, 1979), for anxiety disorders (A. T. Beck & Emery, 1985), for personality disorders (A. T. Beck, Freeman, Davis, & Associates, 2004), and for substance use disorders (A. T. Beck, Wright, Newman, & Liese, 1993). This chapter outlines basic principles of cognitive therapy that are common to most cognitive therapeutic interventions (cf. J. S. Beck, 1995; Wright, Basco, & Thase, 2006), along with suggestions for the manner in which these standard strategies apply to suicidal patients. Strategies that are targeted specifically to suicidal patients are presented in subsequent chapters.

One fundamental characteristic of cognitive therapy is that it is structured and time limited. Patients understand that they will take an active, systematic problem solving stance in session and that they will work collaboratively with their clinician to address their life problems in a goal-directed manner. Unlike cognitive therapy with other types of patients, cognitive therapy with suicidal patients involves work on life problems specifically as they relate to their recent suicidal crisis. That is, a focus on suicide prevention is central to cognitive therapy with these patients, whether it be in a direct manner (e.g., strategies that modify suicide ideation and intent) or in an indirect manner (e.g., strategies that patients can use to find a job, which will in turn instill hope for the future and add meaning to their lives). Patients understand that homework assignments are developed collaboratively with their clinician so that they can apply the strategies discussed in sessions to the life problems that relate to suicidal crises.

Another fundamental characteristic of cognitive therapy is that a large part of the intervention focuses on patients' interpretations of situations and ways to evaluate these situations in a realistic manner. Clinicians educate patients about the cognitive model and the manner in which interpretations or misinterpretations are associated with certain emotional experiences and behavioral reactions. The cognitive model is reinforced using examples from patients' own lives. Patients understand that they will develop skills to identify and evaluate their negative thoughts relating to distress, and suicidal crises. They will then link the thoughts that emerge in specific situations to more fundamental beliefs that color the manner in which they view themselves, the world, and the future, and they will work toward modifying those beliefs.

Cognitive therapy also includes strategies that are primarily behavioral in nature. For example, anxious patients are often taught relaxation skills, and depressed patients often engage in activity monitoring so that they can identify ways to get pleasure from their lives and participate more frequently in those activities. Behavioral strategies are useful in obtaining relief from distressing symptoms and in developing skillful ways to manage symptoms when they arise in the future. However, behavioral strategies also produce cognitive change, in that they demonstrate to patients that they have the ability to tolerate and manage distress and that their problems are not insolvable.

Although much of cognitive therapy is focused on active strategies for producing meaningful cognitive and behavioral changes, it is based on the premise that a sound therapeutic relationship is in place between the clinician and patient. It is imperative that clinicians demonstrate a warm, empathetic, collaborative, and nonjudgmental stance (A. T. Beck & Bhar, in press). The development of a comprehensive case conceptualization that provides the roadmap for treatment is derived from a detailed understanding of the patient's history and current problems. This understanding is best acquired through the use of attentive listening and empathy. Clinicians who have better listening and empathy skills are more likely to foster behavior change than less skilled clinicians because these skills are essential to enhancing the therapeutic alliance. Thus, the goal of cognitive therapy is not for the clinician to advise patients on how to better approach problems in their lives. Rather, it provides a means for patients to discover alternative ways of interpreting and responding to problems in their lives through collaborative empiricism, or the process by which the patient and clinician together approach the patient's problems from a systematic, scientific approach. This aim can only be achieved when the clinician communicates a stance of acceptance and validation.

This chapter is divided into two main sections: (a) session structure and (b) general cognitive therapy strategies. All of the material in these sections is general to most forms of cognitive therapy and is described in detail in books such as Judith S. Beck's (1995) *Cognitive Therapy: Basics and Beyond* or Jesse H. Wright, Monica R. Basco, and Michael E. Thase's (2006) *Learning Cognitive-Behavior Therapy: An Illustrated Guide*. However, we illustrate the manner in which these general strategies are applied specifically to suicidal patients.

SESSION STRUCTURE

Cognitive therapy sessions follow a basic session structure, including a brief mood check, bridge from the previous session, agenda setting, homework review, discussion of issues on the agenda, periodic summaries, homework assignment, and final summary and feedback. Following this session structure allows for ongoing assessment of patients' symptoms and suicide risk, for patients to take an increasingly large amount of responsibility in the therapeutic process, and for the opportunity to systematically address patients' concerns from a cognitive perspective. The session structure described in this section allows for tangible goals to be accomplished within each session and for a thread to run between sessions so that the course of treatment is geared toward meaningful changes in patients' lives.

Brief Mood Check

At the beginning of each session, cognitive therapists briefly assess their patients' mood in the time since the previous session. One efficient way to complete this task is to have patients arrive for their sessions 5 to 10 minutes early so that they can complete standard self-report inventories such as the Beck Depression Inventory—II and the Beck Hopelessness Scale. In the first moments of the session, the clinician can quickly scan patients' responses on these inventories and address symptoms that are particularly problematic or in which there has been marked improvement or deterioration.

We acknowledge that many clinicians do not have ready access to standardized self-report inventories and that some patients express frustration with completing these inventories before every session. In these instances, clinicians can verbally assess patients' mood, such as by asking them to rate their mood on a 0 to 10 scale (0 = *extremely low mood* and 10 = *extremely good mood*). It is also helpful for clinicians to attend to symptoms that are particularly distressing for patients, such as sleep disturbance or fatigue. As described at length in the next chapter, the brief mood check is a time for the clinician to conduct a suicide risk assessment. Furthermore, because suicidal patients are often receiving a number of medical, mental health, addictions, and social services, the clinician uses this time to check in regarding their adherence to other treatment protocols, particularly their use of psychotropic medication, and whether they are regularly attending other appointments. Finally, the clinician who works with suicidal patients assesses patients' alcohol and substance use in the time since the previous session, as these factors are strongly associated with increases in suicide ideation and risky behavior.

The brief mood check should last no more than 5 minutes. One obstacle the clinician may encounter is that patients begin to launch into a detailed description of the difficulties they have experienced in the time since the previous session. We suggest that clinicians gently intervene in these instances with an acknowledgment that their problems sound difficult and an invitation to put them on the agenda for discussion. This subtle intervention socializes patients into the cognitive therapy session structure and models a systematic, problem solving approach to address the issues that they introduce.

The brief mood check serves a number of purposes (J. S. Beck, 1995). First, it helps the clinician to track patients' progress over time and make that progress explicit to patients to instill hope and build momentum. It also provides the clinician with the opportunity to express care and concern for patients about issues that are most salient to them. Moreover, the brief mood check uncovers "red flags" that are important for the clinician to address later in session, such as an increase in substance use, hopelessness, or noncompliance with medication use.

Bridge From Previous Session

The bridge from the previous session is a very brief strategy to ensure that patients accurately understand and remember what happened in the previous session. It also links the content from the previous session to the current session, so that the clinician can follow up on issues introduced in the previous session and work with patients to achieve an adequate resolution. The bridge from the previous session is helpful in weaving a coherent thread across the course of treatment and ensuring that sessions progress in a manner such that the longer term goals of therapy are addressed. To make the bridge from the previous session, the clinician might ask questions such as (a) "What did we talk about last session that was important for preventing another attempt? What did you learn?" (b) "Was there anything that bothered you about our last session?" or (c) "What homework did you do or did not do? What did you learn?" (J. S. Beck, 1995).

At times, patients admit that they do not remember much about the previous session, which can undoubtedly be frustrating for the clinician. This difficulty is particularly common with suicidal patients, who often live with chronically high levels of distress, use alcohol and substances, and exhibit clouded judgment and decision-making skills. We encourage clinicians to have patience in these instances and to be more directive in completing the bridge than they might with their nonsuicidal patients. Although it is ideal for patients to take responsibility in forming the bridge from the previous session, the clinician may need to socialize them into this process and lead by example.

Agenda Setting

Agenda setting is an explicit, collaborative process that occurs between the clinician and the patient to establish the issues that will be a focus of the session. Both the clinician and the patient place items on the agenda. If multiple problems need to be discussed, then agenda setting involves the prioritization of those problems, including an indication of the length of time that is necessary to address each issue. Items for the agenda usually relate to treatment goals set collaboratively in the early phase of treatment so that there is a coherent thread from one session to another. However, at times patients will introduce agenda items that are unrelated to treatment goals. It usually is in the best interest of the therapeutic relationship to address the issues that patients believe are important; in many instances, as these issues are discussed, the clinician finds creative ways to link them to the overall goals for treatment. That is, the clinician gently guides the agenda setting process to ensure that patients' needs are met and that progress is made toward achieving the goals set at the beginning of treatment. As patients become socialized into the process of cognitive therapy, they take more responsibility for setting and organizing the agenda items. In general, agenda setting improves the efficiency of sessions, and it models an organized approach to prioritizing and addressing life's problems. In fact, we have found that agenda setting instills hope in some patients, as it communicates that their life problems can be addressed in a systematic manner.

Agenda setting with suicidal patients involves determining which specific problems or issues will have the greatest likelihood of preventing a future suicidal crisis. Priority should be given to problems or skills deficits that are perceived by the clinician and the patient as the most life threatening or dangerous. We recognize that suicidal patients often have chronic and unresolved problems that make them vulnerable to engage in future suicidal acts. We advise the clinician to first address issues that are most relevant to the recent suicidal crisis rather than focus on more long-standing issues. Thus, the primary focus of cognitive therapy for suicidal patients should be on (a) issues that were the most proximately related to the suicidal crisis, (b) interventions that are perceived by both the clinician and the patient to be the most helpful in preventing a future suicidal act, and (c) thoughts, beliefs, or behaviors that interfere with treatment attendance or treatment compliance. We regard this as the *acute* phase of treatment that is focused on suicide prevention. Long-standing and chronic issues will eventually be addressed during a *continuation* phase of treatment after it is clear that patients have developed and can apply strategies to manage suicidal crises. In chapter 9, we discuss an approach to evaluating whether this goal has been met.

Agenda setting is a central feature of cognitive therapy because it organizes patients' problems, relates them to treatment goals, and ensures that time in session is used efficiently. However, not all patients respond favorably at first to agenda setting, as some patients find that it is unfamiliar and very different from the way they have approached other issues in their lives. Thus, early in the course of treatment, it is important for the clinician to explicitly describe the agenda setting process and explain its rationale. The clinician can ask for feedback to assess whether patients have any reservations about agenda setting or questions about the way it works. Some patients find that they dislike the term *agenda* because it seems too formal or businesslike. In such cases, the clinician can set an agenda by asking, "What is important for us to focus on today?" in a more casual manner and ultimately achieve the same goal.

We have identified a few common problems that occur with agenda setting and have devised strategies for addressing them. For example, some patients begin to describe problems in great detail when asked which items they would like to place on the agenda. When patients launch into a discussion of problems with little structure, they often become agitated and link their problems with other, more tangential issues, which in turn escalates their level of distress. If this occurs, it is important to educate patients that agenda setting involves naming the problem rather than describing it in detail. For example, the clinician can say, "This sounds like an important problem that we should put on the agenda. Should we call this problem 'problem with your boyfriend?' Is there any other problem that we need to get to today?" This process models for patients how to clearly identify the problem and its boundaries.

Sometimes patients respond with "I don't know" when asked which items they would like to place on the agenda. There are many reasons why patients might have this response, including that they truly do not know how best to address their problems, that they are hopeless about the possibility that treatment will be helpful for them, or that they are avoiding talking directly about their problems. In this circumstance, the clinician can summarize the previous session to remind patients of the trajectory of treatment to date and the treatment goals. If this strategy does not elicit any agenda items, the clinician can offer a menu of choices related to the treatment goals or suggest topics from previous sessions that focused on suicide prevention. In addition, the clinician can suggest that patients think about what they would like to talk about at the next session or write a list of agenda items as a homework assignment. The clinician could even devise a worksheet with questions for patients to think about before their next session. All of these strategies help patients develop the skills to identify and organize their life problems.

Sometimes patients have a negative emotional reaction when asked about the agenda. If this occurs, the clinician can identify patients' thoughts by asking them, "What ran through your mind when I asked you what you wanted to put on the agenda?" There are a variety of reasons why patients may have a negative reaction to setting the agenda. For example, they may feel hopeless about treatment and believe that setting an agenda is futile. They may perceive themselves as weak and fear that things will get worse if they discuss specific emotional topics. Once the clinician recognizes and empathizes with patients' concerns, he or she can assist them in developing an adaptive response to these thoughts. In addition, the clinician can help patients to identify the advantages and disadvantages of discussing specific topics and develop strategies for dealing with negative emotional reactions to specific agenda items.

The content of the agenda might change as the session progresses. Even the most experienced clinician finds that he or she occasionally makes inaccurate estimations of the amount of time required to discuss a specific agenda item. In these instances, the clinician makes the dilemma apparent to patients so that together they can problem solve the best way to make adjustments. If patients opt to wait until the following week to discuss a specific item, then that is highlighted in the following session's bridge from the previous session. Moreover, as the clinician and patient discuss agenda items, they might uncover a more pressing issue to address in the remainder of the session. In this case, the clinician makes it explicit that they will deviate from the agenda and the reason for doing so.

Review of Homework

As stated earlier, homework is an essential part of cognitive therapy because it ensures that patients will have the opportunity to apply the skills developed in session to the problems they experience in their lives. We often find that patients become quite adept at talking through problems in session, but that sustained change occurs only when they are able to translate this discussion to their lives in a meaningful way. It is imperative that clinicians include homework review on the agenda and attend to the assignment developed in the previous session. If the clinician does not review homework, then he or she risks giving patients the message that homework is not important.

At times, patients may come to session with a crisis, and particularly with suicidal patients, these crises need to take priority. If the clinician decides that it is in patients' best interest to abandon the homework and focus on the crisis, then he or she makes this decision explicit (e.g., "It's obvious that this new problem is causing you a lot of distress and needs to take first priority in our work together. Let's save discussion of last week's homework assignment for next week").

Discussion of Agenda Items

Discussion of agenda items forms the heart of cognitive therapy. It is here that patients describe situations that have been problematic for them and that clinicians use the general cognitive therapy strategies described in this chapter and the specific suicide-relevant cognitive therapy strategies described in the subsequent chapters to help patients understand the meaning of the situations, identify more balanced construals of the situations, and problem solve ways to cope with the aftermath of the situations or to address similar situations in the future. Typical problems that clinicians experience in this portion of the session include unfocused discussion, inaccurate pacing, and the failure to make an appropriate therapeutic intervention (J. S. Beck, 1995). These problems are easily remedied with supervision from an experienced cognitive therapist and with reflection based on the clinician's own professional experience.

Periodic Summaries

Periodic summaries provide a means for clinicians and patients to summarize the main themes uncovered from different parts of the therapy session. Often the periodic summaries occur after discussion of each agenda item and consist of a restatement of the problem, the main conclusion learned from discussion of the problem, and the manner in which patients plan to address it. Periodic summaries ensure that both the clinician and the patient have the same understanding of the problem and offer the opportunity for the clinician to provide empathy. Periodic summaries are also useful for pacing the session and for allowing time for the clinician and patient to reflect on issues discussed. As with some of the other aspects of the cognitive therapy structure, in the early phase of treatment clinicians often take the lead in providing periodic summaries. Patients take an increasing amount of responsibility for periodic summaries as they become socialized into the cognitive therapy process.

Homework Assignment

Although we discuss the assigning of homework toward the end of this section of the chapter, homework may be addressed whenever it is appropriate during the discussion of agenda items. The importance of putting careful thought into the development of homework assignments cannot be understated. If patients are not invested in their assignments, they will not follow through with completing them, and as a result, therapy may not progress as smoothly or as quickly as it might otherwise. Given the central importance of homework in cognitive therapy, sufficient time should be available so that any problems with the homework assignment may be addressed.

Sometimes patients find the term *homework* aversive, and it is helpful for them to work with their clinician to devise an alternative phrase that would facilitate, rather than inhibit, the completion of the assignment. Sometimes patients perceive that homework is being assigned to them and that they have little say in its development. It is important to remember that cognitive therapy is fundamentally a collaborative process and that all aspects of therapy should be approached from a collaborative stance. Sometimes patients find assignments overwhelming, either because the task is so complex that they do not know where to start when they are outside the clinician's office or because too many components have been assigned. In our experience, we have found that it is most helpful to develop one concrete task for homework on which suicidal patients can fully focus their attention.

The clinician can adopt a number of strategies to ensure that homework assignments are successful. For example, the clinician can ask patients to estimate the likelihood that they will complete their homework assignment on a scale ranging from 0% (*definitely do not plan to do the homework assignment*) to 100% (*definitely plan to complete the homework assignment*). If their estimate is less than 90%, then the homework assignment should be discussed further until the clinician and patient are confident that the patient will do it. The clinician can ask patients to recall the rationale for the homework assignment, which can help to reaffirm their commitment to achieving positive change through cognitive therapy. Once the rationale for homework is clearly understood, the clinician can ask patients to anticipate any obstacles that might interfere with completing the assignment and brainstorm ways to overcome them. Following this discussion, the clinician reassesses the likelihood of patients' expectation that the homework will be completed. If patients continue to indicate that they are less than 90% confident that they will complete their homework assignment, then the assignment may be modified or a new assignment may be considered.

There are several other strategies for improving the likelihood that patients will successfully complete the homework. If at all possible, it is helpful to start the assignment in session so that patients have a model to follow and so that they perceive that they have taken a step toward success. The clinician and patient may also discuss a specific date and time to do the homework. We strongly recommend that the homework assignment be written down by both the clinician and the patient. A written homework assignment reminds patients to complete the task and clarifies the rationale and any specific instructions. We have found that written homework assignments are visual cues that remind patients of adaptive coping strategies and that increase the likelihood that they will actually use them during crises.

Final Summary and Feedback

The last 5 minutes of the session are devoted to a final summary of the material covered throughout the entire session and are an opportunity for patients to provide feedback to the clinician. Sometimes patients find the discussion of specific topics, especially those issues related to suicide, to be aversive or upsetting. Obtaining feedback helps to identify such problems so that the clinician and patient can identify strategies for managing these emotions. These strategies may include assisting patients in recognizing and responding to any negative cognitions using the skills presented in the subsequent section of this chapter, helping patients to engage in any distracting or self-soothing activities, or scheduling a follow-up session or phone call during the next 24 to 48 hours to assess patients' status. Feedback is another way of communicating that therapy is a collaborative process and that the clinician is willing to make modifications if there is an aspect of the experience that is not satisfactory.

GENERAL COGNITIVE THERAPY STRATEGIES

The evaluation of maladaptive or unhelpful cognitions is a central activity in cognitive therapy. After gaining practice with identifying the thoughts and images associated with negative emotional experiences, patients systematically develop strategies for questioning the validity of these cognitions and incorporating all available information in developing an alternative, more adaptive perspective. Over time, themes emerge from the typical cognitions that are reported, which are indicative of dysfunctional thoughts that patients have about themselves, the world, and/or the future. Lasting cognitive change occurs when these dysfunctional beliefs are identified and modified throughout the course of treatment. In addition, behavioral strategies may be incorporated into cognitive therapy as indicated. These strategies often serve the function of increasing patients' activity levels and testing out dysfunctional beliefs in their own environments. In the next sections, we describe some of these standard cognitive and behavioral strategies in more detail.

Evaluating Thoughts and Beliefs

A prominent activity that occurs in cognitive therapy is the evaluation of distorted or maladaptive thoughts and beliefs. In cognitive therapy that is specifically geared toward suicidal patients, most of the thoughts and beliefs that are addressed in session are relevant to suicide ideation, suicidal intent, and hopelessness. The following section describes standard strategies for identifying and modifying these cognitions.

Identifying Automatic Thoughts

Automatic thoughts are thoughts that emerge in particular situations and that are associated with a negative change in mood. They are termed *automatic* because in many instances, they appear so quickly that patients are not fully conscious of them and may not be aware of their emotional or behavioral consequences. A first step in modifying problematic cognitions is to help patients develop tools to recognize when they are experiencing them.

The most straightforward way of identifying automatic thoughts is simply to ask, "What was running through your mind at that moment?" However, in our experience, patients sometimes have trouble answering this question, particularly during the early phase of cognitive therapy. Other approaches to identifying automatic thoughts include, "What would you guess was running through your mind at that time?" or "Would you have been thinking _____ or _____?" Clinicians also should be aware that patients might experience distressing images in addition to distressing automatic thoughts. J. S. Beck (1995) provided excellent examples of ways to elicit patients' automatic thoughts.

When clinicians guide patients in identifying automatic thoughts and images, it is important that they explicitly link those cognitions with patients' emotional experiences to reinforce the cognitive model (i.e., that cognition is closely associated with mood). In addition, it is helpful to have patients rate the intensity of their mood on a 0 to 10 or 0 to 100 scale, with 10 or 100 being the most intense emotion they have ever experienced. This exercise serves several purposes. First, it helps patients to develop a taxonomy of their emotional experiences, so that they become adept at differentiating among emotions rather than using global terms such as *upset*. Second, as is seen in the next section, it provides a basis by which they can judge the effectiveness of the strategies to modify these cognitions. Third, it provides information to the clinician about the seriousness of the reported circumstances and patients' reactions. Finally, it helps patients begin to evaluate the notion that they cannot tolerate strong emotion without engaging in suicidal behavior.

Throughout the clinical chapters in this section, we focus on the patient introduced in chapter 1, Janice, to illustrate these cognitive therapy principles. Janice represents an amalgam of several of the typical female patients whom we have seen in our clinical trials designed to evaluate the effi-cacy of cognitive therapy for suicidal patients. The following dialogue illus-trates the manner in which Janice's clinician began to identify the automatic thoughts that she experienced before she turned in a job application, at the time she turned the application in to the supervisor, and after she left the building. Notice that it takes some time for Janice to identify the thoughts and images that were running through her mind at the time. The clinician creatively uses a number of strategies to construct an accurate picture of the situation, the cognitions that ran through Janice's mind, and her subsequent emotional reaction to them. In addition, when Janice provides thoughts that were mainly descriptive of what was happening in the situation (e.g., "There are too many people on this bus"), the clinician prompts her to discern the meaning behind those events. The clinician verbally repeats the thoughts as they are uncovered so that Janice will begin to make the connection be-tween particular thoughts and her emotional experiences.

> *Clinician:* Let's slow down for a minute and walk through what happened when you turned in the application. Are you up for that?
>
> *Janice:* OK.
>
> *Clinician:* Picture yourself as you were taking the bus to the store. What do you see?
>
> *Janice:* I'm on the bus, and it is really packed. People are getting off at every stop. I wondered whether I would even get there when I told the manager I would drop by.
>
> *Clinician:* What was running through your mind at that time?
>
> *Janice:* I was like, there are too many people on this bus! I just want to get there!
>
> *Clinician:* And what did it *mean* that there were too many people on the bus at that time?
>
> *Janice:* I'm going to be late.
>
> *Clinician:* OK, so you had the idea that you were going to be late. What emotion were you experiencing at that time?
>
> *Janice:* I guess I was sad.
>
> *Clinician:* You felt sad. [pause] Janice, I'm curious about something. Many of the other folks I work with tell me, when they have thoughts that they are going to be late, that they are experiencing anxi-ety or maybe frustration. Where does the sadness come from?
>
> *Janice:* [tearful] Because I knew it would be the last straw. I figured I probably wouldn't get the job anyway, and now this. I was like, what's the use of even going there?

Clinician:	You're on to something very important, Janice. A lot of things ran through your mind at that time, like "There are too many people on this bus" and "I'm going to be late." But what this all *meant* to you was the prediction that being late sealed your fate— that you weren't going to get the job.
Janice:	Exactly.
Clinician:	So when you had the idea that your fate is sealed, that you're not going to get the job, how much sadness did you feel, on a scale of 0 to 100, with 100 being the most sadness you've ever experienced?
Janice:	I was pretty sad. Like an 80 or an 85.
Clinician:	And what effect did that have on you as you walked in the build-ing and asked to speak to the supervisor?
Janice:	I probably looked sad.
Clinician:	Do you think that might have affected the way the supervisor saw you?
Janice:	Maybe, yes. I was almost in tears. [sarcastic chuckle] I guess a supervisor wouldn't want to hire someone for customer service who looks like they can't handle talking to people.
Clinician:	So the thought about your fate being sealed likely had an effect on how you came across?
Janice:	Yes, I'm sure it did.
Clinician:	Then, when you handed him the application, what was running through your mind?
Janice:	I don't know. I just wanted to get it over with.
Clinician:	Do you think you might have been thinking, "I have a good chance of making a good impression?" or instead might you have been thinking, "I'm never going to get this job?"
Janice:	Probably the second one. Like, what's the use? I was like that especially when he gave me a look like there was no way in hell he would hire me.
Clinician:	So you were struggling with the idea that you were never going to get this job and had the thought "What's the use?" What emotion were you experiencing then, on a 0 to 100 scale?
Janice:	Still sad. But now probably even more, like a 95.
Clinician:	So you gave him the application, and then what happened?
Janice:	He was like really short with me and said, "We'll be in touch."

Clinician: And then you left?

Janice: Yeah, I almost ran out of there, I was so afraid I would cry in front of him.

Clinician: What was running through your mind as you left the building?

Janice: Nothing. My mind was a complete blank.

Clinician: Do you recall seeing any vivid images or pictures in your mind?

Janice: Actually, yeah. I was stuck in the same rut as always, locking myself in my room with my stepfather yelling at me outside my door to get out of bed.

Clinician: And what emotion were you experiencing then?

Janice: Even more sadness.

Clinician: How much sadness, using your scale?

Janice: 100.

Clinician: Is that when you started to have the suicidal thoughts again? [Clinician goes on to link Janice's thoughts and images with suicide ideation.]

Evaluating Automatic Thoughts

Once patients have developed the skill to identify automatic thoughts, they and their clinician can turn their attention toward strategies to modify these thoughts and develop alternative responses that reflect more balanced appraisals of their life circumstances. In most instances, the intensity of patients' negative emotion decreases as they widen their perspective of the situation, consider all of the evidence that supports and refutes their automatic thought, and respond to their automatic thought using this information. At first, patients and their clinician conduct these exercises in session to evaluate particularly problematic situations experienced in the time since the previous session. However, over time, patients become adept at using these skills to modulate their emotional response in the moment when confronted with a problematic situation.

Clinicians use *Socratic questioning* to help patients evaluate the validity of their automatic thoughts. That is, they gently guide patients in evaluating the evidence that supports or refutes the automatic thoughts and the likelihood that the catastrophic outcomes they predict will actually occur. Most of the questions clinicians ask do not require yes-or-no responses; rather, they are intended to stimulate critical thinking on the part of the patient. It is important for clinicians to keep in mind that this, like other aspects of cognitive therapy, is a collaborative process. The goal of Socratic questioning is not to directly challenge patients' assessments or pressure them into adopting a different perspective that is judged by the clinician as being more adaptive. In fact, it is helpful for clinicians to remember that there is often a grain of truth in patients' thoughts and that it would be invalidating to adopt the stance that patients' thinking is uniformly unrealistic. Instead, clinicians communicate an understanding of the way in which patients reached a particular conclusion and offer alternative ways of appraising the situation.

Alternative responses are constructed when patients and their clinician collaboratively use Socratic questioning to evaluate the validity of their thoughts. For example, many suicidal patients report the automatic thought "No one cares about me." In response, a clinician might ask questions such as "What is the evidence that supports that thought? What is the evidence that refutes that thought?" A reasonable alternative response might be, "I'd like to have a wider support network. I haven't been good at keeping in touch with my old friends. But they were good friends at one time, and I guess I could try to start spending time with them again." Note that the alternative response is not unrealistically positive, and it acknowledges areas in which the patient would like to see some improvement. However, it makes reference to specific pieces of evidence that refute the global negative statement.

The dialogue that follows is an example of Socratic questioning as Janice and her clinician discuss her difficulties with her job application. The dialogue starts where the clinician helps Janice to identify the most relevant automatic thought that ran through her mind while she was traveling on the bus. However, instead of continuing to identify additional automatic thoughts related to the escalation of her sadness and hopelessness, the clinician decides to intervene using Socratic questioning. Notice that the clinician uses several different types of questions to respond to Janice's appraisal of the situation.

Clinician:	You're on to something very important, Janice. A lot of things ran through your mind at that time, like "There are too many people on this bus" and "I'm going to be late." But what this all *meant* to you was the prediction that being late sealed your fate—that you weren't going to get the job.
Janice:	Exactly.
Clinician:	Let's assume for a moment that you don't get the job. How bad will that be?
Janice:	[tearful] It will be horrible. I'll be stuck with my mother and stepfather forever.
Clinician:	[gently] Are you 100% sure of those consequences?
Janice:	Well, yeah, I don't have any money to put down a deposit on an apartment.
Clinician:	You're right, it sounds like you won't be able to move out *this* month. What would you tell a friend in this situation?

Janice:	[wipes her eyes] Probably that there's always next month, that she should keep trying.
Clinician:	And how does that apply to *your* situation?
Janice:	[despondent] I know, I know. I should keep looking. That I'll *eventually* get a job. [sounds sarcastic]
Clinician:	Your tone of voice suggests that you're not convinced. What's running through your mind right now?
Janice:	I don't have it in me. I'll never be able to hold down a respectable job.
Clinician:	And what emotions are you experiencing when you say that, that you'll *never* be able to hold down a respectable job?
Janice:	Sadness. And a lot of hopelessness.
Clinician:	Janice, you're not the only one in the world who would feel sad or hopeless when you have the idea that you'll never be able to get a respectable job. In fact, I would guess that a lot of people would feel that way if they had the idea that they'd never get a respectable job. But I'm wondering how accurate that statement is. Where's the evidence?
Janice:	Well, I've been out of work for a long time, first when I quit to go back to school, and then for the past few years when I was in and out of the hospital. That doesn't bode well for holding down a good job.
Clinician:	You're right, this has been a tough few years for you. What about before you went back to college? Did you have a steady job then?
Janice:	Well, yes, I worked for about 5 years in a store at the mall.
Clinician:	So what does that tell you?
Janice:	I guess that I have had a job *before*. But I don't know, it just feels so hopeless.
Clinician:	It *feels* hopeless. You've had a rough few years. What if you were to say to yourself, "There are some things I need to do to ensure that I get back on my feet and get a job. But I had a steady job before, so I know I can do it."
Janice:	OK, I guess I can try.
Clinician:	Janice, could you summarize in your own words what I just said?
Janice:	That I held a job once, so I can do it again. But I guess I need to get my act together and put out some more applications.
Clinician:	When you make those statements, what emotion do you feel?

Janice: Still sad, because I think of how much I have to do to find jobs
            and fill out applications. But I guess there is a little bit of hope.

In this example, the clinician constructed an alternative response (i.e., "There are some things I need to do to ensure that I get back on my feet and get a job. But I had a steady job before, so I know I can do it."). This sometimes occurs in the beginning sessions of cognitive therapy as patients are learning the cognitive skills. When clinicians take the lead in constructing alternative responses, they check with patients to make sure they are relevant and use creative strategies to ensure that they will ultimately be useful, such as having patients repeat them in their own words. As therapy progresses, patients take responsibility for constructing alternative responses on their own.

Beliefs

Core beliefs are the fundamental views that people have of themselves, the world, and/or the future. In most instances, these core beliefs drive the automatic thoughts that are elicited in particular situations. Although skills for identifying and evaluating automatic thoughts form the foundation of cognitive therapy, the most lasting cognitive change occurs when dysfunctional core beliefs are identified and modified. As is seen in chapter 8, the three most common categories of core beliefs in suicidal patients include helpless core beliefs (e.g., "I am trapped"), unlovable core beliefs (e.g., "Nobody cares for me"), and worthless core beliefs (e.g., "I am a burden").

Intermediate beliefs are termed as such because they are more easily identified and articulated and more amenable to change than core beliefs, and they form the bridge between core beliefs and the automatic thoughts experienced in particular situations. Often, intermediate beliefs take the form of rigid attitudes, rules, or assumptions about the way the world works. They sometimes take on the form of conditional statements, such as "If I don't get all As, then I am a failure" or "If even one person doesn't like me, it means I am undesirable." Notice that these statements are unrealistic and create an impossible standard to which the individual must conform. It is not surprising that people are at risk of emotional disturbance if they cannot meet these standards, and it is usually the case that they fall short because their standards are so lofty.

Patients often have difficulty articulating core beliefs and intermediate beliefs. However, as described in chapter 7, understanding of these beliefs is the central part of the cognitive case conceptualization and guides the selection of interventions throughout the course of treatment. At the beginning of treatment, the clinician develops hypotheses about patients' beliefs based on their history, clinical presentation, articulated problems, and identified automatic thoughts. The clinician then modifies these hypotheses as more information is gathered throughout the course of treatment. There are several strategies that the clinician can use to identify beliefs collaboratively with their patients. For example, the clinician can summarize themes that characterize the automatic thoughts that have been articulated in several different situations. Additionally, when patients exhibit intense affect while describing the thoughts that ran through their mind, it is likely that they have hit on a core belief.

The *downward arrow technique* is a common approach to identify core beliefs in a systematic manner (Burns, 1980). When patients identify automatic thoughts, the clinician may respond with a question such as "What does that mean to you?" When patients respond, the clinician continues to probe about the meaning of the cognition as many times as is necessary until they collaboratively arrive at the patients' fundamental belief regarding themselves, the world, or the future. Consider the following dialogue with Janice.

Clinician: You know, Janice, I'm struck by the fact that the supervisor did not give you an absolute negative response. What was it that he said when you handed him the application?

Janice: That he'll be in touch. But I *know* that's just another way of saying we don't want you.

Clinician: Maybe yes, maybe no. I have an idea. What if you were to follow up with the manager and inquire about the status of your application?

Janice: [horrified] Oh, no! I could never go back there!

Clinician: What ran through your mind when I made that suggestion?

Janice: That there's no way I'm going back there. I'm not strong right now, and I couldn't bear it if he says he's not going to hire me. [laughs sarcastically] And don't ask me about the likelihood of not getting hired, because I think it's pretty high.

Clinician: So let's say that you don't get this job. *What does that mean to you?*

Janice: That I'll never be able to get a job again.

Clinician: And what does the idea that you'll never be able to get a job again *mean to you?*

Janice: [pauses] Well, it means that I'll live with my mother forever.

Clinician: *And what does that mean?*

Janice: I'm not sure I get what you're asking.

Clinician: Let me put it another way. The idea you'll be living with your mother forever . . . *what does that say about you?*

Janice: [tearful] That I'm nothing. A loser. I'm a worthless human being.

In this example, the clinician identified a powerful core belief in Janice—that she is worthless. The clinician uses this information to revise the cognitive case conceptualization, specifically that many of Janice's automatic thoughts stem from the idea of being worthless and that this core belief drives her to selectively identify cues in her environment that confirm this idea and to ignore cues that suggest she has worth. On the basis of the understanding that a sense of worthlessness underlies many of Janice's difficulties, the clinician can begin the task of modifying this belief by helping Janice to identify ways of acknowledging existing areas of self-worth and to develop additional ways of improving her sense of self-worth, which in turn have the potential to decrease her suicide risk.

Many of the same strategies for evaluating automatic thoughts can be used to evaluate beliefs. For example, the clinician can guide patients in examining the evidence that supports and refutes their belief and in reformulating a more realistic, balanced belief. In our experience, beliefs are not modified in one session. Instead, the clinician uses these strategies over time and frequently assesses the degree to which the patient continues to believe the old belief and now believes the new belief. Patients often believe their old, maladaptive beliefs at a level of 100% at the beginning of therapy, but by the end of therapy, they may only believe them at a level of 10% to 20%, or even not at all.

Cognitive therapy for suicidal patients addresses patients' suicide ideation and propensity to engage in suicidal acts, and it helps patients to develop strategies for coping with suicidal crises in the future. The acute suicide prevention phase of cognitive therapy is relatively brief and often occurs in conjunction with a larger treatment program, including medical, psychiatric, addiction, and social service interventions. Because suicidal patients are often struggling with a number of chronic psychiatric, interpersonal, and situational difficulties, it is not realistic to expect that their beliefs will be fully modified during the period of treatment that is directly focused on suicide prevention strategies. Nevertheless, by the end of this phase of treatment, many patients will have the tools to (a) identify their beliefs and understand the manner in which they influence automatic thoughts, emotional reactions, and behavioral responses and (b) implement strategies to periodically assess the strength of these beliefs and modify them as needed. It is expected that many of these beliefs would be targeted in the continuation phase of treatment, after the risk of future suicidal acts has subsided.

Behavioral Strategies

Clinicians may select among a wide array of behavioral strategies, based on the cognitive case conceptualization, to manage mood as they are warranted. For example, if anxious patients have concerns about their symptoms spiraling out of control, then the clinician might use muscle relaxation as a way for these patients to regain a sense of controllability. In most instances, we find that behavioral strategies reduce symptoms by bringing about cognitive change, as patients learn that they can cope with their symptoms and life difficulties and that the worst-case scenario that they anticipate is either very unlikely or not so bad after all.

A common strategy used by many cognitive therapists is the *behavioral experiment*. In behavioral experiments, patients experientially test the validity of their faulty beliefs or predictions in real-life situations. In other words, patients adopt a hypothesis-testing approach, such that they gather data from their own environment and objectively analyze them before making a judgment or drawing a conclusion. This strategy is powerful in modifying automatic thoughts, predictions, and beliefs because patients see firsthand that their ideas are incorrect or exaggerated. These experiments are often assigned as homework. In the previous dialogue with Janice, the clinician could have gone in a different direction and devised the following behavioral experiment instead of identifying her core belief.

Clinician:	You know, Janice, I'm struck by the fact that the supervisor did not give you an absolute negative response. What was it that he said when you handed him the application?
Janice:	That he'll be in touch. But I *know* that's just another way of saying we don't want you.
Clinician:	Maybe yes, maybe no. I have an idea. What if you were to follow up with the manager and inquire about the status of your application?
Janice:	I think he'd brush me off and say that he'd never hire me in a million years.
Clinician:	So not only do you predict that you won't get the job, you also predict that the manager will be inconsiderate.
Janice:	Yeah, I really do.
Clinician:	Would you be willing to do an experiment this week? Would you be willing to inquire about the status of your application so we can see if your prediction is accurate?
Janice:	[reluctantly] I guess I could try, but. . . . [trails off]
Clinician:	Here's why I am suggesting this. If you do get the job, then you'll learn that the idea that you would not get the job was premature. If you don't get the job, but the supervisor still treats you considerately, then you'll learn that some aspects of your prediction were accurate and some were exaggerated. And if you don't get the job and you perceive that he treated you in an inconsiderate manner, then in the next session we'll work on coping with that as well as continuing to work through obstacles to submitting a successful job application.

Janice: I . . . suppose . . . but I think I would be really devastated if he is inconsiderate. It would make me feel like I am not worth the time of day.

Clinician: OK, let's talk *now* about ways you would cope with that in the event that it does indeed occur. . . .

The clinician proceeded to have Janice imagine that the supervisor was inconsiderate and to articulate the cognitive and behavioral strategies she would use to manage her associated distress. When Janice came back for her subsequent session, she reported the results of her experiment.

Clinician: I'm curious to hear how your experiment went.

Janice: I can't believe I actually went through with it, but I did stop by the store and ask to see the supervisor.

Clinician: That took a lot of courage, Janice. How did it go?

Janice: Well . . . I didn't get the job. But it wasn't as bad as I thought. The supervisor said that they ended up hiring someone who was already working in the company.

Clinician: And how did the supervisor communicate this? Was he rude or inconsiderate?

Janice: No, not at all. He actually apologized for being short with me when I originally turned in the application because he was in the middle of dealing with some problem. And he also told me that I was qualified for the job, that the fact that they didn't hire me had more to do with the other person having an "in."

Clinician: So what did you learn from all of this?

Janice: [sigh] That I get too wrapped up with what other people think and let it get to my self-esteem. That things aren't as bad as I think they are.

Clinician: After getting this new information, how sad did you feel, on a 0 to 100 scale?

Janice: Actually, there really wasn't any sadness at all. I ended up going to a couple of other places to apply for similar jobs, since the supervisor told me I was qualified.

Often, suicidal patients are depressed and report little, if any, enjoyment in their lives. In these instances, the clinician may use another behavioral strategy, *activity monitoring and scheduling,* to identify how patients are actually spending their time and where they might schedule a pleasurable activity (A. T. Beck & Greenberg, 1974). Patients are asked to keep a log of their activity each hour of the day for the time in between sessions. For each activity, they make two ratings on a 0 to 10 scale—the perception of accomplishment they get from the activity and the degree of pleasure they feel when they are doing the activity. To ensure that patients do not make ratings biased by their depressed mood at the time, clinicians prepare them for this activity in session by creating anchors for various points along both continuums and encouraging them to use the full scale. After clinicians gather information about the activities in which their patients are engaging, they can work with their patients to (a) schedule new activities that provide a sense of accomplishment and pleasure and (b) engage more frequently in the activities that provide a sense of accomplishment and pleasure. For suicidal patients, this translates to helping them pursue activities that provide a sense of meaning in their lives and create a sense of connection to their community.

The clinician can implement an abundance of additional behavioral strategies, such as muscle relaxation, controlled breathing, and role playing, to enhance communication and social skills. The clinician can be creative in adopting a behavioral strategy to address symptoms and life difficulties, provided that it follows from the cognitive case conceptualization. We recommend that these strategies be introduced in session and that as homework, patients practice generalizing the strategies to their own environments. In addition, we suggest that clinicians inquire about what patients have learned by using the skills so that they change their beliefs about the degree to which they can influence their environment and cope with adversity.

SUMMARY AND INTEGRATION

Cognitive therapy is a time-limited, structured approach to treatment that helps patients develop cognitive and behavioral strategies to manage their mood, improve their functioning, and ultimately to modify their fundamental dysfunctional thoughts and beliefs. Cognitive therapists follow a session structure, which includes a mood check, a bridge from the previous session, agenda setting, discussion of agenda items, periodic summaries, homework assignment, and a final summary and feedback. Within the session structure, cognitive therapists have flexibility in selecting strategies to address the symptoms and life problems that they and their patients put on the agenda for discussion. The selection of a particular strategy is guided by a cognitive case conceptualization, which contains information about the patient's beliefs and automatic thoughts that emerge in specific situations. In chapter 7, we describe the detailed process for arriving at a cognitive case conceptualization with suicidal patients.

One goal of cognitive therapy is to modify thoughts, images, and beliefs that are exaggerated and associated with high levels of negative affect. Clinicians first guide patients in developing skills to identify these problematic cognitions, and strategies such as Socratic questioning and behavioral experiments are used to evaluate them in an adaptive, realistic manner. Cognitions that elicit intense affect are likely representative of core beliefs. These beliefs facilitate the information to which patients attend or ignore in their environment and color the manner in which patients interpret neutral or ambiguous information. Thus, modification of dysfunctional beliefs is associated with lasting change in cognitive therapy. In addition to cognitive strategies, behavioral strategies are often used by cognitive therapists to reduce distressing symptoms and implement positive changes in patients' lives. Not only does the use of behavioral strategies often result in substantial symptom improvement, it also provides evidence to patients that they can cope effectively with life adversity.

As is illustrated in more detail in the subsequent chapters, our cognitive therapy treatment for suicidal patients shares many similarities with general approaches to cognitive therapy (e.g., J. S. Beck, 1995). The cognitive case conceptualization is paramount in guiding the understanding of the patient and selecting appropriate interventions. One main focus of treatment is the modification of dysfunctional thoughts and beliefs. Sessions follow the structure described earlier in this chapter. The clinician may use the cognitive and behavioral strategies described in this chapter when they are warranted by the cognitive case conceptualization.

However, several features of our protocol are unique to the population of suicidal individuals. The development of strategies to prevent suicidal crises is the primary target for intervention in this approach to cognitive therapy. Although patients may introduce a range of issues in session, such as depression, sexual abuse, or relationship problems, a focus on the patient's suicide ideation and issues associated with the recent suicidal crisis is paramount. We view this as the acute suicide prevention phase of treatment, which is the focus of this book. Once patients demonstrate evidence that they have developed the skills to handle future suicidal crises, the clinician may then turn to treating these underlying issues from a cognitive approach in a continuation phase of treatment. Moreover, because suicidal patients need direct, immediate prompts to deescalate their distress, many of the general cognitive therapy strategies have been modified so they are readily available in times of crisis. Thus, the cognitive therapy protocol for suicidal patients was conceptualized from this general cognitive therapy framework and then optimized for use with suicidal patients in times of crisis.

6

EARLY PHASE OF TREATMENT

Chapters 6 through 9 describe specific strategies for conducting cognitive therapy with suicidal patients, which are based on the treatment package that we found to be efficacious in reducing the rate of reattempts in our clinical trial (G. K. Brown, Tenhave, et al., 2005). Many of these strategies were described previously in an unpublished study treatment manual (G. K. Brown, Henriques, Ratto, & Beck, 2002) and in other articles and book chapters that summarize the treatment (Berk, Henriques, Warman, Brown, & Beck, 2004; G. K. Brown, Jeglic, Henriques, & Beck, 2006; Henriques, Beck, & Brown, 2003); they are presented here in full for the first time. As with the treatment protocol that was implemented during the clinical trial, we envision that these strategies will be used during the time that patients are actively suicidal or shortly after patients have experienced a suicidal crisis.

Some clinicians may already be working with patients who report a substantial increase in suicide ideation or who make a suicide attempt during the course of treatment. In these cases, the clinician would shift the focus of the treatment to the strategies described in this volume to help these patients develop the skills necessary to manage future suicidal crises. Their previous work can resume when it is clear that these patients have the ability to apply the suicide management skills to their lives. Thus, this approach can be used either for new patients who present for treatment following a suicidal crisis or for patients who have a suicidal crisis while engaged in treatment. Either way, when the clinician and patient begin to focus on other problem areas that are unrelated to the suicidal crisis, they have moved out of the acute suicide prevention phase and into the continuation phase of treatment and can address some of the chronic, long-standing diagnostic or psychosocial issues that are associated with distress and functional impairment.

Cognitive therapy for suicidal patients was developed from much of the material presented up to this point in the book, including the major components of the classification system of suicidal acts, the general cognitive model of psychiatric disturbance, specific psychological constructs associated with suicidal acts, and general cognitive therapy strategies. This treatment is based on the premises that suicidal patients (a) lack important cognitive, behavioral, and affective coping skills; (b) fail to use previously learned coping skills during suicidal crises; or (c) fail to make use of available resources during suicidal crises. In the latter two instances, it is often maladaptive automatic thoughts and core beliefs that prevent suicidal patients from using their skills and resources. The primary goal of this treatment is to reduce the likelihood of future suicidal acts, which is accomplished by (a) acquiring adaptive coping strategies; (b) developing cognitive tools to identify reasons for living and instill hope; (c) improving problem solving skills; (d) increasing patients' connection with their social support network; and (e) increasing patients' compliance with adjunctive medical, psychiatric, addictions, and social service interventions. The acute phase of treatment that is devoted to suicide prevention typically involves a limited number of sessions (e.g., approximately 10 sessions in our clinical trial).

Figure 6.1 presents an overview of the progression of phases that occur during cognitive therapy for suicidal patients. The treatment is divided into four main sections—the early phase of treatment, cognitive case conceptualization and treatment planning, the intermediate phase of treatment, and the later phase of treatment. This chapter and chapters 7, 8, and 9 correspond to these four major phases of treatment (see the appendix for an outline of the major components of each phase). This chapter, in particular, focuses on the tasks that are accomplished during the early phase of treatment, represented by the first circle in the flow diagram.

The aims of the early phase of treatment are as follows: (a) obtaining informed consent and socializing patients into the structure and process of cognitive therapy, (b) engaging patients in treatment, (c) conducting a suicide risk assessment, (d) developing a safety plan, (e) conveying a sense of hope, and (f) having patients provide a narrative description of the events that occurred during the recent suicidal crisis. We present topics (a) through (e) in this order as an indication of the typical chronological order in which these issues are addressed during the early phase of treatment. However, clinicians may choose to address these issues in a different order or cover one or more of these areas over several sessions, as indicated by the particular cir-

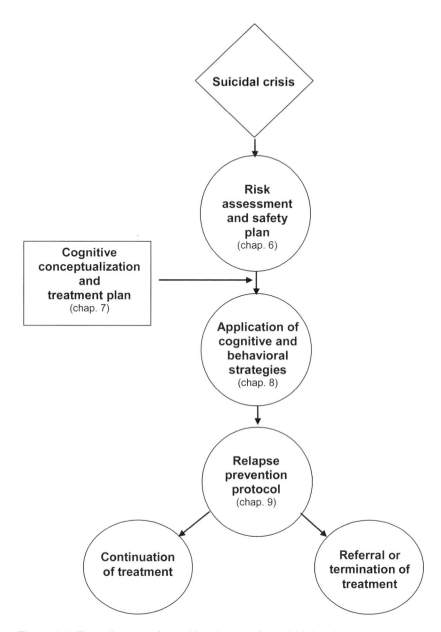

Figure 6.1. Flow diagram of cognitive therapy for suicidal patients.

cumstances and clinical presentation of the patient. We reserve discussion of topic (f) until chapter 7, as it occurs across several sessions in the early phase of treatment and is used to formulate the cognitive case conceptualization.

Many of these topics might strike the reader as important goals to achieve in the early phase of cognitive therapy with any patient. We emphasize them in this chapter because we believe they are particularly important for successful treatment with suicidal patients. These patients often have low expectations for treatment, believing that their situation is hopeless and that nothing can be done to change it. Thus, the clinician must pay careful attention to developing a strong therapeutic relationship, modeling a systematic approach to solving problems, and conveying a sense of hope for the future.

INFORMED CONSENT AND THE STRUCTURE AND PROCESS OF COGNITIVE THERAPY

One of the first steps in any approach to therapy is for the clinician to obtain informed consent from the patient to participate in a psychosocial assessment and subsequent treatment (American Psychological Association, 2002). According to this ethical principle, information is provided to patients using language that is understandable to them. This principle also assumes that patients have the capacity to engage in the informed consent process and that they are able to freely provide consent without any undue influence from others. The ability to consent to treatment may be questionable for patients who are experiencing extreme distress or who have cognitive deficits as a result of a suicide attempt, such as a drug overdose. In such cases, it is best to seek their assent to the intervention while keeping their preferences and best interests in mind. For example, if a patient is intoxicated and spontaneously reports thoughts of suicide, the clinician may decide that it is in the patient's best interest to conduct a suicide risk assessment to protect her from harming herself and to obtain informed consent later once she is able to do so. There are several components of the informed consent process, including providing patients with information about (a) the limits of privacy and confidentiality, (b) the structure and process of treatment, (c) the potential risks and benefits of treatment, and (d) alternative treatments. Each issue is reviewed subsequently. We emphasize that informed consent does not simply involve providing patients with information related to these topics. An important feature of the informed consent process is a dialogue between the clinician and patient so that the patient can ask questions about treatment and the clinician can provide as much clarification as necessary to ensure that the patient comprehends the information that is being presented.

A critical issue to address in the first session is confidentiality, given that these patients are characterized by a number of features that increase the risk for engaging in future suicidal acts. Patients should be informed that their information is kept confidential except under specific circumstances as indicated by state law, such as when they are an imminent danger to themselves or to someone else (American Psychiatric Association [APA], 2003). In these circumstances, confidentiality may be breached only insofar as the clinician needs to take necessary steps to ensure patients' safety or to protect others' safety. Discussion of the limits of confidentiality might not go as smoothly as it does with many nonsuicidal patients, as the clinician cannot promise confidentiality for information associated with the same issue that brought them into treatment and that will be the focus of treatment. Many patients assume that if they mention that they are having thoughts of killing themselves, then they will definitely be hospitalized. In our work with suicidal patients, we refer patients to the hospital when we determine that they are at imminent risk of harming themselves and cannot be treated safely on an outpatient basis. We encourage clinicians to clearly explain the rationale for these limits of confidentiality and provide examples of the range of interventions that will be used, depending on the severity of their suicide ideation and intent (e.g., increasing frequency of sessions, scheduling brief telephone "check-ins," consulting with family members), so that patients understand that hospitalization is only one of many treatment options. If hospitalization is necessary, we encourage clinicians to approach it with patients as collaboratively as possible (e.g., the selection of a particular hospital).

As part of the informed consent process, the clinician should describe the focus and structure of therapy in clear and understandable terms. Thus, we encourage clinicians to be explicit in communicating to their patients that the primary goal of this treatment is to prevent a future suicidal act. Patients are then educated about the particular strategies that will be used to achieve this aim and the manner in which these strategies can be applied during future suicidal crises. At times, patients express a desire to focus on other issues that are unrelated to their suicidality. Although our targeted protocol does not preclude other issues as a focus of treatment, we suggest that they be addressed as they relate to patients' recent suicidal crises and their risk for future suicidal crises. As discussed in the beginning of this chapter, issues and problems that are unrelated to the patients' propensity for suicide can be established as a priority for treatment after patients have demonstrated an ability to generalize the suicide management skills to their lives.

In addition to discussing the rationale and goals of treatment, clinicians have found it helpful to describe characteristics that are unique to cognitive therapy, as many patients have had different types of psychotherapy and may expect a similar structure and format for this treatment. For example, patients are informed that sessions last approximately 50 minutes, that sessions are active and goal directed, that they may be asked to complete inventories before the session starts (e.g., Beck Depression Inventory), and that homework assignments are developed to help them apply cognitive and behavioral skills to their daily lives. In addition, they should be told that this phase of treatment is brief because of the circumscribed nature of its focus on suicide. However, as is seen in chapter 9, the time at which termination of this phase occurs is flexible, on the basis of the degree to which patients demonstrate that they can implement cognitive and behavioral strategies to manage future crises. Thus, patients are informed that progress will be assessed throughout the course of treatment and that the length of this treatment phase will be adjusted accordingly. Clinicians should be aware that they are presenting many details and that patients, particularly those who are in crisis, are not likely to remember all of them. It is often helpful to have a clearly laid-out handout to supplement the information that is presented verbally. Moreover, clinicians can use periodic summaries, described in chapter 5, to ensure that the main points are understood.

The clinician models a cognitive therapy approach by setting an agenda in the first session. As described in chapter 5, the clinician explains the rationale of agenda setting to patients, letting them know that it is a collaborative process that occurs at the beginning of each session. However, the agenda for the first session may seem less collaborative to patients because there are several issues that must be covered to adhere to ethical principles. Usually, the clinician indicates that the agenda topics for the first session include (a) discussion of the structure and process of treatment, including obtaining informed consent; (b) emphasis on the importance of therapy attendance and active participation; (c) completion of a suicide risk assessment; and (d) completion of a safety plan. Feedback is elicited from patients, and additional items they identify as being important are added to the agenda. We realize that there are many agenda items for the first session and that there is the potential for patients (and clinicians) to feel overwhelmed. We encourage the clinician to acknowledge that many of these agenda items are those that are covered in the first session but then apply to other sessions (e.g., confidentiality), so that they will be addressed again only as needed.

After the structure and process of cognitive therapy have been adequately covered, the next step in the informed consent process is to discuss the benefits and risks of treatment. When discussing the benefits of this treatment, patients can be educated about the proportion of patients who have responded to treatment and the evidence for this approach's efficacy. For example, for patients who seek treatment after a suicide attempt, it would be appropriate to inform them that a previous research study found that cognitive therapy helped to reduce the rate of subsequent suicide attempts by as much as 50% (G. K. Brown, Tenhave, et al., 2005). The clinician can also describe his or her own success rate in treating suicidal patients (Rudd et al., in press).

Conversely, patients should also be informed of the potential risks of treatment, such as (a) the possibility of emotional discomfort, (b) the risk that a suicidal act may occur during treatment, and (c) potential negative effects of breaching confidentiality. The clinician can communicate to patients that talking about events and feelings associated with suicidal crises has the potential to be upsetting to them, and he or she can discuss potential strategies that can be implemented should patients feel upset after a treatment session. Suicidal patients, especially patients who recently attempted suicide, should also understand that treatment does not guarantee that they will not make another suicide attempt (Rudd et al., in press). Providing patients with this information helps to underscore the importance of addressing potential crises and treatment compliance (Rudd et al., in press). In addition, there are potential risks associated with the possibility of breaching confidentiality to ensure the safety of patients or others. For example, patients may be told about the negative effects of having to contact the police, emergency personnel, or family members when the risk for suicide is imminent and they will not consent to interventions to reduce those risks. However, the clinician can indicate that he or she will carefully evaluate the potential negative effect of breaching confidentiality on the therapeutic relationship and on other aspects of the patient's life. In addition, the clinician communicates that he or she will inform the patient in the event that confidentiality has to be broken, so that the patient will be fully aware of what is happening. The exception to this is if the clinician uses his or her clinical judgment to decide that disclosing a breach in confidentiality would further increase patients' risk of harming themselves or others.

A final step in the informed consent process involves the discussion of alternative treatments. Patients who recently attempted suicide should be informed that other evidence-based treatments may be effective for preventing suicide attempts, such as interpersonal psychotherapy (Guthrie et al., 2001) and dialectical behavior therapy (Linehan et al., 2006), as described in chapter 4. Information concerning the potential benefit of medications for reducing the likelihood of another attempt may also be provided, such as the benefit of lithium for patients with major affective disorder (Thies-Flechtner, Müller-Oerlinghausen, Seibert, Walther, & Greil, 1996) and the benefit of clozapine for patients with schizophrenia (Meltzer et al., 2003). The clinician should take care to foster a discussion about the advantages and disadvantages of each intervention so that patients can identify the approach they believe would work best for them. For patients who are currently and actively engaged in other psychiatric or addiction treatments, the clinician may also emphasize the importance of treatment compliance and adherence. Although other issues may be discussed as part of informed consent, the most important feature of this process is that the clinician obtains patients' commitment to treatment, including their agreement to attend and participate in the sessions, set session agendas and treatment goals, complete homework assignments, use crisis management strategies, and actively participate in other aspects of treatment as described.

TREATMENT ENGAGEMENT

Obtaining patients' commitment to treatment is especially important because empirical research has shown that only 20% to 40% of individuals who attempt suicide follow through with outpatient treatment after the hospitalization for their attempt (e.g., Kreitman, 1979; Morgan, Burns-Cox, Pocock, & Pottle, 1975; O'Brien, Holton, Hurren, & Watt, 1987). Factors that reduce compliance with treatment include poor economic resources, chaotic lifestyles, negative attitudes toward treatment, severe psychiatric disturbance, drug and alcohol abuse, shame about the suicidal crisis, concern about stigma, and negative culturally based beliefs about mental health services (Berk et al., 2004; see chap. 10, this volume). Thus, it is incumbent on the clinician to take a particularly active stance in engaging and retaining these patients in treatment.

Suicidal patients have often received many courses of psychiatric or addictions treatment and may wonder how this course of treatment is going to be different. Patients who have attempted suicide while they were receiving treatment may feel especially ambivalent or hopeless. Therefore, strategies that engage patients in treatment are paramount in this population, given their poor treatment history. Building rapport with patients may be accomplished by using many of the general cognitive therapy skills described in chapter 5, including (a) demonstrating an understanding of patients' internal reality and empathizing with their experiences; (b) collaborating with patients as much as possible so that the clinician and patient function as a team; (c) eliciting and responding to feedback from patients throughout the session; and (d) displaying optimal levels of warmth, genuineness, concern, confidence, and professionalism. Clinicians who work with suicidal patients must be able to empathize with their patients' experiences while focusing on problem solving and suicide management skills. In addition, clinicians model hopefulness at all times, even when a solution to the presenting problem is not immediately apparent.

We have identified a number of factors that have the potential to increase the likelihood that patients will remain in treatment. First, clinicians should empathize with patients that talking about things that are stressful to them, especially events that preceded a suicidal crisis, may remind them of painful issues or events that they would rather not think about. To address this concern, the clinician can explain the specific manner in which talking about emotional issues will be beneficial in preventing a future suicidal act. In addition, the clinician can work with patients to identify strategies for coping with distress associated with talking about upsetting issues, such as taking a break, talking about upsetting issues for a limited period of time, or using relaxation or breathing to manage negative emotional reactions. These strategies convey that the decision to discuss emotional issues is a collaborative one between the clinician and the patient and that the clinician is keenly aware of potential iatrogenic effects of treatment.

Second, clinicians must pay particular attention to cultural issues that have the potential to be a barrier to seeking services. In one of our clinical trials, 60% of the patients were African American, and African American ethnicity was associated with a negative attitude toward treatment (Wenzel, Jeglic, Levy-Mack, Beck, & Brown, in press). These patients often indicate that they have difficulty connecting with a clinician whom they perceive to be of a middle-class, majority culture. The clinician can use Socratic questioning to identify and address patients' beliefs about working with a clinician whose ethnic and economic background might be different than their own. For example, the clinician might ask, "What runs through your mind when you imagine working with me in this setting?" If patients' automatic thoughts are negative, absolute, or rigid, the clinician might inquire about the evidence that supports and refutes these cognitions. The clinician can also propose a behavioral experiment, such as committing to only a few sessions, for patients to test their negative predictions about remaining in treatment. It is equally as important for clinicians to attend to their own beliefs about working with suicidal patients and patients who are of different cultural backgrounds. If clinicians lack competence in working with people of a particular culture, ethnicity, or sexual orientation, it is their responsibility to acquire this knowledge through reading, clinical experience, and consultation with peers or supervisors.

Third, the clinician can use general cognitive therapy strategies to identify the factors that have the potential to prevent patients from attending therapy and to brainstorm ways to overcome those obstacles. These factors might be cognitive (e.g., low expectations for treatment), behavioral (e.g., easily loses appointment card), or situational (e.g., no transportation) in nature. The cognitive barriers can be particularly challenging to overcome, but they also allow the opportunity to model the application of cognitive strategies. For example, patients might give cues that they are not "buying into" the cognitive model, such as apathetic, single-word responses, lack of eye contact, and facial grimaces. In these instances, clinicians can elicit patients' beliefs about coming to therapy, general expectations for the likelihood of success in treatment, and expectations about the utility of specific features of cognitive therapy. When it is clear that patients' negative beliefs would interfere with therapy attendance or compliance, clinicians can use Socratic questioning to help them evaluate the degree to which the belief is realistic. Furthermore, clinicians and patients can work collaboratively to develop a specific plan for addressing times when patients fail to attend sessions. Consider this dialogue Janice had with her clinician when she expressed ambivalence about committing to cognitive therapy.

> *Clinician:* Janice, the fact that you're responding to most of my questions with one-word answers suggests to me that you're not entirely on board with this treatment. Am I right about this?
>
> *Janice:* [heavy sigh] I don't see how this is going to make any difference. I've been like this for too long.
>
> *Clinician:* So you have the belief that therapy won't be helpful. [Janice nods] What, specifically, makes you think that?
>
> *Janice:* [exasperated] Everything! My other therapists haven't helped! My medications haven't helped! The real issue is that my step-

father makes my life miserable. But my mother would never leave him, and I don't have enough money to get out of that house. [becomes tearful]

Clinician: It sounds like there is some reason to be skeptical, given that you've been in treatment many times before, and you haven't felt much better. But I'm wondering if there's any evidence that this time might be different.

Janice: There *is* none.

Clinician: [gently] Is there anything we've done up to this point that is different than what you did with previous therapists?

Janice: [pouting] I don't know, it's too soon to tell.

Clinician: Fair enough. Think back to earlier, when I was explaining what this treatment was all about. That I would help you to develop specific strategies for dealing with times when you can't cope and you feel like hurting yourself. Have you ever done that before in therapy?

Janice: [reluctantly] I *guess* not. I usually end up talking about my relationships with my mother and my stepfather over and over.

Clinician: How does my approach to treatment sound to you? Is there a potential for it to be helpful?

Janice: I really don't know.

Clinician: Would you be willing to give it a try?

Janice: [reluctantly] I suppose.

Clinician: Good, Janice, I'm glad you can make a preliminary commitment to treatment. [pause] In my experience, when people have doubts about whether therapy will be helpful, it's easy for them to skip sessions, thinking "What's the use?" especially when they are having a down day. Has this ever happened to you?

Janice: Yeah, that's usually when I just stop going to therapy altogether.

Clinician: I wonder if the two of us can develop a plan for dealing with times you start going down the "What's the use?" road.

Janice: I don't know what that would be.

Clinician: Well, how's this for a plan? What if you were to agree to attend four sessions, no matter what? At the end of the fourth session, we can reserve some time to evaluate the "What's the use?" question and critically examine whether this therapy *is* of any use to you.

Janice: Just four sessions, and then we can talk about it?

> *Clinician:* You got it, four sessions. At the end of fourth session, you might have a better idea of exactly what therapy has to offer and how it will be helpful in your life. Then, you'll be able to answer the question "What's the use?" more objectively than you would if you were sitting home, down in the dumps . . . so, four sessions it is?
>
> *Janice:* Four sessions it is.

Finally, we have found that some patients are ambivalent about talking about suicide because they reap secondary gains from their suicidal behavior. Although this may not be readily apparent to patients, often they receive attention, care, and concern from close others and service providers when they are suicidal or otherwise in distress. By developing strategies to manage their suicidal crises, they are putting themselves in the precarious position in which they no longer receive that attention from others. In some instances, it would be detrimental to the therapeutic relationship to explicitly point out this process, as patients would perceive such an assessment of their problems as blaming and invalidating. However, clinicians can use Socratic questioning to gain insight into the processes at work, which would in turn provide an opportunity for them to identify more adaptive ways to receive attention, care, and concern from others.

We have found it helpful for clinicians to "go the extra mile" to reach out to suicidal patients and assist them in scheduling and keeping appointments. Techniques for engaging these patients in treatment include making reminder phone calls, sending letters, having flexible scheduling, and having a willingness to conduct telephone sessions, if necessary. In addition, many suicidal patients have limited social and financial resources. Assisting patients in obtaining funding for transportation (e.g., subway passes), child care, and emergency food money may be essential for treatment engagement. As stated in chapter 4, we used study case managers in our clinical trials who assisted in maintaining contact with patients, reminding them of their appointments, providing referrals for mental health and social services, and serving as a second supportive contact person (G. K. Brown, Tenhave, et al., 2005). The services of a case manager are especially important for patients who have difficulty in regularly attending sessions or who have the potential to have many crises between sessions. Another advantage of using this sort of team approach in treating this population is that it helps to prevent clinicians from feeling overwhelmed or isolated in treating high-risk patients. We realize that it is often not feasible for clinicians to use case managers to track patients, assist with social services, or allow for flexibility in scheduling. Our main message is to suggest that clinicians working with these patients shift their mindset that the responsibility for getting to therapy lies solely with the patient.

SUICIDE RISK ASSESSMENT

Because suicidal individuals constitute a high-risk population, it is incumbent on the clinician to conduct a comprehensive suicide risk assessment at the beginning of treatment and briefer assessments of suicide risk at each subsequent session. A comprehensive suicide risk assessment includes direct questioning of patients' current mental status, the administration of self-report measures, and clinical observation of patients' behavior (cf. APA, 2003). The suicide risk assessment occurs within the context of a psychological assessment that is conducted before or during the early phase; chapter 7 discusses how to use this information for the cognitive case conceptualization and treatment planning. The aims of this comprehensive risk assessment are to (a) identify the risk and protective factors that determine patients' level of risk for suicide, (b) identify concomitant psychiatric and medical disorders that are especially related to suicidal behavior, (c) determine the most appropriate level of care (e.g., inpatient or outpatient treatment), and (d) identify the risk factors that are modifiable with treatment. The guidelines presented in this chapter are focused on conducting risk assessments with patients who are seeking outpatient therapy. We recognize that the risk assessment protocol may be quite different for those patients who are evaluated in the emergency department or during crisis calls (cf. APA, 2003).

The quality of the risk assessment depends on a number of factors, including the clinician's level of skill, the patient's ability and motivation to disclose accurate and complete information, the degree to which there is access to other sources of information (e.g., medical records), and the length of time available to conduct the assessment. It is often helpful to obtain information from the patient's social network, such as family members or friends who can provide information about the patient's mental status, previous suicide attempts, and treatment history. Contact with other clinicians can strengthen the patient's resources and facilitate the coordination of care. We realize that the information described in this section may not always be attainable. In general, it is recommended that a comprehensive risk assessment should be conducted using all sources of information that are currently available and that it should be modified in future sessions as new information becomes available.

Patients and clinicians alike sometimes have the erroneous belief that talking about suicide increases the likelihood of attempting suicide. In actuality, no data exist that support this notion. Quite the contrary, we find that open and frank discussion about suicide minimizes its stigma and mystique. Often, patients are relieved when clinicians address the issue in a straightforward manner, as many people in their lives approach it gingerly or avoid it altogether. Nevertheless, there are times when patients become upset while they are discussing personal issues that are relevant to their recent suicidal crisis. Before beginning the suicide risk assessment, the clinician can inform patients that some of the questions that will be asked may be stressful or remind them about issues or events that they would rather not recall. The clinician can also communicate that he or she anticipates that the benefit of asking the questions related to conducting a risk assessment will outweigh the potential risks. As stated earlier, there are many specific coping skills that can be invoked if patients become distressed as they are discussing issues related to recent and past suicidal crises.

Assessment of Risk Factors

Figure 6.2 displays the main domains of a comprehensive risk assessment, including suicide ideation and suicide-relevant behavior, psychiatric and medical diagnoses, psychiatric history, psychological vulnerabilities (e.g., hopelessness), and psychosocial vulnerabilities (e.g., recent loss). This figure expands on the constructs identified in chapter 2, such that it summarizes the clinical indicators of some of these constructs and identifies situational factors that exacerbate these constructs. We have found it helpful to note these risk and protective factors on one page because it facilitates the efficient evaluation and weighing of the relative strengths of each factor. In this section, we expand on some of the most important risk factors and provide suggestions for their clinical assessment.

It is of paramount importance to carefully assess suicide-relevant cognitions because these variables have been firmly established as risk factors for suicidal acts in the research literature. The clinician often begins the risk assessment by inquiring about suicide-related issues that have the potential to be easier for patients to discuss. For example, the clinician may ask whether patients have a current wish to die and whether this wish to die outweighs their wish to live. Once patients have begun to talk about life-and-death issues, the clinician can bridge to asking patients whether they currently have any suicidal thoughts (or other cognitions associated with suicide, e.g., images or command hallucinations to harm themselves). If patients report that they have been thinking about suicide, then the clinician should assess the duration, frequency, and intensity of the suicide ideation both for a recent time period (e.g., the past 48 hours or the past week) and for the worst time in patients' lives, as research has shown that worst-point ideation predicts future suicidal acts to a greater degree than current suicide ideation (A. T. Beck, Brown, Steer, Dahlsgaard, & Grisham, 1999). If patients report any suicidal thoughts, images, or hallucinations, the clinician determines their level of desire and intent to kill themselves (e.g., "Do you have any desire to end your own life? Is this desire weak, moderate, or strong?"). Subsequently, if patients endorse desire and/or intent to kill themselves, the clinician notes whether they have a plan to kill themselves by asking questions such as "Have you been thinking about how you might kill yourself? Do you intend to carry out this plan?" This line of inquiry assumes that patients will

Suicide-relevant variables (recent)		Clinical status (recent)	
☐	Wish to die that outweighs the wish to live	☐	Major depressive episode
☐	Suicide ideation without intent or plan	☐	Mixed affective episode
☐	Suicidal intent without specific plan	☐	Substance abuse or dependence
☐	Suicidal intent with specific plan	☐	Axis II Cluster B personality disorder
☐	Command hallucinations to hurt self	☐	Hopelessness
☐	Actual suicide attempt ☐ Lifetime	☐	Agitation or severe anxiety
☐	Multiple suicide attempts ☐ Lifetime	☐	Social isolation or loneliness
☐	Interrupted or aborted attempt ☐ Lifetime	☐	Problem solving deficits
☐	Preparatory behavior to kill self ☐ Lifetime	☐	Dysfunctional attitudes (such as perfectionism)
☐	Nonsuicidal self-injury behavior ☐ Lifetime	☐	Perceived burden on family or others
☐	Regrets a failed suicide attempt	☐	Abrupt change in clinical status (improvement or deterioration)
Activating events (recent)		☐	Highly impulsive behavior
☐	Divorce, separation, or death of spouse or partner	☐	Homicidal ideation
☐	Interpersonal loss, conflict, or violence	☐	Aggressive behavior toward others
☐	Legal problems	☐	Chronic physical pain or other acute medical problem (e.g., AIDS, chronic obstructive pulmonary disease, cancer)
☐	Financial difficulties, unemployment, or change in job status	☐	Method for suicide available (e.g., gun or pills)
☐	Pending incarceration or homelessness	☐	Physical or sexual abuse (lifetime)
☐	Other loss or other significant negative event	☐	Family history of suicide (lifetime)
Treatment history		Protective factors (recent)	
☐	Previous psychiatric diagnoses and treatments	☐	Expresses hope for the future
☐	Hopeless or dissatisfied with treatment	☐	Identifies reasons for living
☐	Noncompliant with treatment	☐	Responsibility to family or others; living with family
☐	Not receiving treatment	☐	Supportive social network or family
☐	Refuses or unable to agree to safety plan	☐	Fear of death or dying because of pain and suffering
		☐	Belief that suicide is immoral, high spirituality
		☐	Engaged in work or school

Figure 6.2. Suicide risk assessment.

be honest and forthcoming in response to these questions. Patients who are reluctant to disclose their level of intent or specific plans to commit suicide to their clinician may be at a higher risk for suicide than those patients who report their ideation openly (APA, 2003).

In addition to assessing patients' reports of their desire and plan to kill themselves, clinicians should assess for behavioral indicators of suicide ideation, such as acts of preparation for attempting suicide. Although these behaviors often cannot be observed in the clinician's office, the clinician can ask, "Have you actually done anything to prepare for a suicide attempt? What was that?" Examples of preparatory behaviors include purchasing a gun, rope, or garden hose; stockpiling pills; searching the Internet to determine the best method; writing a suicide note; preparing a will; giving away highly valued possessions; or saying goodbye to friends or family members for no apparent reason. As discussed later in this chapter, it is important to ask whether patients have any access to lethal methods, especially if they describe such methods as part of their plans to kill themselves. Examples of access to such methods include the availability of a firearm (especially a firearm in the home) or the availability of potentially lethal medication.

The risk assessment should also include an identification of other suicide-relevant behaviors such as suicide attempts, interrupted attempts, and aborted attempts (see definitions of these behaviors in chap. 1). Both lifetime and recent suicide-relevant behaviors should be assessed, with an understanding that a recent occurrence of these behaviors is associated with an increased likelihood of subsequent suicidal acts (e.g., in the past month or past year; Hawton, Zahl, & Weatherall, 2003). When assessing for the occurrence of these behaviors, it is helpful to use broad screening questions such as "In the past, have you made a suicide attempt or done anything to harm yourself?" If patients indicate that they have made a suicide attempt or engaged in self-injury behavior, then follow-up questions are asked to assess for suicidal intent experienced during these acts. This line of questioning helps the clinician to determine whether patients engaged in a self-inflicted, potentially injurious behavior with any intent to die as a result of the behavior. The Columbia Suicide Severity Rating Scale (Posner, Brent, et al., 2007) is useful for screening for suicide attempts, interrupted attempts, aborted attempts, and nonsuicidal self-injury behaviors and for other suicide-relevant variables because it includes precise definitions and questions that correspond to these definitions.

As part of the risk assessment, the clinician assesses for other specific characteristics of any previous suicide attempt because, as described in chapters 1 and 2, specific characteristics of past attempts affect the likelihood of engaging in future suicidal acts. For example, clinicians can use questions from the Suicide Intent Scale to assess the level of expectation of death as a result of a previous attempt, whether the purpose of the attempt was to escape or resolve problems, and whether patients took precautions against being discovered. Data from this scale have the potential to play a central role in estimating risk, as patients who have made a previous attempt characterized by high intent are more likely to make another attempt than patients who have made previous attempts characterized by low intent (R. W. Beck, Morris, & Beck, 1974). In addition, the Suicide Intent Scale measures whether patients regret that they survived an attempt, which is important because regretting a failed attempt indicates increased risk of eventual suicide (Henriques, Wenzel, Brown, & Beck, 2005).

As stated in chapter 2, the vast majority of suicidal patients have at least one psychiatric diagnosis. Thus, a comprehensive assessment of suicide risk includes an evaluation of current psychiatric disorders, including major depression, bipolar disorder (especially the presence of a mixed affective episode), alcohol and drug use disorders, and psychotic disorders. Axis II features associated with a Cluster B personality disorder, particularly those associated with borderline personality disorder and antisocial personality disorder, can be assessed using direct questioning, behavioral observation, and reports from others. Screening instruments for psychiatric disorders, alcohol abuse (e.g., Alcohol Use Disorders Identification Test; Babor, Higgins-Biddle, Saunders, & Monteiro, 2001), and drug abuse (e.g., Drug Abuse Screening Test; McCabe, Boyd, Cranford, Morales, & Slayden, 2006) provide an efficient method for determining whether a full assessment of these disorders is clinically appropriate.

Chapters 2 and 3 described many other psychological and behavioral factors that have been associated with increased risk, including severe hopelessness (especially stable levels of high hopelessness), distress that is perceived by the patient to be unbearable, social isolation or loneliness, problem solving deficits, and dysfunctional attitudes such as perfectionism. The presence and severity of all of these variables should be evaluated in the suicide risk assessment. Patients, especially older patients, may be considered at high risk if they perceive themselves to be a burden to family members (Joiner et al., 2002). Observations of agitation or acute anxiety indicate increased risk (cf. Busch, Fawcett, & Jacobs, 2003) because they may be indicative of the emotional and behavioral concomitants of attentional fixation. As mentioned previously, the clinician should assess for any homicidal ideation and for any aggression or violence toward others, as research has demonstrated that these behaviors are associated with an increased risk of suicide (cf. Conner, Duberstein, Conwell, & Caine, 2003; Verona et al., 2001). Finally, any abrupt change in the patient's clinical status—either a rapid deterioration or a dramatic and unanticipated improvement in mood—may indicate increased risk (Slaby, 1998). For distressed patients who have been ambivalent about suicide, an improvement in mood may indicate a decision to engage in a suicidal act.

A detailed treatment history can assist in the risk assessment, as it provides information about patients' responsiveness to previous interventions and their degree of engagement and optimism associated with these interventions. This part of the risk assessment includes the identification of previous psychiatric treatment (especially psychiatric hospitalizations), psychotherapy, and addictions treatment. Clinicians should also assess whether patients feel hopeless, ambivalent, or dissatisfied with any current or previous treatment. Specific characteristics of previous treatment may be noted, including noncompliance (e.g., not taking medication as prescribed or not attending sessions regularly) and unstable, uncollaborative, or poor relationships with clinicians. Patients who have resigned themselves to the idea that there is no effective treatment available for their psychiatric or medical disorder or other problems may be at increased risk for suicide.

Assessment of Protective Factors

In addition to the assessment of risk factors for suicide, a comprehensive risk assessment should include an evaluation of the protective factors that are associated with a decreased risk for suicide (see Figure 6.2). As stated in chapter 2, there is much less empirical research that has identified variables that "protect" against suicidal acts versus those associated with increased risk. However, clinically we have found that many of these characteristics are important strengths of patients that counteract some of the variables that increase their risk level. Many of these protective factors reflect psychological attitudes or beliefs, such as hopefulness (e.g., Range & Penton, 1994); reasons for living (e.g., Strosahl, Chiles, & Linehan, 1992); a wish to live (e.g., G. K. Brown, Steer, Henriques, & Beck, 2005); self-efficacy in the problem area that is associated with the suicidal crisis (e.g., Malone et al., 2000); a fear of death, dying, or suicide (e.g., Joiner, 2005); and a belief that suicide is immoral (e.g., J. B. Ellis & Smith, 1991). Another protective factor is a supportive social network (e.g., Rowe, Conwell, Schulberg, & Bruce, 2006), especially when supportive individuals are available during a time of crisis. Patients who are married or live with a family member may have a lower suicide risk, especially when they have a responsibility to a child or other family member (e.g., Heikkinen, Isometsä, Marttunen, Aro, & Lönnqvist, 1995). Our clinical experience suggests that being actively engaged in treatment is another protective factor.

Determination of Suicide Risk

A final determination of risk is made after examining all of the information that is available, including the patient's self-report, the medical record, and other sources of information. This determination involves evaluating (a) whether each risk or protective factor is present or absent and (b) the severity or weight of each factor that is present in conferring risk. Previous research on risk factors has offered little guidance in weighing multiple risk and protective factors for determining the risk for any one patient. Generally, the characteristics that have been most consistently associated with a high risk for suicide in the literature—such as a previous suicide attempt, stable levels of hopelessness, and the indication of intent to kill oneself with a specific plan—are weighed most heavily in the overall estimation of risk. In addition, the weighing of each risk factor can be based, in part, on those that seem to cause the most distress for the patient. However, the determination of each risk factor's severity should not be based exclusively on patient self-report; it should also involve sound clinical judgment that is based on professional experience, knowledge of empirically supported risk factors, the clinical presentation of the patient, and reports from relatives and other care providers.

After the clinician has estimated the strength of each risk and protective factor, a final determination of risk is made by evaluating the overall strength of all risk factors relative to the overall strength of all protective factors. Suicide risk is lower if the protective factors are judged to outweigh the risk factors, and suicide risk is higher if the risk factors are judged to outweigh the protective factors. Clinicians may then rate the overall risk for suicide as *low*, *moderate*, or *imminent*. We have found that these categories are useful for treatment planning and in determining the appropriate level of care. Chapter 10 describes a range of intervention options for patients who are characterized by varying levels of suicide risk. In addition to deciding on the appropriate level of care, the clinician should also evaluate the need (a) for additional treatment or social service referrals, (b) for additional follow-up evaluations to assess ongoing risk, (c) to inform other treating clinicians or agencies of the level of risk, (d) to contact family members to inform them of the risk, and (e) to obtain additional information from other sources (e.g., medical records).

Debriefing

During and after the risk assessment, the clinician should attend to any adverse effects of the evaluation. To accomplish this, the clinician assesses the current degree of distress, intent to harm oneself or engage in a suicidal act, and urges to use alcohol or drugs before and after the assessment, as well as during the assessment if distress is obvious. If patients' clinical status appears to worsen during the assessment, the clinician can encourage them to take a break, help them to engage in a distracting activity to calm down, and continue with the assessment after their condition has improved. Observation of patients' deterioration may provide valuable information for the risk assessment, as a higher level of care might be indicated for patients who cannot engage in this discussion without experiencing a significant amount of distress. Although debriefing is an important aspect of the clinical evaluation, especially for improving the collaboration between the clinician and patients, we have found that most patients are able to tolerate any potential negative effects of the assessment if they understand that the rationale for the risk assessment is to protect their safety and for treatment planning.

SAFETY PLANS

After a final determination of risk is made and the clinician determines that the patient may be safely treated on an outpatient basis, the clinician works with the patient to develop a safety plan that will address ways to deal with the factors that put him or her at risk for future suicidal crises. The safety plan is a written list of prioritized coping strategies and resources that patients agree to do or to contact during a suicidal crisis. The rationale for the safety plan is that it helps patients to lower their risk of attempting suicide in the immediate future by using a predetermined list of coping strategies and resources. Given that it is often difficult for patients to use problem solving skills during a time of crisis, the purpose of the safety plan is to develop a set of coping strategies while they are not in crisis so these strategies will be readily available in times of distress. The protocol for the safety plan is very similar to other protocols that have been developed by Barbara Stanley at Columbia University and by M. David Rudd and his colleagues (e.g., Rudd, Mandrusiak, & Joiner, 2006).

The basic components of the safety plan include (a) recognizing warning signs that precede the suicidal crisis, (b) identifying coping strategies that can be used without contacting another person, (c) contacting friends or family members, and (d) contacting mental health professionals or agencies. During a crisis, patients are instructed first to recognize when they are in crisis and then to follow each step as outlined in the plan. If following the instructions outlined in the first step fails to decrease suicide ideation and intent, then the next step is followed, and so forth. In our experience, we have noted that the best safety plans are brief, use an easy-to-read format, and generally consist of the patients' own words. We have also found that on occasion, patients find the name *safety plan* aversive. In these instances, clinicians and patients can be as creative as they like in identifying a new title. Alternative titles generated by patients in our studies have included *jeopardy plan* and *Plan B*.

In formulating the safety plan, the clinician is asking patients to use these written strategies to manage their suicidal crisis. However, the safety plan should not be presented as a *no-suicide contract*. A no-suicide contract usually takes the form of asking patients to promise not to kill themselves and to call someone during a time of crisis (Stanford, Goetz, & Bloom, 1994). Despite the anecdotal observation that no-suicide contracts may help to lower clinicians' anxiety regarding suicide risk, there is virtually no empirical evidence to support the effectiveness of no-suicide contracts for preventing suicidal acts (Kelly & Knudson, 2000; Reid, 1998; Rudd, Mandrusiak, & Joiner, 2006; Shaffer & Pfeffer, 2001; Stanford et al., 1994). Clinical guidelines caution against using no-suicide contracts as a way to coerce patients not to kill themselves, as it may obscure patients' true suicidal risk status (Rudd, Mandrusiak, et al., 2006; Shaffer & Pfeffer, 2001). Patients may withhold information about their suicide ideation for fear they will disappoint their treating clinician by violating the contract. In contrast, the safety plan is presented as a plan to illustrate how to prevent a future suicide attempt, and it involves a commitment to treatment in that patients agree to use coping skills and contact health professionals during a time of crisis.

The clinician and patient collaboratively compose the safety plan, such that both individuals actively generate items to include on the form (see

SAFETY PLAN

1. Warning signs (when I am to use the safety plan):
 	
      ☐ Wanting to go to sleep and not wake up
      ☐ Wanting to hurt myself
      ☐ Thinking "I can't take it anymore"

2. Coping strategies (things I can try to do on my own):
 	
      ☐ Listening to rock music
      ☐ Rocking in chair
      ☐ Going for a walk
      ☐ Controlled breathing
      ☐ Taking a hot or cold shower
      ☐ Exercising

3. Contacting other people:
 	
      ☐ Calling a friend to distract myself: _____ Phone: _____
 	
 If distraction does not work, I will tell any of the following people that I am in crisis and ask for help:
 	
      ☐ Calling a family member: _____ Phone: _____
      ☐ Calling or talking to someone else: _____ Phone: _____

4. Contacting a health care professional during business hours:
 	
      ☐ Calling my therapist: _____ Phone: _____
      ☐ Calling my psychiatrist: _____ Phone: _____
      ☐ Calling my case manager: _____ Phone: _____
 	
 The following agencies or services may be called 24 hours a day/7 days a week:
 	
      ☐ Calling the psychiatric ED: _____ Phone: _____
      ☐ Calling National Suicide Prevention Lifeline   Phone: 1-800-273-TALK

Patient Signature: _____   Date: _____

Clinician Signature: _____   Date: _____

Figure 6.3. Example of a safety plan developed during the early phase of treatment. ED = emergency department.

Figure 6.3 for an example). We have found that collaboration is often improved when the clinician and patient can sit side by side and focus on developing the safety plan. Using a template and completing the safety plan on a computer is efficient, but if a computer or template is not available, the clinician can construct one using the subheadings displayed in Figure 6.3. The following four steps are included in the safety plan:

1. *Recognizing warning signs.* The safety plan has the potential to resolve a suicidal crisis only if patients can recognize that they are actually experiencing a crisis. Thus, the first step in devel-

TABLE 6.1
Examples of Warning Signs Leading to Suicidal Crises

Type of sign	Examples
Automatic thoughts	"I am a nobody."
	"I am a failure."
	"I don't make a difference."
	"I am worthless."
	"I can't cope with my problems."
	"Things aren't going to get better."
Images	Flashbacks
Thinking processes	Having racing thoughts
	Thinking about a whole bunch of problems
Mood	Feeling really depressed
	Intense worry
	Intense anger
Behavior	Crying
	Isolating oneself
	Using drugs

oping the safety plan involves the recognition of the signs that immediately precede a suicide crisis. These warning signs can include automatic thoughts, images, thinking styles, mood, or behavior. Patients are asked to list the things they experience when they start thinking about suicide. These warning signs are then listed on the safety plan in their own words. Table 6.1 summarizes some of the typical warning signs identified by patients in our clinical trials.

2. *Using coping strategies.* After patients have identified the signs that lead to suicidal crises, they are asked to list some activities that they could do without contacting other people. At the beginning of treatment, such activities function as a way for patients to distract themselves and prevent suicide ideation from escalating. Examples of coping strategies early in treatment involve engaging in specific behaviors such as going for a walk, listening to inspirational music, taking a hot shower, playing with the dog, or reading the Bible. Other behavioral, affective, and cognitive coping strategies are added to this section of the safety plan as patients learn new skills during treatment, such as those that are described in chapter 8. Thus, although the safety plan is developed during the early phase of therapy, it is reviewed and updated during the intermediate and later phases of treatment as more effective coping skills are learned.

3. *Contacting family members or friends.* The third step consists of a list of those family members or friends whom patients could contact during a crisis. Patients are instructed to reach out to

these individuals if the coping strategies that have been listed in the second step do not resolve the crisis. The list of individuals who may be contacted is prioritized, and phone numbers are included. When contacting others, patients may or may not inform them that they are experiencing a crisis and are in need of help. We have observed that socializing with friends or family members without explicitly informing them of their suicidal state may assist in distracting patients from their problems and alleviate the suicidal crisis. In contrast, patients may choose to inform other close friends or family members that they are experiencing a suicidal crisis, especially when other strategies that have been listed on the safety plan are not effective. In addition, a variation of this step is for patients to indicate the warning signs that other family members or friends might observe during a time of crisis and the manner in which they would like others to respond to them during a time of crisis. Given the complexity of deciding whether patients should or should not disclose to others that they are thinking about suicide, the clinician and patient should work collaboratively to formulate an optimal plan.

4. *Contacting professionals and agencies.* The fourth step consists of listing the telephone numbers of professionals who could assist in a time of crisis, including (a) the clinician; (b) the on-call clinician who can be reached after business hours; (c) the primary care physician, psychiatrist, or other physician; (d) the 24-hour emergency treatment facility; and (e) other local or national support services that handle emergency calls (e.g., the Suicide Prevention Lifeline, 800-273-TALK). Patients are instructed to contact a professional or agency if the previous strategies (i.e., coping strategies or contacting friends or family members) do not work. The safety plan emphasizes that appropriate professional help is accessible in a crisis and, when necessary, indicates how these services can be obtained.

After the safety plan has been completed, the clinician reviews each step of the plan and obtains feedback. The clinician asks whether there is anything else that might be added to prompt further brainstorming of coping strategies. In a similar manner to evaluating the likelihood that patients will complete their homework assignments, the clinician might ask, "On a scale of 0 (*not at all likely*) to 100 (*very likely*), how likely is it that you would be able to do this step during a time of crisis?" If patients express doubt about their ability to implement a specific step on the safety plan, then the clinician uses a problem solving approach to ensure that obstacles to implementing the step are overcome, that alternative coping strategies are identified, or both.

| SAFETY PLAN TO GO |
| Warning signs: |
| Coping strategies: |
| Family/friends: |
| Emergency contacts: |

Figure 6.4. Safety plan to go: crisis card.

Moreover, if patients indicate less than a 90% likelihood of using the safety plan as a whole, then the clinician works with them to identify and modify negative beliefs or assumptions about using the safety plan. A failure to agree to use the safety plan might indicate that a higher level of care is warranted, although the clinician should take care to make a decision about level of care using all available information (see chap. 10), not only the patient's estimate of the likelihood of using the safety plan.

Once patients indicate that there is at least a 90% likelihood that they will use the safety plan during a crisis, then they and their clinician sign it, and the original document is given to patients to take with them. A copy is kept with the clinician so that it may be revised at subsequent sessions as new skills are learned or as the social network is expanded. The clinician also discusses where patients will keep the safety plan and how it will be retrieved during a crisis. The format of the safety plan may be adapted depending on the idiosyncratic needs of the patient. For example, we have observed that some patients may be more likely to use the safety plan if the information is placed on small crisis cards (see Figure 6.4). Such cards consist of very short phrases to remind patients of the specific steps that are described in the safety plan. We are also aware that some patients may have cell phones or other portable electronic devices that they carry with them that will allow for such information to be stored on them. Regardless of the specific medium or format that is chosen, the most important feature of the safety plan is that it is readily accessible and easy to use.

One specific issue related to the development and implementation of the safety plan is the removal of access to lethal weapons. Earlier we mentioned that suicidal intent with a specific plan constitutes a risk factor for suicide. This risk is amplified when the specific plan involves a lethal method that is readily available. The urgency of removing access to a lethal method is even more pronounced when the lethal weapon is a firearm. The amount of time that it takes to kill oneself using a loaded gun is usually much faster than other methods such as overdose or hanging. Thus, gun safety management is a treatment issue that must be addressed during the early phase of treatment if the patient is at risk for engaging in a suicidal act. Discussion of this issue often takes place in the context of developing the safety plan.

If relevant, the clinician and patients discuss the degree of access to lethal methods and agree to focus on ways to reduce access to these methods. Patients should always be asked whether they have a gun in the home or whether they have access to a gun. Patients may also be asked whether they have any plans to purchase a gun. For patients who are at risk for suicide, all guns and ammunition should be removed and stored in a place that is not accessible to them (R. I. Simon, 2007). However, asking patients to remove the gun themselves and give it to a family member or to the clinician is problematic because patients' risk for suicide will increase further, given that they will have direct contact with a highly lethal method of suicide. Instead, an optimal plan would be to have the gun removed from the patient's possession by a designated, responsible person—usually a family member or close friend. This designated person must be able to remove the weapon safely from the home or be willing to contact the police or other person to do so (R. I. Simon, 2007). The clinician and designated person should discuss how the weapon is to be removed and where the weapon will be safely stored so that it is not accessible to the patient. The clinician should have direct contact by phone or in person with the designated individual to confirm that the gun has been safely removed according to the plan that was devised (R. I. Simon, 2007).

The specific plan and the timing of removing a firearm should be decided on a case-by-case basis in consideration of the risk and protective factors. For example, there may be occasions on which patients have an intent and plan to use a gun that is readily accessible to kill themselves, and a designated person is not currently available to secure the gun. In such circumstances, it may be clinically appropriate to hospitalize patients until the gun has been safely removed and the severity of other risk factors for suicide has been reduced. Clinicians should also be aware that the removal of a lethal method does not guarantee patient safety because patients may decide to use another method. Thus, the use of a safety plan and the ongoing monitoring of the patient's intent, plan, availability of lethal methods, and other risk factors are critical aspects for decreasing suicide risk over time.

CONVEYING A SENSE OF HOPE

Although instilling hope is an important element of all approaches to psychotherapy, it is crucial in this intervention because hopelessness is a significant predictor of suicide (G. K. Brown, Beck, Steer, & Grisham, 2000). Even during the first session, the clinician may be able to provide patients with some skills for managing crises (e.g., by including these strategies on the safety plan). In doing so, the clinician helps patients to transform their view that their life situation will not improve and that there is no point in trying to do so. The clinician helps patients to see that "hoping smart" is more functional than hopelessness and despair, as it prompts adaptive problem solving and action rather than inertia. Consider this dialogue between Janice and her clinician, which occurred at the end of their first session after they had developed the safety plan.

Clinician: We've accomplished something very important today. For the first time, you have a plan for dealing with very upsetting situations, such as conflict with your stepfather. What is *your* opinion of the safety plan?

Janice: I don't really know yet. We'll see how it works the next time my stepfather gets in my face.

Clinician: Have you ever had a plan like this before?

Janice: No, this is the first time.

Clinician: Is it preferable to have a plan like this next time you're in crisis, or is it preferable to handle the crises the way you have up to this point?

Janice: Having a plan is preferable, I guess. Maybe it will keep me calm enough so that I can think of something to say back to him, rather than bursting into tears.

Clinician: Ah, so you predict that there is a potential for the safety plan to help you deal with crises, particularly those with your stepfather, differently than you have in the past?

Janice: [affect brightens slightly] Yeah, I guess so.

Clinician: So there's some hope that there is a way for things to be different for you?

Janice: Yes, I feel better about it.

SUMMARY AND INTEGRATION

The early phase of cognitive therapy for suicidal patients orients them to the cognitive therapy approach by focusing on the recent suicidal crisis and by socializing them into the process of cognitive therapy (e.g., setting an agenda at the beginning of sessions). The clinician conveys a sense of hope to patients in two ways—verbally, by explicitly communicating that he or she believes the patient can make meaningful gains in treatment, and nonverbally, by modeling a systematic and manageable approach to dealing with life's problems. The content of the early sessions is geared toward (a) providing a description of the content and process of treatment, including obtaining informed consent; (b) engaging the patient in treatment and addressing any potential problems that may interfere with treatment; (c) assessing suicide risk; (d) developing a safety plan; and (e) instilling a sense of hope.

A final activity that takes place in the early phase of treatment is obtaining a detailed narrative description of the patient's suicidal crisis. In our experience, the very first session of our suicide prevention treatment focuses on obtaining informed consent, conducting a comprehensive suicide risk assessment, and developing a safety plan—the strategies that are the focus of this chapter. It is helpful for clinicians to get some sense of the issues surrounding the suicidal crisis, but there usually is not enough time to obtain appropriate detail. Thus, the additional sessions in the early phase of treatment consist of briefer suicide risk assessments, a check-in regarding whether the safety plan has been effective and whether it requires revision, and a greater focus on a narrative description of the events surrounding the suicide crisis. The narrative description of the events surrounding the suicide crisis forms the basis of the cognitive case conceptualization, which is a comprehensive understanding of patients' clinical presentations based on the cognitive, affective, behavioral, and situational aspects of their suicidal crisis and their psychosocial history. The conceptualization process, particularly strategies for obtaining the narrative description of events surrounding the suicidal crisis, is described at length in chapter 7. The cognitive case conceptualization, in turn, forms the backdrop for the specific intervention strategies presented in chapter 8.

7

COGNITIVE CASE CONCEPTUALIZATION OF SUICIDAL ACTS

As has been discussed in the book to this point, an array of variables interact to increase a person's vulnerability to engage in suicidal acts (e.g., demographic, diagnostic, psychiatric history, psychological variables), and suicidal acts can be understood through many perspectives (e.g., dispositional vulnerability factors, general cognitive processes associated with psychiatric disturbance, suicide-relevant cognitive processes). Moreover, suicidal patients usually report more than one, if not many, factors that contributed to their recent suicidal crisis. Some of the factors involve chronic psychological or social problems (i.e., distal risk factors), and other factors are time limited and occur immediately before the suicidal crisis (i.e., proximal risk factors). Thus, the application of a standardized treatment that addresses only a few of these variables is less likely to be effective than a treatment that uses a flexible approach and is tailored to the specific problems of each individual patient.

Our intervention adopts a case conceptualization approach that focuses on the vulnerability factors and cognitive processes that are associated with the occurrence of a suicidal crisis. According to Persons (2006), case conceptualization–driven psychotherapy "calls for the therapist to develop an individualized formulation of each case that serves as a guide to treatment planning and intervention and to use a hypothesis-testing empirical approach to each case" (p. 167). That is, the clinician applies cognitive theory to understand his or her patient's clinical presentation early in the course of treatment, and over time, he or she modifies the conceptualization on the basis of new information that is learned. Cognitive, behavioral, affective, and situational factors associated with suicidal crises are integrated into the conceptualization, and the conceptualization, in turn, is used to guide the selection and application of specific cognitive and behavioral strategies that may help to prevent a future suicidal act. This chapter describes the major steps of this approach, including (a) conducting a psychological assessment, with a focus on the detailed circumstances surrounding the suicidal crisis; (b) formulating a cognitive case conceptualization of the patient's clinical presentation; and (c) developing a treatment plan based on that conceptualization.

CONDUCTING A PSYCHOLOGICAL ASSESSMENT

A comprehensive psychological assessment must be conducted for any patient who has had a recent suicidal crisis. Although a comprehensive assessment of risk and protective factors, such as that described in chapter 6, may already have been conducted to determine the risk for a future suicidal act, additional psychological assessment is necessary for developing a conceptualization of patients' clinical presentation and a detailed treatment plan that is tailored to patients' needs. The psychological assessment with a suicidal patient has two important components. First, clinicians gather information that is usually collected in most standard intake interviews, including current psychiatric diagnoses, history of psychiatric and addiction treatment, family history of psychiatric disturbance and suicidal acts, medical history, psychosocial history, and mental status examination. Second, clinicians gather detailed information about the circumstances surrounding the recent suicidal crisis.

There are many ways in which clinicians can obtain the standard information on patients' psychiatric diagnoses and various aspects of their history. In some clinics, intake staff members conduct psychological assessments, compile a report, and then assign patients to a clinician. Thus, these clinicians will already have a great deal of relevant information and will be able to develop a preliminary case conceptualization even before they see the patient. Other clinicians will already be in treatment with a high-risk patient, and they will redirect the focus of treatment to address the suicidal crisis and develop strategies for managing future crises. In this case, clinicians will already have much of their patient's history and background from the work that they have done together through that point in time. In both of these instances, the early phase of cognitive therapy will focus on gathering information relevant to the suicidal crisis, and it will not be necessary to gather more general information pertaining to the patient's psychiatric diagnoses and history. In contrast, clinicians who are assigned new cases of suicidal patients and who do not have this background information will need to conduct a complete psychological assessment during the early phase of treatment. Many suicidal patients will continue to be in distress and at risk for future suicidal acts; thus, the suicide risk assessment, described in chapter 6, should always take precedence. The more comprehensive psychological assessment is often distributed across several sessions as clinically appropriate. In addition, the clinician may obtain useful information from standardized self-report measures of psychiatric disturbance, suicide ideation, and previous suicidal acts, such as those described in chapter 1.

The remainder of this chapter illustrates the cognitive case conceptualization process using the example of our patient, Janice. Next, we present the information about Janice that was obtained from the psychological assessment conducted at her intake interview.

> Janice is a 35-year-old, single Caucasian woman who resides with her mother and stepfather. She earned a bachelor's degree in library science a few years ago, but she has been unemployed since graduation. She was recently hospitalized after a suicide attempt in the form of a drug overdose (approximately 20 pills of sleeping medication). Janice reported chronic episodes of recurrent and severe major depression, which lasted for months at a time and never fully remitted. Her Axis I diagnosis is major depressive disorder, recurrent, severe. No diagnoses are specified on Axis II or III, although the intake staff person noted that she exhibits some features of borderline personality disorder. Unemployment and problems in familial relationships are indicated on Axis IV. On Axis V, her GAF (Global Assessment of Functioning) score is 40, and her highest GAF score in the past year is 50.

> Janice reported that she had made three previous suicide attempts by drug overdose; one attempt was 6 months ago, and the other attempts occurred 2 and 6 years ago. She stated that these attempts were not severe enough to warrant medical attention and that she did not tell anyone about them. Janice has had two prior inpatient hospitalizations for depression and suicide ideation, both of which were prompted by her mother's threat to make her find somewhere else to live if she did not get treatment and, ultimately, get a job. During the past several years, she has been prescribed many different types of antidepressants and benzodiazepines, but she regards them as ineffective. At the time of the intake interview, Janice was taking an antidepressant. Her psychiatrist is no longer prescribing a benzodiazepine for sleep disturbance because of its potential lethality.

> Janice's social history reveals that she is socially isolated and engages in few goal-directed activities. She indicated that she had a few close

friends several years ago, but that she decreased her contact with them as her depression worsened. She has had several previous relationships with boyfriends, with the longest relationship lasting about 6 months. She has no children. Although Janice lives in the same house with her mother and her stepfather, she interacts with them infrequently and spends most of her time in her room. Her biological father left the family when she was a small child, and she does not have contact with him. She does not pursue any hobbies or interests.

Janice denied a history of physical or sexual abuse. Her mother had been treated previously for depression, and her maternal uncle had made a suicide attempt when she was a teenager. She denied any current medical illness but reported a history of asthma. She denied current alcohol or substance abuse, although she admitted that she went through several periods of time when she was younger when she used alcohol and marijuana on a regular basis.

Janice received a total score of 25 on the Beck Depression Inventory, indicating a moderate level of depression, and she scored a 2 on the suicide item of this measure, indicating a desire to end her life. She received a total score of 15 on the Beck Hopelessness Scale, indicating a high level of hopelessness. Her suicide attempt was considered to be highly lethal (i.e., loss of consciousness and could not be aroused), as determined by the Lethality Scales. The Suicide Intent Scale revealed many important characteristics of Janice's suicide attempt, including a serious desire to end her own life to escape from her problems. She considered that the amount of medication she took had the possibility to be lethal, but denied that death was a likely outcome. She perceived the attempt to be impulsive and made only minimal preparations to kill herself. She denied any overt communication of her intent to kill herself and did not write a suicide note or make any other arrangements in anticipation of her own death. Although she made the attempt while her mother and stepfather were in the house, they were unaware of the attempt until a few hours after she had overdosed. They had found her unconscious on the bathroom floor and immediately sought medical attention for her condition. She was admitted to an inpatient unit where she was medically stabilized. Janice admitted that she was ambivalent about surviving the attempt, as she had difficulty envisioning how she could improve her life circumstances.

This aspect of the psychological assessment provides important information about the dispositional vulnerability factors and current psychiatric disturbance that may have contributed to the recent suicidal crisis. However, another crucial part of the psychological assessment focuses on characteristics of the patient's recent suicidal crisis itself, such that the clinician (a) obtains a detailed description of the suicidal crisis and (b) constructs a timeline that indicates the major situational events and cognitive, affective, and behavioral factors that were proximal to the crisis. This information is used to understand the specific manner in which dispositional vulnerability

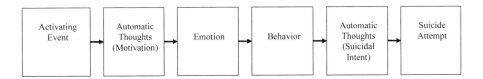

Figure 7.1. Basic cognitive approach to understanding suicidal crises

factors and psychiatric disturbance create a context for suicidal crises to emerge and to identify the suicide-relevant cognitive processes that occur at the time of the crisis and, potentially, culminate in a suicidal act.

Narrative Description of the Suicidal Crisis

Accordingly, a final goal of the early phase of treatment that supplements the aims described in chapter 6 is to obtain an accurate account of the events that transpired before, during, and after the recent suicidal crisis that brought patients into treatment. During this part of the intervention, patients have the opportunity to tell their story about the crisis. The clinician assists patients in this activity by applying the cognitive model described in chapter 3 to the sequence of events that occurred, such that the clinician and patient work together to understand the cognitions, emotions, and behaviors that prompted the suicidal crisis as well as the suicide-specific cognitive processes that were operative once the crisis was in motion. As illustrated in the simplified schematic displayed in Figure 7.1, there are two types of key automatic thoughts that the clinician and patient identify: (a) automatic thoughts associated with the reason or motivation underlying the suicidal crisis and (b) automatic thoughts associated with intent to commit suicide. It is important to acknowledge that the cognitive approach depicted in Figure 7.1 is for understanding a suicide attempt. Patients who have suicidal crises characterized by acute suicide ideation but no accompanying attempt might only have automatic thoughts associated with the reason or motivation to make a suicide attempt, or they might have some automatic thoughts associated with both motivation and suicidal intent but not act on them. The procedure of identifying the sequence of events that occurred before, during, and after the suicidal crisis is very similar to behavior chain analysis that is used in dialectical behavior therapy (cf. Linehan, 1993a).

The clinician sets the stage for obtaining the narrative description of the events surrounding the suicidal crisis by indicating that the beginning of the story may occur at any point in time—it could be the day of the crisis, or it could be weeks or months before. The beginning of the story is the point in time at which patients experienced a strong emotional reaction to a specific event. The specific event could be an external event or situation, such as a significant loss, or an internal event, such as an automatic thought. The clinician notes other precipitants or circumstances, such as the time, date, location, and the presence of other people. Patients are then encouraged to describe everything that subsequently occurred. For patients who attempted suicide, this discussion should focus particularly on the point in time at which a definite decision was made to kill themselves to identify key suicide-relevant cognitions. In addition to describing the method of the attempt, patients are asked to indicate whether they had planned to make an attempt well in advance of the precipitants or whether the attempt was impulsive or reactive (i.e., decision to attempt suicide was made in a matter of minutes). Events that followed the suicide attempt should also be described, including patients' reaction to the attempt and the reactions of others to the attempt to determine whether patients received any positive reinforcement from their behavior (e.g., attention and concern from others).

Occasionally, patients describe only the main external event that led to the crisis without indicating how they reacted to or interpreted the event, such as "I relapsed on drugs, and that's when I attempted suicide." In this instance, the clinician reviews the rationale for obtaining more detailed information and assesses whether patients are reluctant to provide more description. If patients are concerned about providing details, the clinician can use many of the same strategies described in chapter 6 in the context of the risk assessment, such as allowing patients to take breaks as needed or coaching patients in using relaxation or breathing strategies to manage their distress. If patients have no anxiety about providing details but have trouble identifying and articulating them, the clinician can use a Socratic questioning approach to constructing follow-up questions that identify specific thoughts, feelings, and behaviors. For example, the clinician can ask a general question such as "Can you help me understand exactly *how* you went from ____ to deciding to attempt suicide?" To identify automatic thoughts, the clinician asks, "What was going through your mind at that point in time?" To identify a specific emotion, the clinician asks, "How did you feel when that happened?" To identify a specific behavior, the clinician asks, "Then what did you do?"

As patients tell their stories, it is important for the clinician to listen using an empathic and nonjudgmental style. Brief periodic summaries and empathic statements often help patients to feel understood and facilitate a more detailed account of the suicidal crisis. Anecdotally, we have observed that patients who have a trustworthy and collaborative therapeutic relationship are generally more willing to disclose their cognitive and affective responses to their clinician than are patients who do not have a strong therapeutic relationship. It is imperative to obtain a complete picture of what happened without challenging the accuracy or reasonableness of the story. Simply allowing patients to describe what happened helps to build rapport and engage them in treatment. For example, one patient stated that when he was hospitalized for his suicide attempt, he did not perceive that anyone was concerned about what led up to his suicidal act. During the cognitive therapy session in which he was describing his attempt, he said,

> This is the first time I have ever told anyone what happened. Actually, you are the first person who even asked me what happened. It seems that most people either don't care about what happened or they are too uncomfortable to talk about it.

The following dialogue between Janice and her clinician illustrates the process by which clinicians assist patients in providing a detailed narrative description of their recent suicidal crisis.

Clinician: Can you tell me what led up to the suicide attempt?

Janice: Where should I start?

Clinician: At any point where you think that the story begins. Usually a story like this begins when someone has a strong emotional reaction to something.

Janice: OK. On the day that I made the suicide attempt, I was sitting on the recliner and my stepfather came home. He walked in the front door and started walking toward me. At that point, I just knew he was going to be his usual self. My mom was sitting across the room on the couch, and I thought, "Even if my stepfather says something, my mom is not going to defend me because she lets him act like he is king of the house."

Clinician: OK, so then what happened?

Janice: He was an asshole, just like I expected.

Clinician: What exactly did he say?

Janice: He said I should get my lazy ass out of the chair and go fix dinner.

Clinician: [makes a nonverbal facial expression of empathy] So then what happened?

Janice: I got mad because he attacked me like that. I shouted something back to him and just stormed off and went upstairs to my room. I was so angry.

Clinician: What was running through your mind as you were storming off?

Janice: That he has no respect for me.

Clinician: It makes sense that you would feel angry. Then what happened?

Janice: I started to get mad at myself as well. I always let him get the better of me. I thought, "I can't take it anymore. I can't stand this never-ending cycle."

Clinician: That sounds very difficult. How were you feeling when you were in your room and thinking that you couldn't take it? Was the anger getting even more intense?

Janice:	There was so much emotion, both anger and depression. I was overwhelmed, totally overwhelmed with emotion. And then, I think in a matter of a couple of minutes, I was suicidal.
Clinician:	And what was going through your mind at that point, after you became suicidal?
Janice:	I think all the thoughts running through my head were making me crazy. My head was screaming, "That's it. I'm doing it. I want to die. I want to end it. I want it to stop."
Clinician:	I see. Let me summarize the sequence of events that happened before you attempted suicide to make sure I understand what happened. Your stepfather came home and told you to get out of the chair. The thought "He doesn't respect me" came to mind, you became angry, and you stormed out of the room. Once you got to your room, you were overwhelmed with negative emotions, you were critical of yourself, and you thought, "I can't take this anymore." The emotions became increasingly intense, and you thought, "I'm doing it. I want it to end." So, it was at that point that you decided to kill yourself?
Janice:	Yeah, that's when I took a bottle of sleeping pills out of the medicine cabinet.
Clinician:	What pills did you take and how many?
Janice:	About 20 pills, I don't remember the name of them, but they were to help me sleep.
Clinician:	And then what happened after you took the pills?
Janice:	Nothing. The next thing I remember was waking up in the emergency room in the hospital.
Clinician:	So a major trigger for feeling suicidal is intense emotional pain?
Janice:	Yeah.
Clinician:	[links Janice's story to possible treatment goals] OK, this is an important issue for us to address. We need to think about whether there are ways that you can get through intense emotional pain without doing something to hurt yourself.
Janice:	[Blank stare]
Clinician:	So a goal for treatment might be for you to be at the point when you can feel really bad but also have some hope that there are other ways of dealing with your thoughts and feelings that might be helpful. Then, my hope is that suicide would no longer be an option for you. Is that something that you're open to working on?

COGNITIVE THERAPY FOR SUICIDAL PATIENTS

Janice: I guess so, but the reason why it's hard not to have suicide as an option is because I've never really had a time in my life when I felt good. I've never been able to sit through it long enough to stop the suicidal thoughts. I have trouble sitting through the pain part and know that the good stuff is coming because I never have had the good stuff. So it's hard not to feel suicidal.

Clinician: So in the times when you're feeling a lot of pain, it's hard to imagine something hopeful that will get you through that—it's hard to imagine feeling better?

Janice: Right. Because the good feelings have never really been there. Usually, it's either this intense emotional pain when I'm suicidal or an empty, blah feeling. It's just weird. I've never really been happy in my life.

Constructing a Timeline of the Suicidal Crisis

On the basis of the narrative description of the events leading up to the suicidal crisis, the clinician constructs a timeline that incorporates the activating event, cognitions, emotions, and behavioral responses. Figure 7.2 displays a timeline of the sequence of events surrounding Janice's suicide attempt. Key automatic thoughts are noted on the timeline, many of which are accompanied by emotional escalation. As shown in Figure 7.2, Janice's anger escalated when her stepfather was critical of her and when her mother failed to take any action to intervene. At that point, she experienced some automatic thoughts about the situation that led to her emotional response (anger). Next, Janice stormed off and isolated herself in her room, where she began to have several automatic thoughts in reaction to her anger and subsequent behavior. These automatic thoughts (e.g., "I can't take it anymore") were identified by the clinician as the most relevant in understanding the attempt because they were the most proximal to Janice's decision to end her life.

Although Figure 7.2 displays a single activating event, many timelines contain multiple activating events and many different cognitive, emotional, or behavioral reactions to those events. Even though the clinician and patient may be able to construct a complete timeline from the patient's story on the first try, patients often identify additional thoughts, feelings, or behaviors after reviewing an initial draft of the timeline. Thus, several drafts may be required to develop the most detailed timeline that is an accurate representation of what had occurred. This timeline assists in developing the cognitive case conceptualization of the suicidal crisis and in identifying the points in time when interventions or coping strategies can be used to prevent a future crisis. The figure is also a useful resource in preparing for the relapse prevention protocol, which occurs in the later phase of treatment and is discussed in chapter 9.

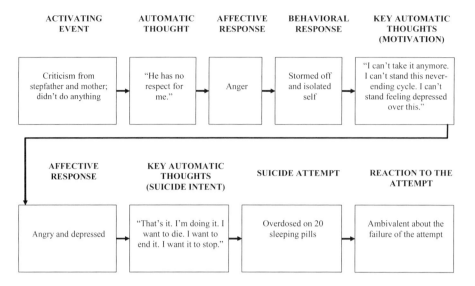

ACTIVATING EVENT	AUTOMATIC THOUGHT	AFFECTIVE RESPONSE	BEHAVIORAL RESPONSE	KEY AUTOMATIC THOUGHTS (MOTIVATION)
Criticism from stepfather and mother; didn't do anything	"He has no respect for me."	Anger	Stormed off and isolated self	"I can't take it anymore. I can't stand this never-ending cycle. I can't stand feeling depressed over this."

AFFECTIVE RESPONSE	KEY AUTOMATIC THOUGHTS (SUICIDE INTENT)	SUICIDE ATTEMPT	REACTION TO THE ATTEMPT
Angry and depressed	"That's it. I'm doing it. I want to die. I want to end it. I want it to stop."	Overdosed on 20 sleeping pills	Ambivalent about the failure of the attempt

Figure 7.2. Timeline of Janice's suicidal crisis.

COGNITIVE CASE CONCEPTUALIZATION

The early phase of treatment culminates with the development of a cognitive case conceptualization. Initially, patients may regard their suicidal crisis as an expression of extreme distress in reaction to one or more proximal events. However, the aim of the cognitive case conceptualization is to develop a more in-depth understanding of the suicidal crisis, which takes into account other factors that are present in the patient's history (i.e., dispositional vulnerability factors, psychiatric diagnoses, relevant contextual factors such as a history of abuse) that supplement the circumstances immediately surrounding the crisis. Thus, not only does the conceptualization include the events and automatic thoughts that were directly experienced in the suicidal crisis, but it also incorporates early experiences and the core and intermediate beliefs that are related to the automatic thoughts, as illustrated in Figure 7.3.

Early experiences, beginning in childhood, include significant acute, chronic, or recurrent events that may have set the stage for the development of the core and intermediate beliefs. As stated in chapter 5, core beliefs are central ideas or absolute truths that patients have about themselves, the world, or the future. They are global, enduring cognitive processes that, once formed, are not easily modified with experience. Core beliefs also influence the development of intermediate beliefs, which consist of rigid attitudes, rules, and/ or assumptions. Intermediate beliefs are the implicit rules that are followed to maintain subjective well-being or avoid harm and generally take the form of conditional statements about the way the world works. Our treatment

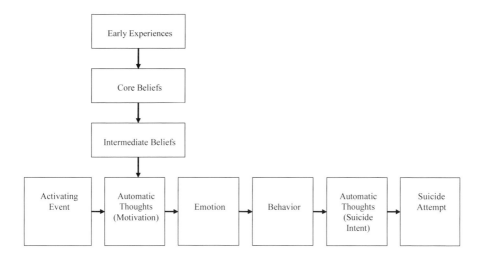

Figure 7.3. Expanded cognitive approach to understanding suicidal crises.

focuses on modifying the core beliefs and intermediate beliefs that are associated with suicide schemas. According to Figure 7.3, the suicide-relevant core and intermediate beliefs influence the automatic thoughts and images that patients experience during a suicidal crisis. Thus, the cognition–emotion–reaction sequence that is part of the general cognitive model (i.e., chap. 3, Figure 3.1) can be applied in treatment to understand and eventually modify the cognitive content that is activated in suicidal crises.

Although the patient and clinician may be able to identify the automatic thoughts that occurred during a suicidal crisis, core and intermediate beliefs are often less obvious. Sometimes, the clinician may ask directly about these beliefs or recognize when a belief is expressed as an automatic thought. However, core and intermediate beliefs are often so fundamental that patients may not be aware of them or articulate them to themselves or others. In these instances, the clinician may examine the patient's thoughts and recognize the common themes that arise when discussing the suicidal crisis, with the common themes providing clues about the patient's core and intermediate beliefs. Clinicians may also be able to illicit these beliefs by using the downward arrow technique. As described in chapter 5, once the key automatic thought is identified, the clinician may ask the patient, "What does that thought mean to you?" To illustrate this strategy in the context of the patient's motivation to commit suicide, consider the following dialogue with Janice:

Clinician: So a critical point occurred when you thought, "This is it. I can't take it anymore. I can't stand this never-ending cycle. I let him affect me too much."

Janice: Yeah.

Clinician:	What do these thoughts mean?
Janice:	I'm not sure.
Clinician:	Let me put it another way. What do they *say* about you as a person?
Janice:	There is something really wrong with me. There has to be since he constantly picks on me, but yet other people get along with him just fine. [pauses and speaks more softly] That I am just a worthless human being.
Clinician:	From what I know about you, it sounds like this worthlessness is a central idea that you have had about yourself, which has been present throughout your life.
Janice:	[sighs] Yes, my life really has very little meaning. There is no joy in my life. Only pain and disappointment.
Clinician:	I'm hearing two core beliefs: "I'm worthless" and "Life has no meaning." Does this sound right to you?
Janice:	[becoming tearful] Yes, that's what it's like almost all the times I am feeling suicidal.

Later in the session, Janice also identified a third core belief—that she cannot bear emotional pain. Thus, Janice's core beliefs fall in the domain of two suicide schemas. Her beliefs of being worthless and of life as being meaningless are associated with trait hopelessness, and her belief about difficulty bearing emotional pain is associated with unbearability.

Intermediate beliefs (i.e., attitudes, rules, assumptions) may be identified in a similar manner. In Janice's case, the clinician used additional Socratic questioning to reveal the following assumptions: "If I cannot control my emotions, then I'm worthless" and "If past treatments have not helped, then it's hopeless." It was determined that these core and intermediate beliefs were influenced by Janice's early experiences in childhood, such as Janice's father leaving when she was a small child and the chronic and recurrent depressive episodes that she had had since the age of 13. Janice recalled that her mother frequently left her with a babysitter to date other men and that her mother scolded her when she expressed her desire that her mother stay at home more often. At times she threw tantrums to capture her mother's attention, and her mother responded by shaming her for her emotional displays. Thus, Janice developed the ideas that she was not worthy of her mother's attention and that she did not have the right to express her desire or show emotion, which, in turn, led to her chronic low self-esteem. Her stepfather's treatment of her reinforced this belief of worthlessness, particularly because Janice did not view him as treating others in the same manner.

The identification of early experiences, core beliefs, intermediate beliefs, and key automatic thoughts form the heart of the cognitive case conceptualization of the suicidal crisis. The central focus of cognitive therapy for suicidal patients is to help them develop strategies for modifying these cognitions. However, two additional pieces of the case conceptualization are important to consider in light of the cognitive model presented in chapter 3. First, the clinician notes the dispositional vulnerability factors that have the potential to (a) activate suicide-relevant schemas and the core beliefs associated with these schemas and (b) exacerbate suicidal crises. Janice was characterized by one dispositional vulnerability factor—deficits in problem solving. Throughout her life, Janice had had trouble making decisions and often became overwhelmed when faced with a large task. She lacked the confidence that she was able to solve her problems (i.e., low problem solving self-efficacy), had trouble identifying options to address her problems (i.e., inability to generate solutions), and often did nothing (i.e., avoidance) rather than taking action. This characteristic is evident in Janice's unemployment, as she was unable to identify the steps one would take to obtain a position as a librarian, and she was deterred by her idea that she would not be good enough to get the job because of her relatively low grades in her library science program.

Second, clinicians describe the suicide-relevant cognitive processes (e.g., attentional fixation) at work during the suicidal crisis, as strategies for breaking the downward cycle will also be targeted in cognitive therapy. Earlier in the chapter, we presented dialogue in which Janice indicated that "in a matter of a couple of minutes," she became suicidal. The clinician might have chosen to focus more specifically on what occurred in this short period of time to identify the manner in which she fixated on suicide as a solution to her problems instead of other solutions. Consider the following dialogue:

Janice: And then, in a matter of a couple of minutes, I was suicidal.

Clinician: Can you think back to what specifically was going on in that matter of a couple of minutes, Janice? Before you made the final decision to hurt yourself?

Janice: I don't know . . . it was all such a blur.

Clinician: What I'm wondering is how you went from the intense emotions of anger and depression, and thoughts of not being able to take it, to making the decision to end your life.

Janice: That's really hard to say; usually, I just get overwhelmed and all of a sudden I feel suicidal.

Clinician: Think back a minute to when you stormed off and went to your room. [pauses to ensure Janice is thinking back to that point in time] What were you doing?

Janice: Just laying on my bed, shaking.

Clinician: Did anything in your room remind you of suicide?

Janice:	No . . . but actually in the middle of everything I had to go to the bathroom, and that's when I saw the medicine cabinet and thought that I might as well end it.
Clinician:	So the medicine cabinet reminded you that suicide was an option?
Janice:	Yeah.
Clinician:	And once you saw the medicine cabinet and thought of suicide, did you think of anything else you could do to feel better or to distract yourself?
Janice:	No, nothing ever works when I get suicide in my head.
Clinician:	It sounds like, instead, you became consumed by the idea that the best way to end it is to commit suicide?
Janice:	Yeah, it was like I was going crazy and that the only way to escape from it would be to swallow the pills. That's when I decided just to do it and get it over with.
Clinician:	Do you think you would have thought of suicide if you hadn't seen the medicine cabinet?
Janice:	Not right away, at least. I probably would have lain on my bed and cried for awhile.
Clinician:	So being in the bathroom and noticing the medicine cabinet seemed to push you past your limit. Is this right?
Janice:	Yes, definitely. I have fights with my stepfather all the time, but I don't usually swallow a bottle of pills, I guess. Usually I don't have enough energy to get up and get the pills, and I just go to sleep.

This line of discussion revealed that Janice saw a suicide-relevant cue (i.e., the medicine cabinet) and became increasingly consumed by the idea of committing suicide (i.e., attentional fixation). The clinician assessed whether Janice was able to see other solutions to her emotional distress, such as doing something to make herself feel better or distract herself, and Janice's response indicated that she was unable to generate other solutions once she was focused on suicide. Thus, this line of questioning revealed that her attentional fixation, along with her automatic thoughts associated with unbearability (i.e., "I can't take it anymore"), pushed Janice past her threshold of tolerance. Had she not seen the medicine cabinet, she likely would not have become as fixated on swallowing the pills. Such a sequence of events often characterizes people who make impulsive suicide attempts.

It is important to note that the clinician would not have obtained this information if he had not been guided by the cognitive model of suicidal acts. At first, Janice indicated that she suddenly became suicidal and that she could not remember the specific sequence of events because everything was a blur. Only when the clinician asked specific questions (e.g., "Did anything in your room remind you of suicide?") were the specific cognitive processes at work in Janice's suicidal crisis revealed. As a result, the clinician had a complete understanding of the cognitive contents associated with Janice's recent suicidal crisis (e.g., thoughts associated with unbearability) and of some biases in the manner in which she was processing information.

The clinician can use a form like that displayed in Figure 7.4 to complete the cognitive case conceptualization. This form summarizes the dispositional vulnerability factors, early experiences, core beliefs, intermediate beliefs, key automatic thoughts, and suicide-relevant cognitive processes that are central in understanding the patient's suicidal crisis. The clinician might not complete all of the boxes if the information is not readily available, or conversely he or she might develop hypotheses about what might have gone in certain boxes, which would be tested as he or she gains more information about the patient during the course of treatment. An important feature of the cognitive case conceptualization is that it is flexible, such that it is modified or refined throughout the course of treatment as more information emerges. Taken together, both the timeline of the sequence of events that led to the attempt (Figure 7.2) and the cognitive case conceptualization (Figure 7.4) facilitate the development of a complete understanding of the dispositional vulnerabilities, underlying beliefs and assumptions, automatic thoughts, beliefs, feelings, and behaviors that culminated in the suicidal crisis. Armed with this information, the clinician compiles a comprehensive understanding of the factors that create a context for suicidal crises to emerge and cognitive, emotional, and behavioral reactions that he or she would expect to occur in a specific crisis.

TREATMENT PLANNING

Treatment plans summarize the specific problems that are presented by patients and the goals of treatment, both of which are informed by the psychological assessment, cognitive case conceptualization, and patients' input. When clinicians develop a treatment plan, they specify (a) the goals for treatment and strategies for achieving those goals and (b) a flexible plan for the activities undertaken in each session. The main purpose of the treatment plan is to determine the specific skills deficits that need to be improved and the dysfunctional beliefs that need to be modified. Moreover, the changes that are targeted are described using language that makes the goals specific, measurable, and observable.

Developing Treatment Goals

The prevention of a future suicidal act is paramount to other treatment goals. Although most patients are in agreement that the prevention of sui-

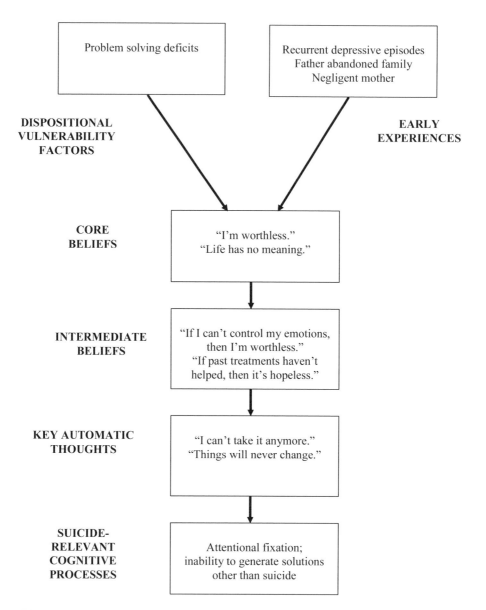

Figure 7.4. Janice's cognitive case conceptualization.

cide is a goal for treatment, occasionally some patients dismiss suicide prevention as a treatment goal because the recent crisis is in the past, and they feel confident that they will never have another crisis. For these patients, it is important to support their decision to live and to offer a rationale for identifying the prevention of suicide as a treatment goal. For example, the clinician might state that one's resolution to live often decreases in times of stress or hopelessness and that now is the time, when patients are feeling better, for them to learn specific strategies to manage suicidal crises in the future. Other patients may refuse the prevention of suicide as a treatment goal because they are ambivalent about their wish to live and their wish to die. It is essential to address these patients' automatic thoughts about these life-and-death issues, with the goal of offering patients a sense of hope that their problems may be resolved.

After patients have agreed that suicide prevention is an important treatment goal, they and their clinician identify additional treatment goals. These goals typically involve addressing the dispositional vulnerability factors (e.g., problem solving deficits) that are associated with suicide risk. Often, patients will prefer that secondary goals be added to the treatment plan, such as psychiatric or substance use disorders that were diagnosed during the psychological assessment or psychosocial problems that they were experiencing around the time of the suicidal crisis. We encourage clinicians to approach these treatment goals in the context of patients' recent suicidal crises and risk for future suicidal acts. Janice's primary treatment goal was preventing another suicide attempt, and her secondary treatment goals included developing strategies to manage her mood disturbance, which she identified as contributing to her suicide ideation, and finding a job, which would help her to attain a sense of self-worth and eventually move out of her mother's home. The clinician expected that addressing the problem of finding a job would help Janice to develop problem solving skills, which she could then use in dealing with other problems and crises. In addition, treatment goals may also involve modifying the core beliefs that are identified from the cognitive case conceptualization. Janice hoped to modify the beliefs that she is worthless, that life is meaningless, and that she cannot bear emotional pain.

Occasionally, patients may wish to include a treatment goal that is vague or for which it is unclear whether it actually can be attained. In these instances, the clinician may ask patients to outline the goal in behavioral terms. For example, if patients indicate that the goal of treatment is to be less depressed, the clinician may ask them to describe how someone else (e.g., a friend or family member) would know that they were less depressed. When Janice was asked to describe how her mother would recognize that she is less depressed, she reported that she would be socializing with her friends more often, crying less often, and doing things to better her life, such as getting a job. The clinician further delineated the treatment goal by asking Janice to describe the type and frequency of these social activities. Janice then decided that a reasonable goal for her was to meet a former classmate for lunch twice a month.

Selecting an Intervention Strategy

After establishing the treatment goals, the clinician and patient select the specific cognitive and behavioral interventions that will most likely prevent a future suicidal act. On the basis of the cognitive case conceptualization, the clinician and patient determine which problems or skills deficits are perceived to be the most life threatening or dangerous. These problems usually include specific automatic thoughts or behaviors that coincided with patients' decisions to end their lives, which were identified in the timeline of the patient's recent suicidal crisis. We recognize that sometimes it is difficult to determine which problems or skills deficits are the most dangerous because there are many different variables that contribute to patients' suicidal acts or because they are still in crisis. If patients have made more than one suicide attempt, they and their clinician may construct additional timelines for previous attempts to identify the most life-threatening or dangerous deficits across suicidal episodes.

Once the key automatic thoughts or behaviors have been identified, specific interventions are chosen to address them. As described in chapter 8, many different cognitive and behavioral intervention strategies can be used to circumvent a future suicidal act. How does a clinician choose the most appropriate one? Clinicians might ask themselves the following questions: (a) Which intervention is perceived by the clinician and patient to be the most helpful for preventing a future suicidal act? (b) Which intervention would have helped to make a difference in preventing a previous attempt? (c) Which intervention builds on the existing resources of the patient? and (d) Which intervention would make the broadest difference in the patient's life? These issues may be addressed directly with patients, with the patients' family members, or with a consultation team.

SUMMARY AND INTEGRATION

The cognitive case conceptualization forms the backbone of cognitive therapy for suicidal patients. It is an understanding of suicidal patients' clinical presentation, on the basis of the cognitive model, that incorporates dispositional vulnerability factors, suicide-relevant beliefs and cognitions, and cognitive processes that were operative at the time of the suicidal crisis. The cognitive case conceptualization is ever evolving. When a clinician first meets a patient, he or she might form the conceptualization on the basis of a combination of the information that the patient discloses, information from the patient's charts, and clinical experience with similar patients; that is, the clinician generates hypotheses about the cognitive, behavioral, affective, and situational factors associated with the patient's recent suicidal crisis. However, the cognitive case conceptualization is modified as the clinician gains more information, develops a relationship with the patient, and observes the patient's behavior over time. Once a timeline of events associated with the recent suicidal crisis has been constructed and a solid cognitive case conceptualization is developed, the clinician and patient move on to the intermediate phase of treatment.

The cognitive case conceptualization serves many purposes. We believe that clinicians make decisions that are informed by theory, and the case conceptualization brings cognitive theory to life for individual patients. It helps to organize large amounts of information and make patients' behavior understandable in light of the schemas that have developed on the basis of their previous experiences. The cognitive case conceptualization also guides the development of the treatment plan and the specific intervention strategies selected by the clinician. For example, when a suicidal patient is in crisis, a clinician might adopt strategies to modify automatic thoughts such as "I can't take this anymore" or to interrupt attentional fixation. When the acute crisis has resolved, the clinician might adopt strategies to modify the core belief that the future is hopeless. As is seen in chapter 8, there are numerous strategies to reach these particular goals.

8

INTERMEDIATE PHASE OF TREATMENT

In the intermediate phase of treatment, the clinician aims to help patients develop cognitive, behavioral, and affective coping skills to manage suicide ideation and reduce the likelihood that they will engage in future suicidal acts. The interventions that are selected in the intermediate phase derive from the cognitive case conceptualization and the treatment plan. Suicidal patients often have many problems, including psychiatric disorders, alcohol or drug use disorders, chronic physical problems, pervasive psychosocial problems (e.g., poor financial resources, limited social network), and restricted access to medical and social services. These multiple and complex problems are challenging for the clinician, given that there are often limited time and resources available to address all of the problems that may have been associated with a previous suicidal crisis. As stated in chapter 5, the primary focus of cognitive therapy for suicidal patients should be on (a) issues that were the most proximately related to the suicidal crisis; (b) interventions that are perceived by both the clinician and the patient to be the most helpful in preventing a future suicidal act; and (c) thoughts, beliefs, or behaviors that interfere with treatment attendance or treatment compliance.

The intermediate phase of treatment should be conducted so that a balance is struck between structure and flexibility. On one hand, clinicians are encouraged to adhere to the session structure described in chapter 5 to maintain an efficient, focused approach to preventing suicide. On the other hand, specific interventions must be implemented in a flexible manner so that acute distress is managed and so that patients can tolerate attention to issues that have the potential to be painful and embarrassing for them. The clinician should keep in mind the cognitive model of suicidal acts, cognitive therapy session structure, the cognitive case conceptualization of the patient's clinical presentation, and the patient's current level of distress as he or she directs the session. Moreover, patients may be referred to the self-help guide *Choosing to Live: How to Defeat Suicide Through Cognitive Therapy* (T. E. Ellis & Newman, 1996) to supplement the strategies targeted in treatment.

The reader who is already familiar with cognitive therapy will notice that many of the strategies described subsequently are similar to those that are incorporated into cognitive therapy for nonsuicidal patients. How is this treatment protocol unique? First, our treatment is a targeted intervention, such that the content of sessions is devoted to understanding the recent suicidal crisis, conceptualizing the recent suicidal crisis in light of the cognitive model, and developing strategies to reduce the likelihood of future suicidal crises. The material that clinicians and patients introduce in session is considered in the context of patients' recent suicidal crisis or current suicide ideation, and specific factors that increase the risk of future suicidal acts assume primary importance in treatment (i.e., the acute phase of treatment). It is only when both the clinician and patient are confident that the patient will be able to manage future crises that the focus of treatment shifts to other areas of importance, such as symptoms of a particular psychiatric disorder or a current psychosocial problem (i.e., the continuation phase of treatment). Second, the strategies used with suicidal patients are concrete and geared toward those that can be accessed easily in times of crisis rather than those that are more complex and require systematic attention. For example, a common cognitive strategy used with nonsuicidal patients is the *Dysfunctional Thought Record* (A. T. Beck, Rush, Shaw, & Emery, 1979; J. S. Beck, 1995), in which patients record situations, thoughts, and emotions in columns to identify and evaluate negative automatic thoughts. In our experience, suicidal patients in a state of hopelessness who are consumed by attentional fixation often do not have the capacity to engage in such an exercise, so it is important for the clinician to devise prompts to promote immediate cognitive, emotional, and behavioral change.

STRUCTURING SESSIONS IN THE INTERMEDIATE PHASE

The basic structure of sessions in the intermediate phase of treatment follows the format presented in chapter 5. That is, the clinician begins with a mood check, encourages patients to form a bridge from the previous session, collaboratively sets an agenda with patients, reviews homework, discusses agenda items, makes periodic summaries, works with patients to develop a new homework assignment, and makes a final summary and obtains feedback. However, there are additional items that are covered in each session of cognitive therapy with suicidal patients. These items include (a) evaluation of suicide risk, (b) evaluation of alcohol and drug use, (c) evaluation of compliance with other services, and (d) review of the safety plan.

Suicide Risk Assessment

A brief evaluation of suicide risk should be conducted at each and every session, as the ongoing assessment of suicide risk is one of the most important steps in securing the safety of patients and for developing an appropriate plan for each session. This assessment is done as part of the brief mood check; thus, the mood check focuses more on suicide ideation and intent and less on mood than do brief mood checks in cognitive therapy for nonsuicidal patients. Although clinicians should monitor suicide risk in all of their patients, it is particularly important for patients who have recently had a suicidal crisis because they are at high risk. Therefore, clinicians should ask a series of questions to assess many aspects of suicide risk, such as (a) "Do you have a wish to die or feel that life is not worth living?" (b) "Do you have a desire to kill yourself?" (c) "Do you intend to kill yourself?" (d) "Do you have a plan to kill yourself?" and (e) "Do you feel hopeless about the future?" Other questions may be asked that are unique to the particular patient's profile of suicide risk, such as triggers, thoughts, beliefs, or behaviors that were associated with a recent suicidal crisis. Alternatively, patients can complete standard inventories, such as the Beck Depression Inventory, before each session, and the clinician can focus on their responses to items assessing suicidal thoughts and wishes and pessimism. The clinician can check in with patients about their general mood as well, but it usually will be of secondary importance to the patient's report of suicide ideation and intent.

A general rule of thumb for clinicians is that any suicide ideation or severe hopelessness, an abrupt change in the clinical presentation, a lack of improvement or worsening of the patient's condition despite treatment, other significant loss, or other warning signs that were listed on the safety plan indicates an increased risk for suicide. When it is determined that increased risk is present, a more detailed evaluation of suicide risk, as described in chapter 6, should be conducted, and an action plan for managing risk should be placed first on the agenda. Often, an action plan involves revisiting the safety plan and modifying or adding to its contents.

Drug and Alcohol Assessment

Many patients who experience suicidal crises abuse drugs or alcohol (e.g., Adams & Overholser, 1992), and when they are actively using substances, their risk for attempting suicide increases, often because of disinhibition and impaired judgment. Clinicians should assess for the use of these substances in the period of time since the previous session, particularly for those patients who have a history of drug and alcohol problems (see chap. 13). If patients respond affirmatively, it is important to identify the frequency of substance use, the amount used, the effects on mood, and the risk for self-injury behavior. The clinician may also assess patients' desire to use drugs and alcohol, especially in instances in which a relapse in substance use was associated with a previous suicidal crisis. For example, the clinician could ask patients, "On a scale from 0 to 100, with 0 indicating *no desire* and 100 indicating *very strong desire*, what is your current desire to use [insert name of substance] right now?" Patients who have reported a relapse on drugs or alcohol or who have a current urge to use these substances should be evaluated further for the likelihood of use so that an appropriate action plan can be developed. Similar to suicide ideation and hopelessness, drug and alcohol use is assessed during the brief mood check.

Assessment of Treatment Compliance

As stated in chapter 2, most suicidal patients are diagnosed with at least one psychiatric disorder, and as a result, many of these patients are taking psychotropic medications. Thus, at each session, the clinician asks patients whether there have been any changes in their medication status. In addition, the clinician asks whether there has been any difficulty in taking the medication as prescribed, the date of the last appointment with the provider who prescribed the medication, and the date of the next appointment with that provider. If there are any problems in taking medications or in keeping scheduled medication appointments, this compliance issue is placed on the session agenda for further discussion, as it likely signals an important problem that has relevance to suicide prevention (e.g., negative attitude about treatment, disorganization). Finally, some medications have the potential to be lethal if taken in large quantities (as in Janice's case with her sleeping pills), so monitoring the use of these medications in particular is an extension of the suicide risk assessment.

Suicidal patients are often in need of other professional services, such as ongoing medical care, addiction treatment, and social services. During the brief mood check, clinicians assess whether patients are compliant with these other services. If patients give an indication that they are not compliant with these services, then the clinician adds this item to the agenda and addresses noncompliance with the strategies described later in this chapter.

Review of the Safety Plan

Periodically, the clinician reviews the safety plan that was developed during the early phase of treatment to update the plan as new skills are learned, new contacts are developed, and any problems arise in using it. This process might begin during the suicide risk assessment, when the clinician asks patients whether the safety plan has been useful in reducing suicide ideation or in helping them to avoid suicidal crises. However, additional work on the safety plan is included as an agenda item when necessary. If patients have not used the safety plan during a crisis, it is important to identify obstacles to using the safety plan in times of need. Clinicians should carefully review patients' automatic thoughts, including their expectation of the degree to which the safety plan will be helpful, and use the cognitive strategies described in chapter 5 to evaluate any negative perceptions of the safety plan. Other issues with compliance can be addressed by modifying the safety plan so that it is more user friendly or more relevant to patients' crises and ensuring that it is close by in times of crisis.

INTERVENTION STRATEGIES

The specific interventions that are applied during the intermediate phase are classified within the behavioral, emotional, and cognitive domains. Strategies in the behavioral domain include increasing pleasurable activities, improving social support, and increasing compliance with medical, psychiatric, addictions treatment, and social services. Strategies in the emotional domain promote affective coping skills, which help to regulate emotional reactivity during times of distress. Strategies in the cognitive domain include modifying dysfunctional beliefs, identifying reasons for living, enhancing problem solving strategies, and reducing impulsivity. Although we separate these strategies into these three major classes, in reality behavioral, emotional, and cognitive strategies are often used in conjunction to achieve a desired outcome. For example, sometimes patients are reluctant to implement the behavioral and emotional strategies discussed in session. In these instances, the clinician assesses negative attitudes toward these strategies and uses cognitive strategies for identifying and modifying those negative cognitions. Moreover, when patients successfully use behavioral or emotional strategies, it is important to identify and articulate the concurrent cognitive change that occurs to increase the patient's sense of mastery. Successful implementation of cognitive and emotional strategies often provides evidence to patients that they can manage distress and decrease suicidal crises. Conversely, cognitive strategies often require a behavioral response from patients, such as engaging in a behavioral experiment to test the validity of a particular belief.

Behavioral Strategies

In our clinical experience, many clinicians and patients choose to focus first on developing behavioral strategies for managing suicidal crises. Patients are often motivated by the relatively immediate changes in their lives that they attain through behavioral strategies, which reduce their emotional reactivity and put them in a better place to evaluate underlying beliefs that lead to suicide ideation and suicidal acts. Moreover, these strategies often achieve some of the same aims as do cognitive strategies, as they instill hope in patients and demonstrate that their problems are bearable.

Increasing Pleasurable Activities

As mentioned in chapter 5, one strategy that can be used with patients who are hopeless and inactive is to increase the amount of time that they engage in pleasurable activities. An advantage of focusing on this behavioral strategy first is that it has the potential to increase patients' engagement with their environment, increase opportunities for positive reinforcement and pleasure, and enhance their motivation to address other problems that are more complex. In chapter 5, we described a strategy in which patients monitor the activities in which they engage every hour of the day and assign ratings of pleasure and accomplishment to each activity. We propose a variation of this activity for suicidal patients, as the goal is to engage them with their environment as immediately as possible rather than after a period of time devoted to monitoring.

The clinician and patient collaboratively generate a list of pleasurable activities that can be easily accomplished. The list should include a mixture of solitary recreational activities and social activities, so that patients are not solely dependent on the presence of others to use this strategy. After a list of activities has been developed, patients and the clinician rank order the activities that they view as most enjoyable and the activities that they are most likely to do. Activities that require more effort, such as organizing a group outing, or more financial resources are often less desirable than activities that can be implemented more easily. Occasionally, patients have difficulty generating a list of activities that they find pleasurable. In these cases, it is helpful to ask them to think about a period in their life when they were happier, or when they were not feeling suicidal, and to ask them to describe the kinds of activities that they used to enjoy. To further ensure that patients follow through with the activity, a worksheet or calendar can be used to record the specific dates and times that the activity is to be pursued. In addition, patients are encouraged to rate the degree of pleasure that is derived from each activity on a scale, with 0 indicating *no pleasure* and 100 indicating *a great deal of pleasure*. Such objective ratings help to provide evidence to patients that they have the ability to experience pleasure in their lives. Obviously, the engagement in pleasurable activities will take place outside of the therapy session, so a logical homework assignment is to pursue one or more of these activities. At the following therapy session, if patients indicate that they successfully completed the activities, then the safety plan should be updated to include them so that they can be used when a warning sign for a suicidal crisis is identified.

The following is an example of the manner in which this strategy was used with Janice. This is the third cognitive therapy session; the first two sessions were spent completing a comprehensive suicide risk assessment and psychological evaluation, developing a safety plan, and obtaining a narrative description of the events leading up to her attempt. She scored in the severe range of the Beck Depression Inventory at the beginning of this session and reported high levels of hopelessness and dejection. The clinician decided to target an increase in pleasurable activities to modify her belief that "life is meaningless and has nothing to offer." Notice that at first Janice had difficulty identifying pleasurable activities and that the clinician used cognitive strategies to evaluate the idea that these activities are trivial and will be unhelpful.

Clinician: [at the conclusion of the brief mood check] I'm sorry to hear that things haven't gotten much better for you over the past couple of weeks. [pause] I have an idea of something we might do together that has the potential to improve your mood and refute the idea that life has nothing to offer you. Would you be willing to put that on our agenda?

Janice: [sighs] I don't know what good it will do. But if you want to, go ahead.

Clinician: [finishes the agenda and moves into the discussion of this item] Here's my idea. What if we were to develop a list together of things you like to do—that is, things that give you a sense of pleasure. Then, when you're feeling especially vulnerable, either very depressed or even suicidal, you can consult this list and figure out something to do that might actually help you to feel better.

Janice: I don't know, I've tried everything already. It's not that simple.

Clinician: You're absolutely right. Feeling depressed and suicidal is very complex. In my experience, I've found that this list is a good first step, but certainly not the *only* step. It won't necessarily cure all of your problems, but it might give you a glimmer of hope that you can do some things that will make you feel good instead of rotten.

Janice: I don't even know where to begin in making a list like that. I don't enjoy anything.

Clinician: Well, when you were feeling better, what sorts of things did you like to do?

Janice: [sniffs] I told you before, I don't think I have ever really felt good.

Clinician:	Yes, I remember. Is what you're telling me is that you've never enjoyed any activities in your entire life?
Janice:	[pausing] Well, no, I guess there are times I had at least *some* fun. But it's all different now. I can't do those things.
Clinician:	[choosing to ignore the idea that she can't do those things until he discovers what those activities are] What kinds of things are you thinking about right now?
Janice:	Before I went back to college, in the 1990s, there were a couple of TV shows that I liked. But they're not on anymore. . . . [trails off]
Clinician:	Anything else?
Janice:	Um, I guess I would read magazines some. I used to have a couple of subscriptions. And I used to go out with friends sometimes, like out to lunch or to a movie. But like I told you, I've lost touch with my old friends.
Clinician:	You've done something very important. You've identified three activities that you find pleasurable that have the potential to improve your mood and refute the idea that life has nothing to offer you. But I also heard you say that it would be harder to do these activities—the TV shows aren't on anymore, your subscriptions ran out, and you no longer have contact with your friends. [pauses] What I'm wondering is if there's a way to get around one or more of these obstacles?
Janice:	[dejected] I don't see how.
Clinician:	Well, reading magazines, for example. Must a person have a subscription to read a magazine?
Janice:	Well . . . no . . . I guess I could pick one up at the store.
Clinician:	[showing enthusiasm] That's a great idea. Any other way to get around these obstacles?
Janice:	I don't think those TV shows are on anymore. But I do think one of the shows has come out on DVD. Maybe I can rent that.
Clinician:	This sounds like a good start. [does not pursue going out with friends, realizing that this is a larger problem that will not be solved in one session] Let's start a list. [grabs a pad of paper and writes] "1. Go to store and buy magazine. 2. Rent [name of TV show] on DVD." We're rolling now, Janice. Are you sure there's nothing else for the list?

After this approach was modeled to Janice, she identified three additional activities: (a) cooking her favorite pasta dish, (b) playing with her cat, and (c) going to a movie with her mother. The clinician attempted to ensure that these activities were simple, straightforward, and manageable, given Janice's high level of depression and hopelessness. Later in the session, the clinician assessed the likelihood that Janice would engage in at least one of these activities in the time between then and the next session and identified a specific time at which she would do that activity. Janice decided that she would rent the DVD on her way home from the therapy session and watch some of the episodes that night. When she returned for her next session, she indicated that she watched several episodes in the series and was pleasantly surprised at how much she enjoyed watching them. Janice also read part of a magazine that she had picked up from the store and played with her cat on several occasions. Thus, the clinician worked with Janice to add these activities to her safety plan.

Improving Social Resources

Many suicidal patients enter into treatment with the idea that no one cares about them (Fridell, Ojehagen, & Träskman-Bendz, 1996). Thus, another goal of our cognitive therapy protocol is to improve patients' social support network, which involves either enhancing patients' existing relationships with family and friends or developing new relationships if there is a paucity of close others in patients' lives. It is important that the clinician does not become patients' only social support; instead, it is best to help patients reestablish ties with others, preferably with the healthiest persons already in their support network. In most instances, these support networks are not particularly strong or well developed, but their mere existence can provide patients with a sense of belongingness and hope that these relationships can be strengthened. We recognize that it is not realistic to expect patients to mend all wounds in existing relationships or to establish close, supportive relationships with many new people in a short-term, targeted intervention such as this. However, work on this issue can begin in the acute phase of treatment, and long-standing relational difficulties can be addressed in the continuation phase.

Thus, we encourage clinicians to start by asking patients to develop a list of others who have the potential to be part of their social support system, even if those individuals can only offer limited support or one specific kind of support. In many instances, patients are pleasantly surprised to see that they have some sort of support network in place. Then, using a calendar, patients can be encouraged to schedule as many positive social activities as possible with individuals on their list. In addition, the clinician can support patients in contacting old friends, neighbors, members of their church, and other community resources. In both of these cases, the clinician should use cognitive strategies to evaluate unrealistic ideas that (a) family members and friends do not care for their well-being, (b) family members and friends will not offer assistance in times of need, and (c) they will be uniformly rejected by others.

At times, it is clear that patients are behaving in self-defeating ways that sabotage their close relationships. For example, suicidal patients are often unresponsive to kind words and interactions with others because of their sense of despair, hopelessness, and low self-esteem. In such instances, the clinician might encourage these patients to actively look for kind gestures or words from others and to accept invitations from others instead of automatically declining invitations. Conversely, the clinician might encourage patients to be proactive in giving compliments and extending invitations. Behavioral experiments can be devised to test assumptions that their kind acts will go unnoticed, not be reciprocated, or be rejected. Moreover, many suicidal patients are in such emotional pain that they are unable to focus on the needs of others. To improve their relationships, it is imperative that patients work toward the goal of treating the most important people in their lives with consideration and respect.

We have noted that suicidal patients often underuse their family resources, in particular. Although these patients sometimes conclude that their family members are unhelpful or critical, in many instances it is later revealed that there are several family members who care and who make efforts to be more involved in patients' lives. We have also observed that at times, family members may give up because they are overwhelmed by their own sense of helplessness or because repeated efforts are not reciprocated or noticed. Thus, we have found it helpful to devote one or two sessions to a family meeting, when clinically indicated, to understand and capitalize on patients' family resources. The family meeting helps the clinician determine the degree to which patients' beliefs that they are alone are true versus the degree to which they are a distortion. Furthermore, during the family session the safety plan can be reviewed with family members with the patient's consent. Family members may be taught (a) how to recognize the warning signs of an impending crisis, (b) the specific questions that can be asked of patients to determine whether they are in crisis, and (c) how to help patients implement coping strategies to deal with a crisis or assist them in contacting other professionals during a time of crisis. Finally, as mentioned in chapter 6, family members may be helpful in making the environment safer, such as removing lethal weapons from the home.

Janice clearly had deficits in her social support system. Not only had she lost contact with her friends, but she also had difficult relationships with her mother and her stepfather, with whom she resided. Janice perceived her stepfather to be overtly hostile and critical toward her, and she resented her mother for not coming to her aid. The clinician judged that a first logical step in improving Janice's social support network was to attend to her relationship with her mother, as that relationship was associated with the least amount of conflict, it was a relationship that was already in place (instead of one that would have to be rebuilt, as with her friends), and at times Janice mentioned that her mother expressed care and concern toward her. The following dialogue occurred in Session 4, after Janice had some success in engaging in pleasurable activities.

Clinician: So what was the end result of doing these activities?

Janice: Well, I didn't feel suicidal this week, if that's what you're asking.

Clinician: That's great news, Janice. And how did doing these activities affect your view that life has nothing to offer you?

Janice: I still don't think it does. I mean, what kind of a person locks herself in her room and reads magazines and watches DVDs? I still have no friends. I still don't really *go* anywhere with people.

Clinician: It sounds like the activities helped to stabilize your mood and distracted you from thinking about other problems in your life, but that those problems are still there.

Janice: Yeah.

Clinician: You just mentioned friends and going places *with people*. Does this suggest that you'd feel better about your life if your relationships with others were to improve?

Janice: Yeah, but I don't see how I can do that.

The clinician proceeded to evaluate possibilities of attending to Janice's relationships with her mother and stepfather and reinitiating contact with former friends. Janice eventually agrees that the greatest likelihood of immediate success might come from focusing on the relationship with her mother.

Janice: I *guess* I could try to spend more time with my mother. But I think chances are slim that it will help. She's *always* with my stepfather and doesn't have time for me.

Clinician: How do you know she doesn't have time for you? Did she say that?

Janice: Well, no, but it seems like every day they are going out and doing things, and I'm not invited.

Clinician: Oh, I didn't realize that you *wanted* to be invited to go along on their outings.

Janice: I don't most of the time, but it would be nice to be asked.

Clinician: Let's turn the table for a moment. Let's say you are your mother, and your mother is you. Your mother has been having a hard time lately and spends most of the time in her room. When you do talk to her, it is pretty tense. Would you anticipate that she'd want to go on an outing with you?

Janice: I . . . suppose . . . not. I guess I'd just think that she wants me to leave her alone.

> *Clinician:* Do you think it's a possibility that she doesn't ask because she thinks *you* just want to be left alone?
>
> *Janice:* [reluctantly] Probably. Especially because I've actually told her I just want to be left alone.

The clinician proceeded to help Janice identify activities that she has done with her mother in the past and would like to pursue again. Then they engaged in a role-playing exercise, with Janice playing her mother and the clinician playing Janice, to practice ways of asking her mother to spend time with her. Throughout the process, negative automatic thoughts were identified (e.g., "She'll say no") and modified (e.g., "She might not be able to do something the day I ask her. But we've spent a lot of time together in the past, so there's no reason to think we'll *never* spend time together again"). Throughout the course of treatment, Janice made greater efforts to connect with her mother, and toward the end of the suicide prevention phase of treatment, her mother agreed to attend a session. Also, the astute reader will recognize that Janice has had four sessions of cognitive therapy—the amount to which she agreed at the beginning of treatment. Although Janice still expressed doubt that her life could improve, she opted to remain in treatment, stating that she liked that the approach was "problem focused."

Increasing Compliance With Other Services

As has been stated many times in this book, suicidal patients often face psychiatric, substance abuse, and physical health problems as well as social and economic problems. It is likely, therefore, that they would benefit from a range of services to address these needs. In many cases, the need for such services is urgent. For example, a patient with a serious chronic health problem may require a referral for specialist treatment, a patient abusing cocaine may require a referral to a substance abuse counselor, and a patient who is unemployed and homeless may require a referral to a social worker. In each case, increasing patients' compliance with such referrals should be an integral part of the treatment for patients at risk for suicide, as these problems are often triggers for suicidal acts.

When working with patients to increase their compliance with adjunctive services, clinicians must have an extensive knowledge base about the range of problems with which suicidal patients present and the services that are available to these patients. Nevertheless, it is likely that clinicians will encounter problems and service needs with which they are not familiar, and at such times they will need to research referral options and consult with other professionals in the community as appropriate. In fact, consulting with appropriate professionals and services is central to working effectively with this patient population insofar as the types of problems with which patients present are unlikely to be addressed by one service alone. Therefore, integration of services and inclusion of adjunctive services are often keys to overall treatment success. Moreover, the more knowledge clinicians have about their patients' problems, available services, and the specific services patients are receiving, the more they can provide education to their patients, help their patients to evaluate various treatment options, and work with their patients to comply with these services.

The clinician and patient should collaboratively establish goals regarding compliance problems with adjunctive medical, psychiatric, addiction, and social services. Because many suicidal patients have had problems with compliance in the past (cf. Morgan, Burns-Cox, Pocock, & Pottle, 1975; O'Brien, Holton, Hurren, & Watt, 1987), it is likely that the clinician will need to be proactive. For example, some patients are not compliant because they have difficulty calling the clinician's office and scheduling an appointment, which suggests that they lack the necessary skills to complete this task. In these cases, the clinician can role play the steps necessary for calling and scheduling appointments, first by modeling for patients how to approach these tasks and then by role playing the person on the other end of the telephone call as patients role play what they would say in this situation. Time permitting, the clinician can coach patients in calling to schedule appointments in session, providing encouragement and support as patients are making the calls and immediate feedback after they have completed the call. This activity can also be assigned as homework. When clinicians focus on making these telephone calls as therapeutic material, they should be sure to follow up at each session to determine whether patients kept their appointments and are compliant with treatment recommendations.

Many patients endorse maladaptive beliefs about the nature and treatment of their problems, and these can be especially apparent in their concerns about or resistance to medication. Some of the beliefs that we have observed in suicidal patients include (a) "Being forced to take my medication infringes on my freedom;" (b) "Being on medication implies that I am sick and/or crazy;" (c) "If I take my medication, I will be admitting that something is seriously wrong with me;" and (d) "I am never going to get better anyway, so what is the point of taking medication?" We have found that modification of these beliefs using the strategies discussed in chapter 5 often leads to important, and adaptive, behavioral changes.

Sometimes patients maintain fairly positive attitudes toward the medications they are taking but still fail to comply because of lack of concentration or disorganization. In such cases, stimulus control techniques can maximize the likelihood that they will remember to take their medications in the prescribed fashion (cf. O'Donohue & Levensky, 2006). Patients can be instructed to keep activity schedules that highlight their daily patterns of behaviors. Then patients can note the activities in which they usually engage during those times of day when they are supposed to take their medication. Finally, they can pair the activity with the medication on a regular basis, leading to the formation of a routine. Clinicians can also help patients generate a system of prompts and reminders to help them stick to the plan even if their concentration levels are not at their best. Although these tasks might be overwhelming for patients in crisis, they can be helpful when patients have made some concrete positive changes in their lives and feel more hopeful about solving life's problems.

A final obstacle that can contribute to noncompliance with adjunctive services is perceived and actual stigmas attached to their problems. Normalization of patients' problems may enable them to overcome this stigma, such as by presenting statistics on the percentage of the population that struggles with similar problems. Referral to patient organizations and support groups may be indicated. In addition to providing normalization and support, such organizations can produce cognitive change by providing a context for patients to view their problems from the perspective of others who have had similar experiences.

Affective Coping Strategies

Affective coping strategies enable patients to better regulate their emotionality without resorting to self-injury and suicidal acts (cf. Linehan, 1993a, 1993b). These skills are grouped into three categories—physical self-soothing, cognitive self-soothing, and sensory self-soothing.

Many patients report that engaging in vigorous physical activities decreases stress, depression, and anxiety. Mood-boosting neurotransmitters, increased body warmth, muscle relaxation, distraction, and a sense of accomplishment all contribute to the physical activity's effect in decreasing emotional pain. Patients can also be taught progressive muscle relaxation and controlled breathing exercises to decrease the physiological arousal associated with distressing emotions. It is difficult to think constructively and solve problems in a systematic manner when one is physiologically charged. Therefore, these strategies may be especially useful for patients as they learn to manage intense emotional reactions to use cognitive and problem solving strategies to address their life problems. A demonstration of relaxation methods can be conducted in session, and audiotapes can be given so patients can practice on their own.

From a cognitive perspective, patients may be taught distraction techniques to counteract their volatile emotions and desire to flee from situations by focusing their attention on any of a number of neutral or positive thoughts. For example, they can try to recall positive memories or imagine a pleasant scene. Distraction is also achieved when patients engage in another activity (e.g., housecleaning, calling a friend). It should be emphasized that distraction is a short-term coping strategy, in that it helps patients get through the distress without harming themselves, but that it does not address the problem that originally caused the distress (cf. Linehan, 1993a). Time and care should be dedicated in session to teaching the difference between distraction and avoidance and when it is and is not appropriate to use distraction strategies.

From a sensory self-soothing perspective, patients can learn to manage distress by using senses such as smell, sound, and touch (Linehan, 1993b). For example, patients can take a warm bath or hot shower, listen to soothing music, or use scented candles to calm themselves. It is often helpful to devise self-soothing strategies that are uniquely relevant to a given patient, insofar as those that are useful are often idiosyncratic. For example, one suicidal young man associated the smell of baby shampoo with feeling loved. His caretaker had shampooed his hair when he was a toddler, and he was particularly fond of this person. A strategy was devised whereby he would wash his hair with baby shampoo to create a feeling of being lovable. Although this did not solve his problems, it reduced the severity of his suicide ideation and allowed time for future interventions. This self-soothing strategy was ultimately included in his safety plan.

Affective coping strategies achieve several goals in light of the cognitive model and cognitive case conceptualization. First, these strategies have the potential to prevent the onset of attentional fixation or decrease its intensity by shifting patients' focus of attention. In addition, they address beliefs about unbearability, such that successful use of these strategies demonstrates to patients that they can ride out times of distress. Consider the following dialogue, in which Janice's clinician uses affective coping strategies to address the belief that she cannot bear distress in times in which she is feeling suicidal. Because Janice was initially resistant to using these strategies, the clinician worked with Janice to devise a behavioral experiment (see chap. 5) for her to evaluate, on the basis of data, the degree to which these strategies would be useful in achieving this goal.

Clinician: It seems that you've made many positive changes in your life, such as doing more things that you find enjoyable and reaching out more to your mother. What effect do you think these changes have had on your life?

Janice: They're OK; I do feel better at times. But then there are other times, like 2 nights ago, when I was feeling suicidal again. It was the same old, same old—my stepfather was on my back for not getting that job. He says I should be trying a lot harder.

Although Janice did not make another suicide attempt, the clinician worked with her to identify the sequence of events leading up to her episode of suicide ideation in a manner similar to what was done when he elicited the sequence of events leading up to her recent attempt (see chap. 7). Through this exercise, he identified a key automatic thought associated with unbearability—"I can't take it anymore."

Clinician: When you have the idea that you can't take it anymore, what might help to reduce your distress?

Janice: Taking pills. It's like a relief, an escape.

Clinician: Would you agree that taking pills is something we're trying to avoid in the future?

Janice: [softly] Yes.

Clinician: Would you be up for brainstorming some alternatives that you can use in a time of crisis like this?

Janice: You mean like reading the magazine? I don't think that would work. I can't concentrate on anything during times like that.

Clinician: You're right; in my experience, many people have trouble concentrating on complex tasks when they are in such distress. [Clinician goes on to educate Janice about the affective coping strategies presented in this section]

Janice: I don't know, these seem pretty basic, and I doubt they would do much good. When I feel like that, like I can't take it, that goes on for *hours*, and nothing can stop it unless I can go to sleep or pass out.

Clinician: I have an idea. What if you were to choose a few of these strategies to try the next time you find yourself in this situation, so we can see for sure whether they would decrease your level of distress and reduce the amount of time you are in this state?

Janice reluctantly agreed to do this behavioral experiment. She chose three affective coping strategies—listening to loud music using her headphones, petting her cat (which also reminded her of a reason to live), and taking a hot shower. It is important to acknowledge that these affective coping strategies are unique to Janice and that these same three activities might not be effective for another person. The point is for patients to identify the affective coping strategies that they anticipate would be most soothing to them, regardless of what might be soothing for other people. A few days later, Janice found herself in a similar situation, and once again she experienced the thought "I can't take it anymore." She consulted her list of affective coping strategies and took a hot shower, followed by listening to music with her cat in her lap. Although Janice continued to be angry at her stepfather, her suicide ideation subsided after approximately 10 minutes. The following dialogue illustrates the manner in which this behavioral experiment affected her belief about unbearability.

Clinician: I'm glad to hear that you were able to get through this, Janice. What did you learn from all of this?

Janice: [laughs] I *really* need to get away from my stepfather and get my own place. [pause] But seriously, I thought that these crises basically last for hours and hours, either until I'm so tired that I go

TABLE 8.1
Common Core Beliefs in Suicidal Patients

Helpless core beliefs	Unlovable core beliefs	Worthless core beliefs
I am incompetent.	I am unattractive.	I am broken.
I am trapped.	I will be rejected.	I'm a waste.
I am inferior.	I have nothing to offer.	I'm a burden.
I can't deal with things.	I am boring.	I don't deserve to live.

> to bed or I pass out from taking a lot of pills. This one only lasted a few minutes.

Clinician: What does that tell you about your ability to take it?

Janice: [pauses] I guess I *can* take it if I put my mind to it. It's hard; it's a lot easier just to take a bottle of pills and end it all. But I guess it's what I have to do if I want to get better.

Clinician: That's an important point, Janice. Do you *want* to get better?

Janice: Yeah, I really do.

Cognitive Strategies

Modifying Core Beliefs

Cognitive therapists assist patients in developing skills to identify negative thoughts and beliefs and helping them to understand the manner in which these cognitions affect feelings and behavior. Patients begin to understand the core beliefs that were active at the time of their suicidal crisis through examination of recurrent themes in their automatic thoughts, discussion of early memories, and experiences related to their viewpoints of themselves or others. Core beliefs in suicidal patients often reflect one of three themes—helplessness, unlovability, and worthlessness (see Table 8.1 for examples). It is often helpful to communicate to patients that others have reported similar core beliefs, as at times they are so potent and shameful that patients believe they are the only ones who have ever viewed themselves in this manner.

Clinicians may use the general cognitive therapy strategies presented in chapter 5 to identify and evaluate suicide-relevant core beliefs, including Socratic questioning and behavioral experiments. The application of a behavioral experiment to modify a belief was illustrated in the previous dialogue. The following dialogue occurred in Session 6 of Janice's treatment, in which the clinician used Socratic questioning to help Janice evaluate her belief that life has nothing to offer her, which is representative of her hopelessness schema.

Janice: Things are getting a little bit better. I'm not so sad and "blah" all the time. But, really, nothing major has changed. I still don't have anything to live for. I can't read magazines and watch TV the rest of my life.

Clinician: Last week we identified the belief "Life has nothing to offer me" as being important in understanding the times when you feel suicidal. Am I hearing that this belief is active right now?

Janice: Yeah, I guess so.

Clinician: What makes you think that life has nothing to offer you?

Janice: I'm 35 and still living with my parents, I have no job, I'm not in a relationship, and my biological clock is ticking. Isn't that enough?

Clinician: You've identified three important areas that we can work on in the longer term, after you've developed skills to manage the times when you feel suicidal—housing, employment, and relationships. It's true that those areas aren't going the way you'd like them to. But can that change in the future?

Janice: It sure doesn't seem like it right now.

Clinician: Has there ever been a time in your past when you thought an area of your life wasn't going well, and you made positive changes to turn that around?

Janice: Well . . . I guess when I was in my 20s and was working at the mall. I knew I would never go anywhere with that job and that I didn't want to stay in retail. So I went back to school and got my degree to be a librarian.

Clinician: Do you recall feeling the same way before you went back to school, that life had nothing to offer you?

Janice: Yeah, that's exactly why I moved back with my mother and went back to school.

Clinician: Let me see if I understand all of this. Before, you had the idea that life had nothing to offer you, and you realized that going back to school would give you some meaning in life, and you did that. Is that correct?

Janice: Yeah.

Clinician: And now you're in a situation again where you feel like life has nothing to offer you. Can you think of anything that might change that idea now, in the same way that going back to school changed that idea back then?

Janice: Well, sure, getting a job and getting my own place. Ugh. It just seems like so much work now.

Clinician: I agree, it will take hard work. Are those goals that you want to achieve in the long term, after we address your tendency to become suicidal in times of distress?

Janice:	Yes, I think I would like to work on those with you.
Clinician:	As we're planning like this for these longer term goals, how much do you believe the idea that life has nothing to offer you?
Janice:	I still think that life has been really hard for me. And I'm not looking forward to all the work it will take to change things. But, I guess it's like it was when I went back to school, that there are some things that life has to offer, but I have to go out there and get them myself.

Imagery can be a particularly effective tool for modifying beliefs related to hopelessness in suicidal patients. Often patients report that their future looks empty and that they cannot imagine what their life will look like in the future. Future time imaging helps patients create pictures of their future that are designed to improve their mood and motivation. Clinicians ask them to choose a time in the future and to note the date, how old they are, and what is happening in their life at that time. They can ask patients where they are, what they see around them, and whom they are with. As with other imagery exercises, patients are encouraged to involve all of their senses as they participate in this activity. Images can be created for 1 year, 5 years, and 10 years into the future. The clinician can then shift to a problem solving mode to help patients consider what they would have to do to make those positive outcomes happen. Often clinicians find that patients' hopelessness scores drop as their future becomes less vague and as positive images are generated.

These cognitive strategies become a model for the manner in which patients can deal with crises in their own lives. Instead of having the emotional knee-jerk reaction of feeling suicidal, they now have the tools to ask themselves what they were thinking, what belief was triggered, and whether there might be other or more benign ways to view the situation. Patients have evidence that these strategies have achieved their desired effect when the intensity of their suicide ideation has decreased, dispelling the emotional crisis.

Identifying Reasons for Living

Suicidal patients are readily able to list various reasons for dying. However, many patients report that when they are in an emotionally charged state, they have difficulty recalling reasons to live, which increases the likelihood that they will engage in a suicidal act. Thus, it is important for patients to have easy-access reminders of reasons for living when they are in a crisis. One straightforward manner of achieving this aim is for patients to write down their reasons for living when they are not suicidal so that they can consult them in times of crisis. These lists often contain reasons such as family members and friends, unfinished business, a goal they hope to attain in the future, spirituality, and/or negative attitudes about suicide. The Reasons for Living Inventory (Linehan, Goodstein, Nielsen, & Chiles, 1983) that was described in chapter 2 is a useful tool that helps to achieve this goal.

However, even when reasons for living are written down on a piece of paper, some patients find that they are not particularly compelling in times of crisis, and so their suicidal acts are not deterred. To address this concern, clinicians who work with suicidal patients often encourage them to develop a *Hope Kit.* The Hope Kit is a memory aid consisting of a collection of meaningful items that remind patients of reasons to live and that can be reviewed during times of crisis. Patients often locate something as simple as a shoebox, and they store mementos such as pictures, postcards, and letters. Often, patients include inspirational or religious sayings or poems. For example, one patient's kit consisted of pictures of her children and her dog, a finger painting that her grandson had made her, a letter from a friend, inspirational music on a compact disc, a passage from the Bible, and a prayer card. She decorated the box with her grandson and pasted inspiring words and pictures on the outside of the box. She then put the kit in a conspicuous place in her home, with the idea that she could use it in a time of crisis. In our experience, this exercise is quite enjoyable for patients and is one of the most meaningful strategies learned in therapy to address their suicidal thoughts and behaviors. Moreover, during the course of constructing a Hope Kit, patients often find that they identify reasons for living that they had previously overlooked.

Like many suicidal patients, Janice had difficulty identifying reasons for living in the early sessions of cognitive therapy. After she became more engaged with her environment, she acknowledged that she did not want to put her mother through the pain of suicide. She also viewed taking care of her cat as a reason to live, as she was its primary caretaker. In Session 6, after the clinician used Socratic questioning to help Janice reevaluate the belief that life had nothing to offer, they collaboratively decided to assign the Hope Kit for homework. She included a portrait of her and her mother that had been taken when she was younger, a few pictures of old friends, her diploma from college, a description of an opening for a part-time job at a local branch library, and advertisements for apartment rentals from the classifieds.

Sometimes using a shoebox for the Hope Kit is impractical or uninteresting to patients. In these instances, the Hope Kit can be implemented in other ways. For example, patients may enjoy creating a scrapbook, a collage, a painting, or even a Web page to identify reasons for living. One patient obtained clothing from people who are important to her and made a quilt. Regardless of the specific configuration of the Hope Kit, the most important characteristic is that it serves as a visual cue to remind patients of the people, places, or things that provide meaning in their lives.

Developing Coping Cards

Coping cards are small, preferably laminated cards that contain useful reminders from therapy for dealing with distress that has the potential to be associated with hopelessness and suicide ideation. The primary purpose of coping cards is to facilitate adaptive thinking during a suicidal crisis, particularly when patients are being drawn into the cycle between state hopelessness and attentional fixation. Usually, the clinician and patient work on constructing coping cards during the session. We have found that coping cards that are brief, to the point, and use the patient's own words are most effective during a suicidal crisis. In addition, patients are encouraged to read coping cards when they are not in crisis so that they can practice more adaptive ways of thinking and make them more automatic. Also, the coping cards may include emergency numbers for the clinician or other crisis services.

Figure 8.1 displays four types of coping cards that are typically used in this intervention, as applied to Janice's life circumstances. One type of coping card assists the patient with evaluating negative automatic thoughts and beliefs. For example, a suicide-relevant automatic thought that was identified when discussing the timeline of the suicidal crisis may be written on one side of the card, and the alternative, adaptive response is written on the other side. To assist the patient in developing an adaptive response, the clinician uses the strategies described in chapter 5 to construct questions such as (a) "What is the evidence that the automatic thought is true? Not true?" (b) "Is there an alternative explanation?" (c) "What is the worst that could happen? Could I live through it? What is the best that could happen? What's the most realistic outcome?" (d) "What is the effect of my believing the automatic thought? What could be the effect of changing my thinking?" (e) "What should I do about it?" and (f) "If [friend's name] was in this situation and had this thought, what would I tell him/her?" (J. S. Beck, 1995, p. 126). Adaptive responses are formed by answering one or more of these questions. This type of coping card achieves a similar goal as the Dysfunctional Thought Record, but is designed to be less complex and easier to use during a time of crisis.

A second type of coping card lists pieces of evidence that refute a core belief, such as the idea that a patient is a failure. A third type of coping card lists coping strategies from which patients can choose when they are in the midst of a suicidal crisis (which is similar to a safety plan). Such strategies might include calling a friend or family member, practicing a distraction technique, or engaging in a pleasurable activity. Finally, a fourth type of coping card contains statements that motivate patients to take measures to reach goals or to practice adaptive coping skills. Our experience has taught us that patients respond well to coping cards because they are concrete prompts to counteract the negative thought processes that lead to distress or crises. We encourage patients to keep coping cards in an easy-access location, and many patients find that it is best to keep them near their safety plan. Some patients keep specific coping cards with them, such as in their wallet, if they know there is the potential for them to experience distress that day (e.g., going on a job interview).

> **Automatic thought: I can't take this anymore.**
>
> Alternative response: It is true that things are hard right now. But I just proved to myself that I can take it by using my self-soothing skills. And I'm going to work with my therapist on ways to get out of my current living situation.

> **Reasons why I'm not a failure**
>
> - I graduated from college
> - I've held down jobs in the past
> - I'm improving my relationship with my mother
> - I have survived many crises in the past

> **Coping skills for when I am feeling suicidal**
>
> - Review my safety plan
> - Listen to loud music with my headphones
> - Go to my Hope Kit
> - Take a hot shower

> **Steps for applying for a job**
>
> - Look for openings on the Internet
> - Bring my resume to locations I think would be a good match
> - Make a follow-up phone call a week later
> - Acknowledge that I am doing something to better myself

Figure 8.1. Janice's coping cards.

Enhancing Problem Solving Skills

As treatment progresses, clinicians work with patients to address life problems associated with their recent suicidal crisis. In the early phase of treatment, the clinician and patient work collaboratively to clearly define each problem, prioritize the importance of problems, and identify a concrete goal that will begin to address each problem. The clinician maintains the problem solving orientation throughout the remainder of treatment. Problems identified in the early sessions are included as agenda items in the intermediate sessions. It is hoped that the acquisition of problem solving skills will improve patients' ability to handle life stressors and reduce the degree to which they focus on suicide as the only solution to their problems.

When addressing a specific problem, the clinician's task is to help patients list as many potential solutions as possible without debating their feasibility or likelihood of success. The clinician should be alert to signs that patients' beliefs or negative cognitions interfere with generating alternatives. The more ideas generated, the higher the likelihood that an effective solution will be found. When this brainstorming activity is completed, clinicians encourage patients to weigh the advantages and disadvantages of the proposed solutions. Patients can be taught to consider both the short- and long-term consequences of the solutions and the manner in which their proposed decisions would affect the lives of others and themselves. Moreover, patients can be encouraged to use cognitive rehearsal to imagine a number of proposed solutions and their effects. Multiple images can be surmised, and probability estimates of the degree to which the solution would be successful can be made for each image. Such an exercise may increase patients' confidence in their problem solving abilities, alert the clinician and patients to potential pitfalls, and give both parties a better sense of the likely outcome for a given course of action. Next, the patient settles on one solution, and discrete steps involved in implementing the solution are identified. A useful homework assignment is to anticipate and plan for difficulties in carrying out the proposed solution by writing down potential obstacles that might arise in implementing each step of the proposed solution and ideas for overcoming them.

If the observed outcome matches the desired outcome, the clinician should encourage self-reinforcement through positive self-statements. The clinician can also encourage the patient to consider the manner in which this success can be generalized to future problems. However, patients often report partial success. This situation provides valuable information for facilitating further discussion about what needs to happen differently to achieve the goal. It also provides the opportunity to modify lofty expectations about problem solving, as more often than not problems are not solved optimally, but the solutions are nonetheless generally desirable. When a satisfactory solution has been implemented, clinicians ask patients to reexamine their former beliefs that it is hopeless to try to solve problems or that they cannot control events in their lives.

Reducing Impulsivity

As previously stated, impulsivity is a risk factor for suicidal acts because impulsive patients, by definition, do not systematically think through the decision to harm themselves. Although impulsivity is most evident in an individual's behavior, we regard strategies to reduce impulsivity as being cognitive in nature because they require patients to apply careful thought to their actions. In working with impulsive suicidal patients, it is important to illustrate that the suicidal crisis will pass and that often these crises come in "waves," such that patients' suicide ideation is sure to decrease if they make the commitment to "ride out the wave." Some patients do not readily accept this explanation, and in these cases, it is helpful to create a diagram in which the clinician charts the patient's mood and suicide ideation over time. This sort of visual aid provides compelling evidence to support the clinician's stance that the patient will not remain suicidal indefinitely.

Another cognitive strategy for managing impulsivity in suicidal patients is to generate a systematic list of advantages and disadvantages of acting on the impulsivity. The sheer act of creating this list will deter the individual from acting immediately on suicidal urges. Moreover, this approach models the problem solving stance emphasized through treatment, in which patients develop skills to systematically evaluate circumstances before taking any one course of action or drawing any one conclusion. It sometimes helps patients to think about deterring suicidal acts as "procrastinating suicide." Finally, the clinician can draw on the coping skills developed throughout the course of therapy to identify the most potent strategies for deterring impulsive behavior. Short-term coping strategies for this purpose include sleeping, talking to another trusted individual, calling the clinician, or engaging in ordinary tasks. Impulsive suicidal patients are strongly encouraged to implement the long-term strategy of safeguarding their environment and disposing of lethal means within their reach. By making their environment unfriendly to suicide, patients will buy time to safely to get through difficult periods.

SUMMARY AND INTEGRATION

In the intermediate phase of treatment, clinicians and patients work together to develop specific, concrete strategies for managing suicidal crises and reducing the factors that make patients vulnerable to future suicidal acts. The particular interventions the clinician selects emerge from the cognitive case conceptualization of patients' recent suicidal crises and clinical presentation. Behavioral and emotional coping strategies are often targeted first in treatment, as they have the potential to provide immediate relief of patients' continued distress. Behavioral strategies for improving patients' social support network and increasing their compliance with adjunctive services reduce patients' vulnerability for future suicidal acts by connecting them with their community. Cognitive strategies accomplish three main goals: (a) to modify the beliefs associated with the recent suicidal crisis, which in turn reduces the strength of patients' suicide schemas; (b) to remind patients of reasons for living when they are in crisis and likely to focus exclusively on reasons for dying; and (c) to develop the skills to approach problems—even impulses to engage in future suicidal acts—in a systematic, reasoned manner.

As stated at the beginning of this chapter, we encourage clinicians to make their interventions as concrete and specific as possible so that they are easily implemented in times of crisis. Visual cues, such as the Hope Kit, are especially effective in reminding patients of reasons to live during suicidal crises and breaking patients out of the cycle of attentional fixation. Although this phase of treatment will not modify all negative schemas associated with comorbid psychiatric disorders, it is designed to modify aspects of suicide schemas (e.g., the belief that one cannot bear emotional pain) and curb suicide-relevant cognitive processes before they propel patients past their threshold of tolerance to engage in a suicidal act. In fact, it is likely that these strategies modify the threshold of tolerance itself by demonstrating to patients that they *can* stand crises for a longer period of time than they had thought. Once it is evident to the clinician that patients have acquired these skills, they move into the later phase of treatment, described in chapter 9, to conduct a formal assessment of skill acquisition.

9

LATER PHASE OF TREATMENT

As stated many times throughout this volume, the primary goal of treatment is to reduce the likelihood that patients will engage in a future suicidal act. The main focus during the later phase of this treatment is to evaluate whether patients have learned and can apply specific skills that may help to diffuse a suicidal crisis. Therefore, the later sessions of cognitive therapy consolidate, review, and apply strategies that were most helpful for patients in coping with distress throughout treatment. There are four main tasks that the clinician undertakes in the later phase of cognitive therapy for suicidal patients, including (a) summarizing and consolidating skills that were learned during the intermediate phase of treatment; (b) applying these skills in a series of guided imagery exercises; (c) reviewing progress toward treatment goals; and (d) planning for the continuation of treatment, referring for other treatment, or preparing for the termination of treatment.

REVIEW AND CONSOLIDATION OF SKILLS

During the final phase of this treatment, the clinician and patient review all of the skills that were learned and practiced. This comprehensive review is appropriate when (a) patients no longer report any desire to commit suicide; (b) patients perceive that most, if not all, of the issues that triggered their recent suicidal crisis have been addressed; (c) the severity of patients' acute symptoms has diminished, as evidenced by lowered scores on the Beck Depression Inventory and Beck Hopelessness Scale; and (d) patients have demonstrated that they have acquired skills for coping with future distress or crises. Although other significant psychiatric and substance use disorders may continue to persist and require further treatment, if the major problem areas that were associated with the recent suicidal crisis have been adequately addressed, the focus on suicide prevention can be ended, and longer standing problems and issues can then assume the primary focus of treatment in a continuation phase.

To facilitate the review and consolidation of skills, the clinician and patient review the treatment plan that was developed in the early phase of treatment and the safety plan that has been modified throughout treatment. The clinician asks patients which skills were most helpful in dealing with distress or crises that emerged during the course of treatment. If it becomes evident that patients are having difficulty generating a list of cognitive, emotional, and behavioral coping strategies, then it is likely that they are not ready to move into the later phase of treatment. Conversely, if patients are readily able to generate such a list, then those strategies are applied to the next activity in the later phase of treatment, the relapse prevention protocol. In many instances, it is helpful to develop a coping card that lists the most helpful strategies for coping with future crises, so that patients have easy access to those strategies after the acute phase of treatment has ended.

RELAPSE PREVENTION FOR SUICIDAL CRISES

The relapse prevention protocol is a set of guided imagery exercises in which patients imagine their previous suicidal crisis and systematically describe the manner in which they would cope with suicide-relevant thoughts, feelings, behaviors, or circumstances. This protocol serves as a way to rehearse coping with future crises and to assess treatment progress. The objective of the relapse prevention protocol is to prime, in session, the thoughts, images, feelings, behaviors, and circumstances that were associated with the recent suicidal crisis and to determine whether patients are able to respond to these events in an adaptive way. Although some clinicians have likened this procedure to an exposure exercise, we instead regard the purpose of this exercise as gaining practice in applying coping strategies and consolidating what has been learned in treatment. If the clinician determines that patients have difficulty applying the skills developed during the course of treatment, then additional sessions that focus on learning to apply these skills are warranted. Closure of the suicide prevention phase of treatment is not advised until patients are able to complete the relapse prevention protocol successfully.

The relapse prevention protocol consists of five steps: (a) preparation phase, (b) review of the recent suicidal crisis, (c) review of the recent suicidal crisis using skills, (d) review of a future suicidal crisis, and (e) debriefing and follow-up. Steps (b), (c), and (d) consist of guided imagery exercises in which patients vividly imagine circumstances surrounding a real or hypothetical suicidal crisis. Exhibit 9.1 provides a summary checklist of the major activities that occur in each step of the relapse prevention protocol.

Preparation Phase

Before conducting the first Socratic questioning exercise, the clinician introduces the relapse prevention protocol to patients and obtains their consent for participation. The clinician describes the rationale for the protocol and explains its main components. Specifically, patients are informed that by imagining the suicidal crisis and reliving the pain that was experienced, they will have the opportunity to assess whether the coping skills learned in therapy can be recalled and applied. The clinician helps patients to recognize that the purpose of the exercise is to prepare them for a future suicidal crisis and to ensure that they have the necessary skills to manage it. In other words, patients are informed that they will have the opportunity to test the skills learned during the treatment. Because this task will undoubtedly be uncomfortable for patients, it is imperative that the clinician approach it in as collaborative a manner as possible and ensure that patients perceive the sequence of events in the relapse prevention protocol as controllable and predictable.

The clinician and patient enter the preparation phase of the relapse prevention protocol at least one session before they actually engage in a guided imagery exercise. One reason for this is so that patients have time to become familiar with the exercises' requirements and mentally prepare themselves. In addition, it allows time for the clinician and patient to recall the timeline of events that occurred during the suicidal crisis and review the skills learned during treatment. The careful review of the suicidal crisis and skills learned will facilitate their recollection during the guided imagery exercise. Because the success of the relapse prevention protocol depends on patients' ability to vividly imagine the suicidal crisis, it is important that this information be easily accessible during the guided imagery exercises.

Not surprisingly, some patients are reluctant to participate in the guided imagery exercises. In these instances, the clinician identifies their concerns about completing the exercise and works with them to brainstorm ways to address their reservations. For example, patients may be concerned that aversive emotions are likely to arise when recalling the details of their recent suicidal crisis. The clinician should empathize with patients' feelings and assure them that he or she will help them address any unpleasant thoughts or feelings that are elicited during this exercise. In addition, the clinician should

EXHIBIT 9.1
Relapse Prevention Protocol Checklist

Step 1: Preparation

Provide a complete rationale and description of the steps involved in this protocol.
Confirm that the patient understands the protocol.
Describe the potential for negative emotional reactions.
Discuss strategies for dealing with negative emotional reactions.
Address the patient's feedback and concerns.
Obtain the patient's consent.

Step 2: Review of the recent suicidal crisis

Assess whether the patient is able to produce a vivid image, and if not, teach the patient to do so.
Set the scene of the attempt or crisis.
Ask the patient to describe in the present tense the sequence of events that led up to the suicidal crisis.
Focus on the key thoughts, emotions, behaviors, and circumstances that were most relevant to the suicidal crisis.

Step 3: Review of the recent suicidal crisis using skills

Ask, again, the patient to describe in the present tense the sequence of events that led up to the suicidal crisis.
Prompt the patient to describe the coping strategies and adaptive responses to the key activating events.

Step 4: Review of a future suicidal crisis

Ask the patient to imagine and describe the sequence of events that could lead to a future suicidal crisis.
Focus on key thoughts, emotions, behaviors, and circumstances that are most relevant to eliciting suicide ideation.
Prompt the patient to describe the coping strategies and adaptive responses to the key activating events.

Step 5: Debriefing and follow-up

Ask the patient to summarize what he or she has learned from these exercises.
Describe the manner in which changes the patient made in treatment were reflected in his or her handling of the imagined suicidal crises.
Identify any issues elicited in these exercises that remain problematic for the patient.
Determine whether the patient is experiencing suicide ideation and, if so, collaboratively develop a plan to address it.
Review the safety plan.
Offer additional treatment sessions or follow-up telephone calls as clinically indicated.

ensure that he or she will be available for additional sessions or by telephone to address any adverse reactions that emerge after the session. Moreover, costs and benefits of participating in the guided imagery exercises can be weighed so that patients can articulate their benefit in managing future distress. Some patients anticipate that they will experience feelings of guilt or shame about their behavior; in these instances, the clinician can structure the exercises so that they focus on what the patients learned from this experience rather than on what they did wrong.

Sometimes patients not only express apprehension about the possibility of experiencing painful emotions but they also fear that they will deteriorate if they revisit the details of the previous suicidal crisis. In these instances, the clinician can apply several of the standard cognitive strategies reviewed in chapter 5 to evaluate their concerns. Specifically, clinicians can use Socratic questioning to test the validity of the notion that participation in the relapse prevention protocol will make things worse by asking questions such as (a) "What is the worst thing that could happen? The best thing? The most realistic thing?" and (b) "If the worst thing were to happen, what strategies or skills could be used?" (J. S. Beck, 1995). If these cognitive strategies are unhelpful, the clinician may offer to focus the relapse prevention protocol only on a future high-risk scenario and not discuss the previous suicidal crisis. Although we believe that the relapse prevention protocol facilitates the greatest amount of consolidation of skills if patients engage in guided imagery tasks pertaining to past and future crises, completion of even one guided imagery exercise is preferable to completing none. In rare cases, patients choose not to participate in the guided imagery exercises even when the clinician has used cognitive strategies to evaluate the validity of their concerns. In these instances, the clinician can ask patients to articulate in detail the specific manner in which cognitive and behavioral strategies can be implemented in the future to evaluate the degree to which they have acquired adaptive coping skills.

Review of the Recent Suicidal Crisis

During the session in which the first guided imagery exercise is conducted, the clinician obtains verbal consent to continue. The clinician should, once again, review the rationale for this exercise and ask patients to summarize it in their own words to ensure that it is comprehended. Any concerns that patients express about experiencing unpleasant or suicidal thoughts or urges should be fully addressed. The clinician forewarns patients that they may have a strong emotional response to this experience but that it is to be expected and that there will be time to discuss what happened before the end of the session or, if necessary, in additional sessions or interim telephone content. Finally, the clinician works with patients to identify active coping strategies for dealing with unpleasant thoughts or emotions if they are experienced, such as (a) taking a break, (b) discontinuing the task and talking about something else, or (c) empathizing with the thoughts and feelings that were experienced. The clinician may also suggest using a "stopping rule" that consists of a word or phrase that patients can use to discontinue the task immediately.

After obtaining verbal consent, the clinician uses guided imagery to help patients imagine in detail the events leading up to the suicidal crisis that brought them into treatment. The clinician should have a copy of the notes that were taken during the early phase of treatment to assist in identifying appropriate prompts. The following dialogue illustrates how the initial guided imagery exercise can be introduced.

Clinician: Janice, would you be willing to relive the day of the attempt and experience the feelings again?

Janice: I'm not exactly looking forward to it, but I'll do it.

Clinician: Based on what we discussed in last week's session, why do you think it is important to do this?

Janice: To face my problems head-on. To show me that I can get through them without swallowing a bunch of pills.

Clinician: Good. Now I would like you to close your eyes and think about the day that you made the suicide attempt. I would like you to imagine the point in time just before the event that seemed to trigger the sequence of events that led to the attempt. Picture in your mind what happened on that day, and describe these events and your reactions to these events to me as if you were watching a movie of yourself.

The clinician encourages patients to speak about the events in the present tense, as if the events are occurring in the moment. A detailed discussion of the objects, people, or other situational aspects helps to facilitate vivid imagery, as illustrated in the following dialogue.

Clinician: Where are you right now?

Janice: I'm in the living room of my house.

Clinician: Who are you with?

Janice: My mother is sitting on the couch.

Clinician: What does the room look like?

Janice: Well, my mother is on the brown couch. There is a coffee table in front of the couch, and there is a television in front of the adjacent wall. There is also a large reclining chair across from the couch. I'm sitting in the chair.

Clinician: What color is the chair?

Janice: It is a light brown, made of corduroy. It's very comfy.

Clinician: So you are sitting in the chair right now. What else are you doing?

Janice: I'm watching the news on TV.

Clinician:	What time of day is it?
Janice:	It's about 6:00 p.m. I've been cooking dinner, and my stepfather is coming home soon.
Clinician:	I see. What are you making for dinner?
Janice:	Spaghetti and meatballs. It smells really good.
Clinician:	OK, so you are sitting in the big comfy chair and waiting for your stepfather to get home. What happens next?
Janice:	Well, I hear their car pull into the driveway.

Next, the clinician asks patients to focus on the sequence of events that triggered them to become upset. These events may be cognitions, feelings, or behaviors, but most often they are some sort of external situation, such as an argument with someone. If the events surrounding the trigger involved conflict with another person, then the specific conversation should be recalled. Following a detailed description of the trigger, the clinician asks patients how they responded to the event. For example, the clinician can ask, "What is going through your mind right now?" "How are you feeling right now?" "What are you doing?" or "What happened next?" These questions are designed to elicit the thoughts, behaviors, feelings, and circumstances that were identified during the early phase of treatment as being associated with the timeline of events.

Patients should recall as much detail as possible about the period of time that was proximal to the suicidal crisis. Most important, the clinician should focus on key thoughts, assumptions, or behaviors that seemed to be most critical in the escalation of the suicidal crisis. Consider the following dialogue:

Clinician:	Your stepfather comes home; what happens next?
Janice:	I get really upset.
Clinician:	How come?
Janice:	I see my stepfather come through the front door, and I just know that he's going to say something really condescending to me.
Clinician:	Does he?
Janice:	Yes, he comes in and starts in on me.
Clinician:	What does he say?
Janice:	He says, "Get your lazy ass out of the chair and fix dinner."
Clinician:	So what do you do?
Janice:	I get up out of the chair and tell him to go to hell. That I am making dinner for them, and he treats me like dirt.

Clinician:	What is running through your mind?
Janice:	He has no respect for me!
Clinician:	And then what happens?
Janice:	I stomp up the stairs, go into my bedroom, and slam the door so hard that it knocks a picture off the wall. And then I start to blame myself for getting so angry about my stepfather asking me to get out of the chair. I'm laying in bed, feeling really overwhelmed. I think that there must be something really wrong with me because this stuff happens all the time. And then I have to go to the bathroom, and while I am in there I see the medicine cabinet and decide that I should just end it.
Clinician:	So at the point that you decided to end it, what is going through your mind?
Janice:	I feel I just can't take it anymore. The pain is unbearable. I've been this way my whole life, and I don't see any way for things to improve.
Clinician:	What happens next?
Janice:	I grab a bottle of sleeping medication and swallow all the pills in the bottle.

The monitoring of suicide-relevant thoughts and images is important for determining when the suicide ideation is most acute and for identifying accompanying thoughts, feelings, and behaviors. During the guided imagery exercise, the clinician asks patients to rate the degree of suicide ideation at different times in the sequence. For example, the clinician can ask, "On a scale from 0 to 100, with 0 indicating *no thoughts about suicide* and 100 indicating *extremely suicidal*, how suicidal are you right now?" The purpose of this rating is to monitor ideation so that when there is an increase, it can be targeted in the subsequent guided imagery exercise that incorporates the application of cognitive and behavioral skills to manage suicidal crises. The guided imagery exercise continues until patients have described in detail all of the events surrounding the suicidal crisis. After the exercise is completed, patients are asked to open their eyes. The clinician elicits feedback from patients to (a) identify any residual suicide ideation and begin to address it before proceeding to the next agenda item or ending the session, (b) assess whether patients view the suicidal crisis in a different manner now than they did when they entered into treatment, and (c) identify anything the clinician can do in future guided imagery exercises to make them run smoothly and maximize their effectiveness. At times, new information is revealed during the guided imagery exercise. If this occurs, the clinician and patient can discuss how this information may be used to modify the cognitive case conceptualization or change the safety plan (e.g., identification of warning signs).

EXHIBIT 9.2

- How would you cope with this thought using the skills you learned?
- Is there an alternative explanation for this idea?
- How else might you solve the problem?
- Picture yourself thinking of other options right now. What might those be?
- Who might you call on the telephone?
- What would you do differently?
- What on your safety plan might be helpful?
- Picture yourself using your safety plan right now. What does it say?

Review of the Recent Suicidal Crisis Using Skills

After the initial guided imagery exercise, the clinician again leads patients through the same sequence of events, but this time patients are encouraged to imagine using the skills learned in therapy to cope with the event. This second guided imagery exercise is usually conducted during the same session as the first exercise so that the session is concluded with a sense that patients can actively manage these crises. When a key thought, behavior, feeling, or situation is identified, the clinician asks patients to indicate the current level of suicidal thinking using the 0 to 100 scale. Then, the clinician prompts patients to describe what they might do differently. Exhibit 9.2 summarizes approaches to helping patients generate different ways of coping with the suicidal crisis during the relapse prevention protocol. The identified skill or coping strategy should be described in as much detail as possible to create a vivid image of putting this strategy in action, as illustrated in the following dialogue:

Clinician: When you decided that you couldn't take it anymore, what could you have done differently?

Janice: I guess I could get my safety plan.

Clinician: Good. Imagine that you are going to get your safety plan. Where is it?

Janice: In the drawer in my bedroom.

Clinician: Imagine that you are reading the safety plan right now. What does the safety plan tell you to do?

Janice: It says that one of the warning signs is when I feel that life is unbearable. It says to try to do something to distract myself like reading a magazine, but I don't think that this is going to work. I can't get my mind off of my problems.

Clinician: Are there any other suggestions on the safety plan?

Janice: Yes, it says I could take a hot shower.

Clinician: So imagine that you are taking a hot shower; what does it feel like?

After the coping strategy is described, patients again rate the degree of suicidal thinking on the 0 to 100 scale to determine whether the coping strategy helped to decrease suicidal thoughts and wishes. If patients' suicide ideation continues to be high, or even if it is low but still distressing to them, then the clinician continues to prompt patients to implement additional coping strategies until the crisis has resolved. In fact, in many instances it is preferable for patients to generate as many coping strategies as possible for them to see that there are several adaptive ways to handle the triggers of suicidal crises. At the conclusion of this guided imagery exercise, patients open their eyes and provide feedback to the clinician. It is often helpful for clinicians to obtain an estimate of patients' confidence that they would be able to implement these strategies during an actual crisis. If patients' confidence level is low, then the clinician can reinitiate this relapse prevention exercise or verbally discuss ways of making these strategies even more helpful.

If patients are unable or unwilling to use imagery during the relapse prevention protocol, the clinician and patient can simply summarize the events that occurred before the suicidal crisis and describe the manner in which they would use the coping skills. The rationale and procedure during this review is similar to the rationale and procedure for the guided imagery exercise. The clinician reminds patients of the circumstances associated with the previous suicidal crisis and assesses whether patients are able to respond to maladaptive thoughts, feelings, and behaviors in an adaptive way. However, this is achieved in a straightforward, factual manner using the past tense, rather than through vivid imagery and use of the present tense. Role playing can also be used to elicit coping responses. For example, the clinician could have patients imagine that they are advising a close friend who is suicidal, such that they provide suggestions for coping, or the clinician can implement a reverse role play, such that the clinician plays the role of the patient, and the patient plays the role of the clinician.

Review of a Future Suicidal Crisis

The final guided imagery exercise in the relapse prevention protocol is for patients to imagine a future suicidal crisis and describe, in detail, the manner in which they would use cognitive and behavioral strategies to reduce the likelihood of engaging in a future suicidal act. This third guided imagery exercise can be conducted in the same session as the two exercises described earlier. However, in many instances there is not enough time left in the session to do so or patients are fatigued from the previous exercises, so it is best to reserve this exercise for the subsequent session.

The clinician should use patients' cognitive case conceptualization to develop a realistic scenario in which they would likely experience suicide ideation. This guided imagery exercise is conducted in much the same way as the others described in this chapter, such that patients close their eyes, speak in the present tense, and respond to their clinician's prompts. As patients generate possible solutions and describe the manner in which they would implement learned coping strategies, the clinician praises them for adaptive responding but also introduces additional challenges. These additional challenges are posed to evaluate the depth and flexibility of patients' adaptive responding. If patients are unable to generate any coping skills, the clinician can prompt them more directly to imagine using tools learned in therapy, such as consulting the safety plan, reading a coping card, problem solving, or using controlled breathing. In Janice's case, the clinician selected another conflict with her stepfather as an event that might lead to a future suicidal crisis. He proposed this idea to Janice, and she agreed that it would be a relevant focus for the final guided imagery exercise.

Clinician: Imagine that you are at home tonight, sitting in the brown reclining chair, and your stepfather walks in the house. The frown on his face suggests that he is in a bad mood. He is stomping over to the closet to hang up his coat, and he pauses, looks back at you, and shakes his head. What might he say next?

Janice: He says, "Nothing will ever change. You're going to live off of your mother and me forever. I should win a prize for how much I have to put up with you."

Clinician: What runs through your mind?

Janice: I hate you! I can't stand living with you.

Clinician: And how do you feel?

Janice: Horrible! Depressed and ashamed.

Clinician: And what do you do next?

Janice: Same thing as usual. Run up to my room, throw myself down on the bed, and cry.

Clinician: Picture yourself laying on your bed and crying. Do you have a vivid image of that?

Janice: [nods]

Clinician: Is this the point where you often have the idea "I can't take this anymore?"

Janice: [nods again]

Clinician: On a scale of 0 to 100, how intense are your suicidal thoughts right now?

Janice:	Like an 80.
Clinician:	What can you do to respond to the thought "I can't take this anymore"?
Janice:	I could say, "I know I can get through this. I've done it before. And I'm not going to be here much longer, since I'm finally making some money and will get my own place in a few months."
Clinician:	On a scale of 0 to 100, how intense are your suicidal thoughts after coming up with that alternative way of looking at things?
Janice:	It's better. Like a 40 or so.
Clinician:	So, the suicidal thinking has decreased, but some is still there.
Janice:	Yes.
Clinician:	What else can do you to manage your distress?
Janice:	I can look at my safety plan.
Clinician:	Imagine reaching for your safety plan in the drawer of your nightstand. What does it say?
Janice:	It says read magazines, take a hot shower, talk to my mother, read my coping cards, and look through my Hope Kit.
Clinician:	Which one would be most effective in reducing your suicidal thinking to 0?
Janice:	Um . . . looking through the Hope Kit.
Clinician:	Good. Now imagine looking through the Hope Kit. [pause] What's in there?

The clinician goes on to have Janice focus on the contents of her Hope Kit and what the items mean to her, and he subsequently has her rate the intensity of her suicidal thinking. In addition, the clinician presents Janice with some alternative scenarios, such as her stepfather following her up the stairs to yell at her some more. Janice was able to imagine using every coping skill that had been helpful to her throughout treatment in responding to these various scenarios.

Debriefing and Follow-Up

Following the three guided imagery exercises, patients should be provided with support and encouragement for conducting this task (e.g., "You've come a long way"). In addition, patients should be given the opportunity to reflect on what they learned from this exercise. The clinician can work with patients to identify the specific changes they have made over the course of treatment. How might these skills be used in the future? How will the safety plan be used in the future? Are there issues that were identified in this exercise that still remain a problem? The clinician should consider designing a homework task that is related to issues raised during this exercise.

Also during debriefing, patients rate their current suicidal thinking on the 0 to 100 scale. This rating is different from the rating obtained in the context of the guided imagery exercises because it pertains to the degree of suicide ideation that the patient is experiencing in the present, as a result of completion of the relapse prevention protocol. If any suicide ideation is noted, then the safety plan should be reviewed, and the clinician should encourage patients to articulate the specific manner in which they will manage any thoughts or urges to engage in a suicidal act. In other words, the clinician works carefully with patients to ensure that any suicide ideation has deescalated after the relapse prevention exercises and that they will be safe when they leave the clinician's office. We find that most patients are able to tolerate these exercises because they have successfully developed an array of coping strategies and have already made many positive changes in their lives. However, if patients are struggling after the relapse prevention protocol, then the clinician should offer additional treatment sessions or follow-up telephone calls as clinically indicated. The goals of these sessions or calls are to (a) empathize with patients' concerns, (b) identify patients' automatic thoughts in response to the imagery exercise, and (c) assist patients in developing adaptive responses to these automatic thoughts.

An important aspect of the relapse prevention protocol is to determine whether patients are able to complete all aspects of the exercise in a satisfactory manner. Patients who successfully complete this task are able to engage emotionally, have a clear visualization or provide a detailed description of the events, and generate appropriate responses. The following questions may serve as a guide for the assessment of the successful completion of this protocol:

1. Is the patient able to imagine the sequence of events that led up to the suicidal crisis?
2. Is the patient able to recall and clearly describe the behaviors, thoughts, and feelings that led up to the suicidal crisis?
3. Is the patient able to imagine problem solving or responding more adaptively in the future, and can the patient generate many adaptive responses and resources?
4. Is the patient confident that his or her situation will improve and that he or she will be able to handle future crises differently?
5. To what extent is the patient able to experience affect during the exercises and show a decrease in negative affect after the exercises are completed?

If patients do not complete this task successfully, then additional sessions may be warranted to review the skills learned during treatment.

REVIEW OF TREATMENT GOALS

After the successful completion of the relapse prevention protocol, the clinician and patient evaluate progress that has been made toward the treatment goals that had been established at the end of the early phase of treatment. A risk assessment should be conducted to determine whether patients continue to have any suicide ideation, suicidal intent, or thoughts about a plan to attempt suicide. Patients who continue to report suicide ideation should not be discharged from treatment unless an alternative treatment has been identified and they are fully engaged in another type of treatment. In addition, patients' expectations about the likelihood of making a future suicide attempt should be assessed. If patients anticipate that they will make a suicide attempt in the future or if they are ambivalent about making an attempt, then further treatment with a focus on suicide prevention is clinically appropriate.

Other goals that were discussed during the early phase of treatment should also be reviewed. Because many of these goals relate to concurrent psychiatric or substance use disorders or to long-standing dispositional vulnerability factors, they may not be fully resolved because the primary focus of treatment was on suicide prevention. Together, the clinician and patient can identify the goals that will be targeted in continuation or maintenance treatment, as well as goals that need to be revised or added now that the acute suicidal crisis has resolved.

ADDITIONAL TREATMENT PLANNING

After the successful completion of the relapse prevention protocol and review of treatment goals, the clinician and patient discuss three treatment options: (a) continuation of treatment, (b) referral for additional treatment, and (c) termination of treatment.

Continuation of Treatment

Although the focus of the continuation phase of treatment is on issues that are not directly related to suicide ideation and suicidal acts (e.g., psychiatric disturbance, relationship problems), the clinician should encourage patients to keep their safety plans close by in the event that they experience another suicidal crisis. In addition, the clinician should prepare patients for any setbacks or lapses. Typically, patients who experience a setback, such as a relapse in drug use or depression, often experience hopelessness. This pessimism is often associated with an all-or-nothing thinking pattern that leads patients to conclude that treatment was not effective. This belief is especially dangerous because patients may generalize this setback to indicate that any treatment will not be helpful, which in turn could prompt another suicidal crisis. To prepare patients for possible setbacks or lapses, unrealistic expectations should be addressed, along with potential strategies for dealing with setbacks.

If there are other issues to be addressed, then the clinician and patient revisit treatment goals for the continuation phase of treatment and negotiate the frequency of sessions. The continuation phase of treatment may go on as long as necessary to address patients' multiple, long-standing problems. These sessions follow the same general session structure, including agenda setting, ongoing risk assessment, discussion of cognitive and behavioral coping strategies, and homework assignments. If it is decided that there are no other major issues to be addressed, then the clinician and patient can consider tapering the frequency of visits to biweekly or monthly sessions. Booster sessions, or sessions scheduled as needed by the patient, are another option to use during this phase of treatment. The clinician and patient might agree on specific guidelines for scheduling booster sessions, such as the emergence of suicide ideation, an exacerbation of life stress, or a worsening of dispositional vulnerability factors. Often the clinician decides on a change in the frequency of sessions in consultation with a treatment team or other professionals who are providing care for the patient. On occasion, family members are consulted in determining the best approach for scheduling additional sessions during the continuation phase of treatment.

Referring for Additional Treatment

Occasionally, patients need further treatment that is beyond the expertise of the treating clinician. Clinicians are advised to seek out appropriate referrals in these cases. These referrals may include addictions treatment for alcohol or drug dependence disorders or specialized care for other psychiatric disorders, such as bipolar disorder or schizophrenia. Clinicians often find it helpful to assist patients in scheduling appointments with other professionals. Moreover, it is important to follow up with patients to determine whether they kept the appointment and to evaluate their reaction to and expectations for additional treatment. Contact with other clinicians who are providing additional treatment is highly recommended for optimal continuity of care.

Termination of Treatment

Some patients who have experienced a suicidal crisis and successfully completed the relapse prevention protocol will be asymptomatic or report minimal psychiatric symptoms over an extended period of time. The discontinuation of treatment may be clinically appropriate for these patients. Nonetheless, establishing a watchful-waiting period to monitor for the recurrence of symptoms, including suicide ideation, is recommended. Patients should always be provided with additional referrals, and the circumstances for pursuing additional treatment should be discussed.

Finally, an important component of the termination of treatment is continuing to build on the patients' skills and encouraging patients to use other resources that may serve as protective factors that reduce the likelihood of future suicidal acts. The clinician and patient may review the reasons for living or revise the contents of the Hope Kit that was constructed during the intermediate phase of treatment. In addition, patients should review the list of individuals who are able provide social support. The important aspect of termination of treatment is the transition from an acute, crisis-oriented treatment model to a model of sustained recovery management.

SUMMARY AND INTEGRATION

The focus of the later phase of treatment is on the (a) consolidation of cognitive and behavioral strategies learned in treatment, (b) application of those strategies to imagined suicidal crises, (c) review of treatment goals, and (d) decision of how best to continue with treatment. The heart of the later phase of treatment is the relapse prevention protocol, when patients can engage in guided imagery exercises that are designed to elicit cognitions, emotions, and behaviors associated with suicidal crises and describe the manner in which they would reduce their distress to prevent a suicidal crisis from escalating. The successful completion of the guided imagery exercises demonstrates to patients that they can manage situations that may have led to suicidal crises in the past. Moreover, the successful completion demonstrates to clinicians that their patients have retained and can apply the skills learned in therapy. When patients complete the relapse prevention protocol, the close of the acute suicide prevention phase of treatment is indicated. Patients may remain in treatment with their clinician in a continuation phase of treatment, in which they focus on other issues associated with their clinical presentation (e.g., psychiatric disorders). In contrast, the clinician may opt to refer patients to other professionals for more specialized treatment (e.g., addictions treatment), or he or she may decide to terminate treatment but see patients periodically for booster sessions. Regardless of the specific treatment plan that is followed, the clinician ensures that patients have readily available their safety plan and reminders of reasons to live.

10

CHALLENGES IN TREATING SUICIDAL PATIENTS

Suicidal patients are among the most challenging patients treated by clinicians (cf. Ramsay & Newman, 2005). When clinicians add a suicidal patient to their caseload, they often expect that they will have to deal with multiple crises, hospitalization, and extensive documentation. Moreover, many clinicians are hesitant to treat suicidal patients because they fear the possibility of legal and ethical ramifications if a patient ultimately commits suicide (Bongar, Maris, Berman, & Litman, 1992). Although suicidal patients are in serious need of care, paradoxically, it is often difficult to find a clinician who is willing to treat them.

We acknowledge that there are times when many of these complications are very real; however, they can be managed in a systematic manner using the cognitive therapy framework. Some of these challenges were addressed in chapter 6—we indicated that suicidal patients often have a negative attitude toward treatment, and we suggested strategies for addressing these attitudes to ensure that treatment is successful. This chapter discusses additional challenges that clinicians face in treating suicidal patients and presents ways to address them from a cognitive therapy perspective. All of these challenges have been expressed by clinicians whom we have trained to treat this population. Areas of challenge identified by these clinicians include (a) challenges in patients' lives that prevent them from fully using therapy, (b) challenges in implementing the cognitive therapy protocol, and (c) challenges arising from clinicians' reactions to working with suicidal patients.

CHALLENGES IN PATIENTS' LIVES

It is not uncommon for clinicians who work with suicidal patients to face challenging clinical presentations. At times, suicidal patients' attendance is sporadic because their lives are unstructured, and they are dealing with multiple life stressors. In other instances, patients continue to be at risk for engaging in suicidal acts and require the clinician's attention in between sessions to ensure their safety. Some patients present for sessions under the influence of alcohol or drugs or with concurrent homicidal ideation. The following section describes strategies for handling these challenges within the cognitive therapy framework.

Chaotic Lifestyles

In our experience, we have seen that suicidal patients often have chaotic lifestyles. Housing, transportation, and employment problems often prevent them from attending regularly scheduled therapy sessions. Patients often have repeated "crises" that require the majority of the time allocated to any one therapy session. Thus, at times clinicians perceive that the course of therapy is disjointed or that they repeatedly have to start over from scratch. In these instances, it is difficult to bridge from the previous session because so much time has passed and so much has happened in the patient's life.

When clinicians find that they have a patient with sporadic attendance, we encourage them to attend closely to the cognitive case conceptualization (see chap. 7). Clinicians already will have assimilated the information that was learned in previous sessions into a cognitive case conceptualization, and they can determine whether the new information supports the preliminary conceptualization that has been formed or, conversely, whether the conceptualization must now be modified. Over time, the cognitive case conceptualization will be solidified, which will facilitate the clinician's understanding of cognitive, affective, behavioral, and situational factors that contribute to the patient's difficulties and guide the clinician's choice of strategies implemented in sessions. Thus, clinicians should keep the cognitive case conceptualization in the forefront of their minds during the session and ask the following question: "Based on what I suspect are this patient's key automatic thoughts and dysfunctional core beliefs related to the recent suicidal crisis, what strategy would be most successful in ultimately modifying these thoughts and beliefs?"

After not seeing a patient for some time, it is tempting for clinicians to spend the majority of the session getting an update on the events that have transpired in the patient's life. Given the likelihood that some patients with chaotic lifestyles may not return for several weeks, it is important to take every opportunity to make an intervention based on cognitive theory and the cognitive case conceptualization. For example, we recommend that clinicians maintain the session structure described in chapter 5 to model systematic prioritizing and problem solving for the patient. In addition, we encourage clinicians to take appropriate opportunities to link patients' reported life stressors to the general cognitive model to continue to reinforce the manner in which thoughts, emotions, and behaviors are interrelated. The safety plan developed in the first session can be reviewed to ensure that patients have concrete steps to follow in a crisis. Finally, as discussed in chapter 5, we have found it helpful to select a straightforward, concrete homework assignment that can be started in session to increase the likelihood that patients will make positive changes in their lives outside of session.

Crises Outside of Session

Many clinicians who work with suicidal patients are fearful that they will be required to spend a good bit of time managing patient crises outside of session. There is some truth to this concern; in our clinical trials, we have found that patients contact study staff for reasons such as feeling suicidal, having difficulty coping with overwhelming life stressors, having trouble with the law, and needing help with referrals to hospitals or addictions treatment programs. Thus, clinicians who work with suicidal patients should have readily available a standard plan for risk management, which includes an assessment of the risk and protective factors for suicide and an action plan for reducing risk. As described in chapter 6, the clinician completes the risk assessment as clinically indicated and determines whether patients are at low, moderate, or imminent risk.

The action plan that follows this risk assessment should correspond to the degree of risk. For patients with lower suicide risk, the action plan may include identifying the key elements in the timeline of events that led to the escalation of suicide risk and addressing these factors using the cognitive, emotional, or behavioral strategies described in chapter 8. The clinician also reviews the implementation of the safety plan with low-risk patients and evaluates its effectiveness in reducing risk. At this time, the clinician and patient can revise the safety plan and address any problems or obstacles that were encountered in using it. Appropriate follow-up actions with low-risk patients may include but are not limited to (a) scheduling a follow-up risk assessment, (b) scheduling the next therapy session, (c) scheduling the next telephone contact, (d) contacting other agencies or providers who are also responsible for patient care, (e) obtaining or reviewing medical records for more information that could influence the final determination of risk, or (f) contacting family members or other individuals.

For patients at a moderate level of risk and who can be safely treated on an outpatient basis, clinicians may follow some of the same strategies that they would use for lower risk patients. However, clinicians often schedule a follow-up risk assessment, therapy session, or telephone contact at an earlier point in time with higher risk patients than they do with lower risk patients. For example, a follow-up appointment may be scheduled the next day instead of the following week. In addition, the clinician working with higher risk patients should more strongly consider contacting other providers, agencies, or family members who may be able to provide additional assistance. The clinician may also refer higher risk patients to other providers or agencies for additional evaluation and alternative or adjunctive treatment, such as pharmacotherapy, or for programs that offer a higher level of care, such as intensive outpatient or inpatient services.

If the clinician determines that the patient is an imminent risk to himor herself or others, then it is imperative that more intensive interventions be considered to prevent harm. However, the evaluation of imminent risk is often a difficult task because of the inherent difficulty in predicting dangerous behavior within a very short period of time. Many of the standardized measures of suicide ideation and related constructs have been validated for suicide over a lengthy period of time (i.e., years) and have not been adequately tested for predicting imminent behavior. Thus, the determination of imminent suicide risk is based on the relative strength of risk factors as compared to the strength of protective factors (see chap. 6). Parenthetically, the period of time defined as "imminent" is also open to clinical judgment. Imminent behavior may refer to behavior that is about to occur within the next few minutes, or it may refer to behavior that is about to occur within the next 24 to 48 hours. Regardless of the time frame that the clinician chooses to adopt, a standardized protocol for the determination of risk and the implementation of an action plan should be followed.

Once the clinician has determined that the patient is at imminent risk for suicide, the clinician may recommend that he or she be evaluated for admission to a hospital. The *Practice Guideline for the Assessment and Treatment of Patients With Suicidal Behaviors* (American Psychiatric Association [APA], 2003) recommends that hospital admission is *generally indicated* after a suicide attempt or aborted suicide attempt if

(a) the patient is psychotic;
(b) the attempt was violent, near lethal, or premeditated;
(c) precautions were taken to avoid rescue or discovery;
(d) a persistent plan or intent is present, distress is increased, or the patient regrets surviving the attempt;

(e) the patient is male and older than age 45 years, especially with new onset of psychiatric illness or suicidal thinking;

(f) the patient has limited family and/or social support, including lack of stable living situation;

(g) the patient demonstrates current impulsive behavior, severe agitation, or poor judgment or refusal of help is evident; or

(h) the patient has a change in mental status with a metabolic, toxic, infectious, or other etiology requiring further workup in a structured setting. (APA, 2003, p. 31)

In addition, hospital admission is *generally indicated* for patients with suicide ideation accompanied by a specific plan with high lethality, high suicide intent, or severe anxiety, agitation, or perturbation (American Psychiatric Association, 2003). We encourage clinicians to be familiar with their state laws regarding the decision to involuntarily commit patients who are at imminent risk for suicide and who refuse to be hospitalized.

In contrast, hospital admission *may* be necessary after a suicide attempt or an aborted suicide attempt, except in circumstances when hospitalization is generally indicated as described previously or in the presence of suicide ideation for patients with

(a) psychosis;

(b) a major psychiatric disorder and a history of previous suicide attempts;

(c) a possibly contributing medical condition;

(d) a lack of response to or inability to cooperate with outpatient treatment;

(e) a need for a supervised setting for a medication trial or electroconvulsive therapy;

(f) a need for skills observation, clinical tests, or diagnostic assessments that require a structured setting;

(g) limited family and/or social support, including lack of stable living situation; or

(h) lack of an ongoing clinician–patient relationship or lack of access to timely outpatient care. (APA, 2003, p. 31)

Hospital admission may also be necessary in the absence of suicide attempts or reported suicidal ideation, plan, or intent if evidence from the psychiatric evaluation or history from others suggests a high level of suicide risk and a recent acute increase in risk (American Psychiatric Association, 2003).

In instances in which the clinician determines that patients are at imminent risk, a specific plan must be made for them to be transported safely to a hospital. It is not advisable to leave patients unattended when it has been determined that they are at imminent risk. Because it is imperative to be able to observe patients at imminent risk or to stay on the telephone with them, clinicians should have some method in place for contacting a colleague or other member of the treatment team so that they can make the necessary travel arrangements. Transportation options may include calling the police, ambulance service, or mobile crisis service. At times, patients who proactively contact the clinician in crisis volunteer to get themselves to the hospital. Unfortunately, we have found that such an arrangement often gives the clinician a false sense of hope that the crisis is averted; in actuality, many patients do not make it to the hospital agreed on with the clinician because additional life stressors arise in the meantime, or they decide they want to go to a different hospital but do not inform the clinician of the change in plans. We have found it helpful to contact the psychiatric emergency department of the local hospital for guidance in choosing the most clinically appropriate method of transportation for a patient who is at imminent risk for suicide and to notify the emergency department staff of a patient's impending arrival.

In addition, family members may also be contacted to accompany the patient to the hospital. In many respects, this arrangement is preferable so that patients are monitored at all times and because patients are often more comfortable with family members than with emergency transportation personnel or the police. However, we encourage clinicians to have a contingency plan in place if patients and their family members do not arrive at the hospital within a certain time frame.

Finally, it is also helpful for the clinician to have an understanding of what will happen once patients arrive at the hospital. Often, patients must wait several hours before being admitted or seen by a physician. Sometimes patients are released if the emergency department staff members decide that they are no longer at imminent risk of harming themselves. Thus, clinicians can use their knowledge of the hospital's procedures to help clarify any unreasonable expectations, such as that staff will attend to them immediately on arrival. Moreover, clinicians should take care not to promise that patients will receive a certain type of care, such as actually being admitted to the hospital.

Concurrent Substance Abuse

In our clinical trials in which we are evaluating the effectiveness of our cognitive therapy protocols with suicidal patients, we have found that most of the patients meet criteria for a substance dependence disorder. Many of the clinicians we have trained struggle with whether they can effectively treat patients who are actively abusing drugs. One clinician noted that this situation presents an approach–approach dilemma. When patients are in session with their clinician, they express a legitimate desire to get help, stay sober, and put their lives back together. However, the temptation of using often wins out, particularly when patients have yet to develop other strategies for coping with adversity. We have found that when patients begin using again, clinicians often do not hear from them for several weeks.

A fundamental tenet of our protocol for suicidal patients is that they receive many different services to address their diverse needs, such as from general practitioners, psychiatrists, social workers, and addictions counselors. As stated in other chapters, one goal of cognitive therapy for suicidal patients is for patients to increase their compliance with these services. Thus, clinicians should refer patients for these various services as needed. We find that this strategy delegates the responsibility for patient care to a number of professionals and relieves clinicians' sense that they have sole responsibility for their patients' well-being.

Unlike many clinicians who practice other forms of psychotherapy, we do not necessarily recommend that the clinician refuse to see patients who come to their sessions under the influence of alcohol or drugs. Because many suicidal patients have a weak social support network or core beliefs related to unloveability or abandonment, a perceived rebuff from their clinician has the potential to activate suicide ideation. In addition, because substance use is associated with an increased likelihood of impulsive and aggressive behavior, patients under the influence are at greater risk to act on suicide ideation. Instead, we encourage clinicians to choose the appropriate course of action on the basis of the degree of intoxication and the cognitive case conceptualization. A comprehensive risk assessment should be conducted as described in chapter 6, and if necessary, a safety plan should be generated collaboratively so that patients have a safe place to go after they leave the clinician's office.

Concurrent Homicidal Ideation

As mentioned in chapter 2, sometimes suicidal patients also reveal homicidal ideation during crises. Often, homicidal ideation coincides with a significant stressor or disappointment, such as the breakup of a relationship or being asked to vacate a place of residence. We encourage clinicians working with suicidal patients to assess for homicidal ideation at the beginning of the session during the risk assessment. When patients endorse homicidal ideation, it is important to obtain specific information along many of the same dimensions that are relevant to suicidal ideation, including the frequency, intensity, and duration of the ideation; the degree of intent to harm another individual; the presence or absence of a specific plan to harm another individual; and whether the patient has access to lethal means. Clinicians should keep in mind the state laws that indicate their duty to warn potential victims of patients who express a desire to harm them. It is important that clinicians explicitly discuss this responsibility with suicidal patients at the beginning of the course of treatment, and if a situation arises in which patients express a desire to harm another individual, clinicians should remind them of this duty and its rationale.

CHALLENGES IN IMPLEMENTING THE COGNITIVE THERAPY PROTOCOL

Given the problems described to this point, clinicians sometimes find it difficult to implement the cognitive therapy protocol as effectively as they might like. Many beginning clinicians observe a tension between responding to patients' distress and adhering to the cognitive therapy protocol, particularly in maintenance of the session structure, homework compliance, and suicide prevention as a primary focus of treatment. Here, we remind readers that cognitive therapy is not a mechanistic approach to treatment, with a protocol that should be followed sequentially without regard to the patient's clinical presentation. Safety is of utmost concern for any suicidal patient, and clinicians must use their clinical judgment to determine the most appropriate response in a crisis. Instead, we encourage clinicians to view cognitive therapy as a framework for understanding the patient's suicidal crisis, for organizing information that the patient is providing, and for selecting the intervention that has the potential to meet their patient's treatment goals. As clinicians gain experience with cognitive therapy, they view it as an organizational guide as they attempt to process many disparate emotional experiences, acute problems, and other life events described by patients in crisis. In fact, we find that these fundamental characteristics of cognitive therapy are assets in the treatment of difficult patients, rather than detriments.

Challenges in Maintaining Session Structure

As has already been stated in this chapter, some patients attend therapy sporadically, some patients come to many sessions with a crisis, and some patients are in such distress that they are disorganized or have difficulty focusing. Many clinicians have found that these challenges present difficulties for bridging from the previous session and setting agendas. We appreciate the complexities that they face with a highly aroused or agitated patient. However, it is important to recognize that responding with a similar level of activation will escalate the patient's distress. Setting an agenda with an even, soothing tone of voice provides one means of calming a patient who is otherwise in distress. In fact, this approach demonstrates that patients' difficulties can be approached in a reasonable manner. Although the clinician will likely take the lead in bridging from the previous session and setting the agenda in these circumstances, collaboration can be established by checking with patients every step of the way to ensure that they are on board with the clinician's conceptualization of their difficulties.

At times, patients introduce so many difficult life events and areas of crisis that have occurred since the previous session that it is clear that all of the material will not be able to be covered in a 50-minute session. In these instances, the clinician can use the cognitive conceptualization to discern whether there are underlying themes to some of the patient's current concerns. If so, the clinician can make that observation and ask the client whether there is one underlying theme that might constitute one major part of the agenda. For example, for a patient who is distressed about many conflicts with family members or friends since the previous session, the clinician might identify problems with social support as the underlying issue and address it as one agenda item during the session, using the particular conflicts to illustrate the scope of the problem and to brainstorm ways that interactions might be approached differently in the future.

Patients who are visibly agitated might also benefit from the alternative approach of conducting an affective coping exercise at the beginning of session, such as muscle relaxation, controlled breathing, or guided imagery. These exercises help to "slow down" patients so that they are in a better position to systematically address the issues that are causing distress. Moreover, the clinician can use this procedure as an example of ways to calm down and gather oneself to address a problem rather than doing something impulsive or getting caught up in the barrage of negative thoughts that occur in a time of crisis. In fact, clinicians might obtain a rating of depression, hopelessness, and/or anxiety before and after the exercise to demonstrate empirically to patients that taking the time to engage in one of these strategies has tangible benefits. These exercises, then, could be included in the safety plan as one of the first steps to take when patients experience overwhelming thoughts and emotions associated with suicidal crises.

Challenges With Homework Compliance

Homework is an integral part of cognitive therapy (cf. J. S. Beck, 1995), and evidence has suggested that homework compliance is associated with better treatment outcome (Addis & Jacobson, 2000; Kazantzis, Deane, & Ronan, 2000). However, homework is a challenge that is especially evident with suicidal patients, perhaps because of the multitude of problems in their lives, the severity of their psychiatric symptoms, or their hopelessness about making positive gains in treatment. Thus, the clinician working with suicidal patients needs to be especially creative in ensuring patients' collaboration in the homework process, designing homework assignments that are meaningful to patients and facilitate tangible change in their lives, and creating a sense that homework is important to the treatment process without shaming patients if they do not comply.

The suggestions about increasing homework compliance that we presented in chapter 5 cannot be understated. That is, homework should be assigned collaboratively by the clinician and patients, the assignment should be started in session if possible, and the clinician should obtain an estimate of the likelihood that patients will complete the assignment, addressing any obstacles that may account for low ratings. We have found that homework assignments for suicidal patients should generally consist of only one concrete item, such as calling a friend with whom there has not been much recent contact or making an appointment with a psychiatrist for medications. Assigning more than one item to complete for homework often overwhelms patients. A clear link between that homework assignment and its relation to suicide prevention should be given. The clinician should help patients think of other times in their lives when they successfully completed similar tasks.

Despite clinicians' best efforts in designing relevant, seemingly easily achievable homework assignments, many suicidal patients will be chronically noncompliant with their homework. In these instances, clinicians might assume some accountability for the circumstances (e.g., "I've been emphasizing writing down the negative thoughts that occur during the week, and now that I know you better, I understand that perhaps writing is aversive for you"). Not only does this approach demonstrate that the clinician is sensitive to patients' preferences, it also models responsibility taking. In addition, the clinician can work with patients to identify the advantages and disadvantages of doing homework and patients' beliefs about the degree to which these assignments will create positive life changes. Once negative ideas about homework are identified, the clinician can use Socratic questioning to evaluate the validity of those beliefs. The clinician might design a behavioral experiment to test out any negative predictions that homework assignments will not be helpful.

Challenges in Maintaining a Focus on Suicide Prevention

As stated previously, many patients resist focusing on suicide because they claim they are no longer suicidal or because they believe that there are other, more pressing issues to address in session. Clinicians can also get overwhelmed by the perceived enormity of patients' problems and often get caught up with wanting to address the issues that are causing distress in the moment. Moreover, many of the clinicians we have trained struggle with the fact that some of their suicidal patients must cope with issues such as childhood sexual abuse and speculate that addressing these issues would, in turn, reduce the likelihood of future suicidal crises.

Issues such as childhood sexual abuse are central to consider in the case conceptualization, as they undoubtedly contributed to the development of maladaptive core beliefs about the self, world, and future. However, the suicide prevention phase of cognitive therapy was designed as an intervention composed of a framework and specific strategies that directly modify suicide ideation and reduce the likelihood of future suicidal crises. Thus, we recommend that the clinician initially focus on developing skills to prevent future suicidal crises, which will help to ensure patients' safety, and then address other important issues during the continuation phase of treatment. In other words, the clinician first works to ensure that patients can handle severe distress and then turns to other issues that are part of the more general cognitive case conceptualization.

In addition, the astute clinician will realize that many of the currently distressing problems that patients introduce in session can indeed be considered in light of the recent suicidal crisis. Thus, after patients give tangible indicators that they are learning a specific coping strategy, the clinician can use Socratic questioning to encourage them to consider the manner in which the strategy would be useful at other times in their lives, particularly the times in which they are suicidal. Consider this dialogue with Janice that occurred in the seventh session of cognitive therapy, when the clinician was working with her to identify strategies that would improve her relationship with her mother.

> *Clinician:* For homework, you were going to make a list of the ways you could reconnect with your mother, and you were going to choose one and test it out.
>
> *Janice:* [hands clinician her homework]
>
> *Clinician:* [reading over items on Janice's list] This looks like a solid list. Which one did you end up choosing?
>
> *Janice:* I actually did *two* of the things on the list. I offered to help cook dinner the other night, and while we were cooking, I suggested that we go shopping together.
>
> *Clinician:* How did your mother respond?
>
> *Janice:* I think she was relieved that I am finally out of my room and wanting to get out of the house!
>
> *Clinician:* So she agreed to go shopping?
>
> *Janice:* Yeah. And she didn't even suggest that we take my stepfather along. We're going to go on Saturday afternoon.
>
> *Clinician:* What did you learn from doing this exercise, Janice?
>
> *Janice:* You know how I am. Ever since my mother remarried I've felt that she puts him before me, and since I've been having trouble with depression over the past few years, I've gotten the feeling that she barely tolerates me. I still think she bows down to my stepfather, which ends up hurting both of us. But I learned that I probably was the one who shut down the relationship, not the other way around, and that if I make the effort, we can start

spending more time together and maybe even get the relationship back to the way it was.

Clinician: Those are good insights. When you took a step back and realized that you *were* able to do something to improve the relationship, you felt more connected to her.

Janice: Yeah, that's right. I don't know why I can't do this on my own. I overreact a lot.

Clinician: Well, let's see if you can apply these new skills to another situation. For example, let's say you're in your room and feeling very lonely. That's a situation when you begin to believe that life has nothing to offer and start to feel suicidal, right?

Janice: [nods]

Clinician: How would you apply these relationship-building skills to address this in the future?

Janice: I would definitely just go and talk to my mother if she was alone. Now that we're talking more, I no longer believe that she doesn't want anything to do with me. But I'm not sure if I would go talk to her if my stepfather is around, since most of the time he either ignores me or says something critical.

Clinician: I do understand that you have a difficult relationship with your stepfather and that it might not be the best option to interact with him when you are feeling down. Are there any other people you could talk with?

Janice: Well . . . remember I told you awhile ago that I let go of many close friendships when I started feeling depressed? I bet Jody, the person who was my best friend, would be surprised to hear from me.

Clinician: So your strategy would be to reach out to a different person. What would you say?

Janice: I'd call her and tell her that I miss our friendship and that I'd like to get together with her for coffee.

Clinician: Let's say that you did this. Do you think you would have the same idea that you've had in the past, that life has nothing to offer you?

Janice: [hesitates] Well, I still wouldn't feel great because I have a long way to go to feel that I have meaningful relationships.

Clinician: But would those thoughts consume you to the degree that you would become suicidal?

Janice: No, I guess they wouldn't because I'd be looking forward to seeing Jody again and that I was doing something to better my situation.

In this example, the clinician worked with Janice to develop skills to enhance her social support network to address a problem that she believed was important to put on the agenda, which was her relationship with her mother. However, the clinician linked this issue to the cognitions and emotions that have been associated with Janice's past suicide ideation. He then coached her to articulate the specific steps she would take in applying these skills the next time she experiences these potential triggers for a suicidal crisis. In this way, Janice developed strategies that will prevent another suicidal crisis, and at the same time she addressed issues that are important to her in the moment.

CHALLENGES IN CLINICIANS' REACTIONS

While managing patients' reactions to talking about their suicide ideation and subsequent crises, clinicians working with this population often find that they experience their own distressing thoughts and emotions that affect their treatment delivery. It is not uncommon for clinicians to experience anxiety when working with suicidal patients, as they expect that they will not be able to deal with patients' multiple crises. In fact, Pope and Tabachnick (1993) found that more than 97% of clinical psychologists endorse a fear that their patient might commit suicide. Because suicidal patients constitute a high-risk population, they are indeed more likely than most other patients to engage in future suicidal acts. Clinicians must maintain a delicate balance between responding skillfully to patients' suicide ideation and tolerating the fact that many suicidal patients experience chronic suicide ideation or hopelessness.

In addition to this anxiety, many clinicians who work with suicidal patients report anger and defensiveness. Almost 65% of psychologists in Pope and Tabachnick's (1993) survey indicated that they feel angry at patients who make suicide threats or attempts. Some of the clinicians we have trained indicated that at times, they felt manipulated by patients' reported suicide ideation. They described "contingent suicidality," such that patients report that they might attempt suicide in a particular circumstance, but they refuse to divulge when and where this might occur so that the clinician does not have grounds for involuntary hospitalization. Other study clinicians observed that at times, there is little evidence that patients want to improve, and they wondered whether they had higher expectations for their patients than patients have for themselves. These patient characteristics are associated with clinician hopelessness and burnout.

In our experience, peer supervision is a highly effective means of addressing the fear, anger, and hopelessness that emerge when working with suicidal patients. Peer supervision provides the opportunity for other professionals to validate the array of emotions that the clinician is feeling toward his or her patient, and at the same time to use cognitive strategies to help the clinician gain perspective and take into account information he or she might otherwise be ignoring. Many clinicians indicate that peer supervision creates a teamwork environment and reinforces the notion that they are part of a community of care providers who share the same goals. We find that clinicians leave peer supervision sessions feeling refreshed, recommitted, and equipped to address their patients' difficulties. Thus, we highly recommend weekly or biweekly peer supervision sessions for clinicians who have suicidal patients in their caseloads.

We also understand that many clinicians practice in an environment in which there is little, if any, opportunity to establish regular peer supervision. As has been stated several times in this chapter, we encourage the clinician in this situation to keep in mind that suicidal patients often receive many services and are being seen by many different professionals. Patients are encouraged to seek whatever medical, psychiatric, social service, or addictions interventions are necessary to address the multiple layers of difficulties in their lives. Having a number of professionals with well-defined roles providing care to suicidal patients helps to spread around the responsibility for their well-being. This allows the cognitive therapist to focus solely on suicide prevention with the confidence that other needs in the patient's life are being addressed by competent professionals.

Finally, clinicians can keep in mind that the principles of cognitive therapy apply to themselves as well as to patients. Are they labeling their patients as resistant? Are they mind reading by assuming that their patients are just trying to get attention? Are they personalizing their perception of patients' lack of progress? Are they caught up in their own cycle of dichotomous thinking (e.g., "Things will never change with this patient")? Clinicians would be advised to monitor their own negative automatic thoughts about particular patients and general beliefs about working with suicidal patients and to use cognitive strategies to systematically evaluate those ideas to take on a more balanced perspective.

WHEN A PATIENT ATTEMPTS OR COMMITS SUICIDE

Survey research has shown that up to 30% of practicing psychologists have had a patient die by suicide while actively enrolled in treatment (Chemtob, Bauer, Hamada, Pelowski, & Muraoka, 1989; Pope & Tabachnick, 1993). Clinicians who have had a patient commit suicide may experience intense adverse emotional and cognitive reactions, including shock and disbelief, grief, shame and embarrassment, anger and betrayal, a sense of inadequacy, a sense of isolation from colleagues, fear of blame or a lawsuit, a crisis in their faith in psychotherapy, and even posttraumatic stress (e.g., Chemtob et al., 1989; Gitlin, 1999; Hausman, 2003; Hendin, Lipschitz, Maltsberger, Haas, & Whynecoop, 2000). In the aftermath, some clinicians are so vigilant for suicide risk that they conduct extensive risk assessments in instances in which they are not warranted, which has the potential to damage the therapeutic relationship (Gitlin, 1999). In many cases, the reaction is similar to that of any human being who has suddenly lost a close relationship. Unfortunately, agencies have few systematic guidelines for assisting clinicians through this difficult time (Hausman, 2003).

Very little has been written on guidelines for clinicians' coping when patients commit suicide. Many clinicians indicate that in hindsight, they would have made different choices in the treatment of the patient (Hendin et al., 2000), even if they are confident that they maintained an adequate standard of care. Although "psychological autopsies" of the completed suicides can be educational for the clinician and colleagues for dealing with suicidal patients in the future, in many instances they leave the clinician feeling inadequate and blamed for the patient's death (Kleespies & Dettmer, 2000). Thus, it might be more helpful to clinicians to work through the case of a suicide with a trusted colleague, such as a former mentor (Gitlin, 1999). Collins (2003) recommended that support from colleagues is crucial in the immediate aftermath of patient suicide, although Hendin et al. (2000) noted that many clinicians who have experienced a patient suicide perceive offers of support as being disingenuous. Thus, we recommend that agencies institute a mechanism for support ahead of time. In particular, some clinicians in these circumstances have found it helpful to be part of an informal support group with other clinicians who have endured similar experiences (Kleespies & Dettmer, 2000). Moreover, agencies can hold case conferences, highlighting difficult cases, to provide ongoing training for clinicians in dealing with suicidal patients (Kleespies & Dettmer, 2000).

Given that there are far more attempted suicides than completed suicides, it is even more likely that clinicians will, at some point in their careers, have a patient who attempts suicide while the patient is receiving treatment from them. Ramsay and Newman (2005) proposed several guidelines for clinicians who work with a patient who has made an attempt during the course of treatment. They suggested that in most instances, the clinician should remain the mental health professional of record to ensure that the patient is receiving consistent care. However, they also pointed out that resuming treatment after an attempt provides an opportunity to renegotiate the ground rules of therapy. For example, the clinician and patient can collaboratively agree on the frequency of sessions, the nature and frequency of crisis contacts between sessions, and the types of issues that will be addressed in session. Bongar et al. (1992) noted that the frequency of sessions will often need to be increased, and special arrangements may need to be made to accommodate patients' needs during evenings, weekends, and clinicians' vacations. In addition, Ramsay and Newman (2005) recommended that issues of trust between the clinician and patients should be addressed sensitively but directly. The treatment plan might be revisited, such as by involving other professionals to address other clinical issues relevant to the attempt (e.g., substance abuse) or by obtaining permission from patients to involve family members or significant others in the treatment process.

BENEFITS TO WORKING WITH SUICIDAL PATIENTS

To this point, this chapter has focused on the challenges and struggles in working with suicidal patients. However, it is equally as important to acknowledge the benefits of working with suicidal patients. Aspects of this cognitive therapy protocol would undoubtedly be useful in working with other challenging populations. In addition, many of the clinicians we have trained have indicated that their experience with this protocol has given them confidence and knowledge in dealing with patients in their caseloads who become suicidal during the course of treatment. Moreover, witnessing a patient's transformation from being hopeless and suicidal to being active in managing life's problems is gratifying for even the most seasoned clinician. Thus, successful treatment with a patient who has recently experienced a suicidal crisis has the potential to be a particularly meaningful professional experience.

SUMMARY AND INTEGRATION

Suicidal patients are quite challenging for the clinician in terms of the difficulties that they pose (e.g., repeated crises) and of the fear that they elicit in those who treat them. We have identified some concrete strategies for addressing these challenges from a cognitive therapy perspective. We believe that implementation of these procedures and the use of good judgment in reasonable follow-up with suicidal patients and in maintaining sound documentation of contacts with suicidal patients constitutes an acceptable standard of care (cf. Bongar et al., 1992).

Nevertheless, our experience has taught us that each suicidal crisis differs to some degree and that no one rule of thumb will precisely guide the clinician in making decisions about imminent risk. Thus, we encourage clinicians, if possible, to consult with their colleagues during crises and document the decisions arrived at as a result of those consultations. Moreover, regardless of how prepared clinicians who work with at-risk patients are for a patient's suicide, they may experience a tremendous amount of grief, guilt, anger, and fear of the consequences if the unfortunate event of a patient suicide indeed occurs. We strongly advise that agencies have a mechanism in place to assist clinicians in these unfortunate times. Finally, we suggest that clinicians balance these recommendations with a sense of optimism. Our research has indicated that patients who recently attempted suicide and received cognitive therapy reattempt at approximately half the rate of attempters who receive usual care (G. K. Brown, Tenhave, et al., 2005). These results suggest that cognitive therapy has much promise in helping suicidal patients develop the skills to avert future suicidal crises, which has the potential to be a gratifying professional experience for the treating clinician.

III

APPLICATIONS TO SPECIAL POPULATIONS

11

COGNITIVE THERAPY FOR SUICIDAL ADOLESCENTS

According to the Centers for Disease Control and Prevention (CDC; 2008), suicide accounts for approximately 2,000 adolescent deaths per year and is the third leading cause of death of children between the ages of 10 and 19. Researchers have estimated that approximately 2 million adolescents attempt suicide annually, resulting in approximately 700,000 emergency department visits per year (Shaffer & Pfeffer, 2001). Moreover, within a 1-year time frame, approximately 20% of adolescents consider attempting suicide and 15% develop a plan to do so (Spirito, 2003). Thus, adolescent suicidal behavior is a matter of great public health significance. Adolescence is a time of substantial developmental and psychosocial transition, and not surprisingly, many of the changes that occur during this period increase the likelihood that teens will engage in suicidal acts.

This chapter describes the adaptation of the cognitive therapy protocol to the treatment of suicidal adolescents. First, a general overview of research on the correlates of and risk factors for adolescent suicidal acts is provided to assist clinicians in formulating a cognitive case conceptualization and in selecting appropriate intervention strategies. Second, the manner in which the cognitive therapy protocol for suicidal adults, as described in chapters 6 through 9, can be implemented with adolescents is illustrated. Issues that are unique to working with adolescents are highlighted, and a case example is provided.

SUICIDAL ACTS IN ADOLESCENTS

Because of the substantial public health significance of adolescent suicide, much research has been conducted to identify the correlates of and risk factors for suicidal behavior in this population. Many of these variables are similar to those identified as correlates of and risk factors for suicidal behavior in adults, including those falling in the broad categories of demographic variables, diagnostic variables, psychological variables, and suicide-relevant variables. One relatively unique feature of research with suicidal adolescents is a greater focus on social variables, as the social environment (e.g., family, peers) is often central to explaining acute episodes of adolescents' distress. The relation between these categories of variables and adolescent suicidal acts is considered in this section.

Demographic Variables

Many of the same demographic variables that were important in explaining adult suicidal behavior also apply to the understanding of adolescent suicidal behavior. Epidemiological research has suggested that the likelihood of suicide in adolescence increases as teens get older; in fact, the incidence of suicide increased dramatically for teens between the ages of 16 and 19 in the United States between 1999 and 2005 (CDC, 2008). Suicidal behavior in adolescence also varies as a function of gender—although girls are more likely to attempt suicide than are boys, boys are nearly five times more likely to die by suicide than girls (CDC, 2008). In addition, there are differences in rates of suicidal behavior depending on the racial or ethnic group under consideration. For example, American Indian/Alaskan Native males between the ages of 10 and 19 constitute one of the highest risk groups for suicide (15.12 suicides per 100,000 people), and African American females in this same age range are one of the lowest risk groups (0.96 suicides per 100,000 people; CDC, 2008). Research has also shown that American Indian adolescents have a lifetime history of suicide attempts that is almost twice the rate of other ethnic groups (Borowsky, Resnick, Ireland, & Blum, 1990). These demographic variables are distal risk factors, as the vast majority of older, male, and American Indian adolescents do not engage in suicidal acts. Nevertheless, these background factors assume increased importance when they exist in conjunction with additional risk variables.

Sexual orientation is another demographic variable that has the potential to be important in understanding adolescent suicidal acts. Although there are no national statistics available that speak to the prevalence of suicide among gay, lesbian, and bisexual adolescents, several rigorous research studies have investigated the degree to which suicide attempts vary as a function of sexual orientation. Relative to peers who identify themselves as straight, boys who identify as gay or bisexual are approximately seven times more likely to attempt suicide, whereas girls who identify as gay or bisexual are only slightly, if not at all, more likely to attempt suicide (Garofalo et al., 1998; Remafedi, French, Story, Resnick, & Blum, 1998). Faulkner and Cranston (1998) reported that 27% of adolescents who had same-sex sexual contact endorsed having made a suicide attempt, as compared to 14% of adolescents who had only heterosexual contact. In a nationally representative study, Russell and Joyner (2001) found that adolescents with a same-sex orientation were twice as likely to report a suicide attempt than adolescents who did not report a same-sex orientation and that this association remained significant but attenuated when analyses adjusted for hopelessness, depression, alcohol abuse, family members' suicidal behavior, friends' suicidal behavior, and experiences of victimization. Taken together, these studies indicate that adolescents, especially boys, who self-identify as gay or report having same-sex sexual contact are especially likely to indicate a history of suicide attempts.

Diagnostic Variables

According to Spirito (2003), 80% to 90% of adolescents who attempt suicide are diagnosed with a psychiatric disorder. The most common diagnosis in suicidal adolescents is major depression (e.g., Kingsbury, Hawton, Steinhardt, & James, 1999; Pelkonen, Marttunen, Pulkkinen, Laippala, & Aro, 1997). The presence of a comorbid psychiatric disorder significantly increases the risk of suicide attempts (e.g., Laederach, Fischer, Bowen, & Ladame, 1999), particularly conduct disorder (Feldman & Wilson, 1997) and substance abuse (Andrews & Lewinsohn, 1992; see Crumley, 1990; Mehlenbeck, Spirito, Barnett, & Overholser, 2003, for reviews). Some research has demonstrated that anger (e.g., Lehnert, Overholser, & Spirito, 1994) and anxiety (Trautman, Rotheram-Borus, Dopkins, & Lewin, 1991) are important in understanding adolescent suicidal acts, although many studies have shown that these emotional states are characteristic of adolescent psychiatric patients in general and are not necessarily unique to those who are suicidal (see Wolfsdorf, Freeman, D'Eramo, Overholser, & Spirito, 2003, for a review). Wolfsdorf et al. (2003) noted that clinicians may not see evidence of depression, anxiety, or anger during assessments with suicidal adolescents, as these negative mood states are often transient, peak immediately before a suicidal crisis, and quickly subside.

Psychological Variables

As with suicidal adults, there are a number of modifiable psychological correlates of and risk factors for adolescents who engage in suicidal acts. According to a review by Esposito, Johnson, Wolfsdorf, and Spirito (2003), adolescents who attempt suicide are characterized by hopelessness, but it may be time limited, such that it is most prominent immediately before an attempt rather than after an attempt. Moreover, it is unclear whether it predicts suicide ideation and suicidal acts above and beyond symptoms of depression (cf. Gould, Fisher, Parides, Flory, & Schaffer, 1996). When confronted with problems, suicidal adolescents often demonstrate wishful thinking (e.g., Rotheram-Borus, Trautman, Dopkins, & Shrout, 1990) and a paucity of active coping strategies (Asarnow, Carlson, & Gutherie, 1987). Although some research has shown that suicidal adolescents generate an adequate number of possible solutions to their problems, they report using fewer of the solutions and perceive their problems as less controllable than adolescents without psychiatric problems (Fremouw, Callahan, & Kashden, 1993).

Impulsivity and aggression have been studied extensively in suicidal adolescent patients (see Esposito, Spirito, & Overholser, 2003, for a review). Research has shown that impulsivity is not necessarily a stable personality trait in all suicidal adolescents (e.g., Kingsbury et al., 1999), but that it is characteristic of adolescents who do not plan suicide attempts ahead of time (Wetzler et al., 1996) or who have a poor outcome after treatment (Pfeffer, Hurt, Peskin, & Siefker, 1995). Kashden et al. (1993) determined that suicidal adolescents are characterized by impulsivity in the form of acting without forethought but not by impulsivity in the form of difficulty sustaining attention. Suicidal adolescents, particularly those with conduct disorder (Pfeffer, Newcorn, Kaplan, Mizruchi, & Plutchick, 1988) or who have made unplanned attempts (T. Simon & Crosby, 2000), endorse high levels of aggression. However, in their review of these behavioral correlates of suicidal acts, Esposito, Spirito, and Overholser (2003) concluded that impulsivity and aggression should be considered indirect vulnerability factors rather than direct vulnerability factors for adolescent suicidal acts, as not all empirical studies have found an association between these constructs, and these variables often become nonsignificant when considered in conjunction with other variables, such as depression and hopelessness.

Suicide-Relevant Variables

Research has shown that 90% of adolescents who make a suicide attempt also report suicide ideation (Andrews & Lewinsohn, 1992); however, the fact that 10% of attempters do not report associated ideation indicates that it would be premature to conclude that adolescent patients are not at risk for suicidal behavior if they deny ideation. Other research has demonstrated that the likelihood of an adolescent making a suicide attempt increases as the severity of suicide ideation increases (Dubow, Kausch, Blum, Reed, & Bush, 1989) and as attitudes toward suicide become more favorable (Stein, Witztum, Brom, DeNour, & Elizur, 1992). Although clinicians sometimes attribute adolescent suicidal acts to manipulation or attention seeking, there are limited empirical data to support this assumption. In fact, the vast majority of suicidal adolescents report that they made an attempt because they perceived their situation to be unbearable, impossible, or excessively painful and wanted escape or relief (Boergers, Spirito, & Donaldson, 1998; Hawton, Cole, O'Grady, & Osborne, 1982).

Perhaps the strongest risk factor for adolescent suicidal acts is a previous suicide attempt (Lewinsohn, Rohde, & Seeley, 1994; Shaffer, Garland, Gould, Fisher, & Trautman, 1988). Boergers and Spirito (2003) reviewed research suggesting that 10% of adolescents who attempt suicide reattempt within 3 months, 12% to 20% reattempt within 1 year, and 20% to 50% reattempt in 2 to 3 years. Those who make multiple attempts are more likely than those who make single attempts to experience more severe psychiatric symptoms, more stressful events, more functional impairment, and poorer school performance (Gispert, Davis, Marsh, & Wheeler, 1987; Hawton, Kingsbury, Steinhardt, James, & Fagg, 1999; Stein, Apter, Ratzoni, Har-Even, & Avidan, 1998). Thus, any adolescent who has a history of suicide attempts should be monitored for additional suicidal behavior, particularly in the context of an exacerbation of psychiatric disturbance or life stress.

Adolescents who make highly lethal attempts are at a high risk for death by suicide (Brent, 1987). However, an attempt of low lethality does not necessarily indicate the absence of a desire to die. Many adolescents attempt suicide by a minor drug overdose (Nakamura, McLeod, & McDermott, 1994) or by some other means of low lethality that on the surface seems less serious than highly lethal attempts (Asarnow & Gutherie, 1989). Up to 50% of adolescents, however, overestimate the lethality of their attempts (H. E. Harris & Myers, 1997); thus, clinicians should not assume that adolescent patients did not "really" want to commit suicide in instances of attempts characterized by low lethality. As stated in chapter 1, a variable that is more potent in predicting suicidal acts is suicidal intent. Research has shown that adolescents who die by suicide have particularly high levels of intent, as evidenced by isolating themselves from others during the attempt, communicating suicidal intent before the attempt, and taking precautions against discovery (Brent et al., 1988).

Social Variables

Characteristics of adolescents' social environment may make them vulnerable to suicidal acts. Although there are higher rates of divorce in the families of suicidal adolescents than in the families of nonsuicidal community control patients, the rates of divorce are similar in suicidal adolescents and psychiatric control patients (Spirito, Brown, Overholser, & Fritz, 1989), and the small effect of divorce on adolescent suicide may be explained in large part by parental psychopathology (e.g., Gould, Shaffer, Fisher, & Garfinkel, 1998). However, other research has shown that aspects of the postdivorce social environment, such as parental remarriage (D. H. Olson, Portner, & Lavee, 1985) and residential instability (Brent et al., 1993), are more common in suicidal adolescents than in nonsuicidal adolescents. A history of physical and sexual abuse is common in suicidal adolescent populations (e.g., Bensley, Van Eenwyk, Spieker, & Schoder, 1999), although rates might not be higher than for other adolescents who receive treatment for psychiatric problems (Hollenbeck, Dyl, & Spirito, 2003). In addition, suicidal adolescents' family relationships are often characterized by conflict (Brent et al., 1993), hostility (Kosky, Silburn, & Zubrick, 1990), a lack of communication (King, Raskin, Gdowski, Butkus, & Opipari, 1990), and perceived lack of support (Dubow et al., 1989). Many of these types of family dysfunction are modifiable through psychosocial intervention.

Although far from conclusive, there is some evidence that disrupted peer functioning is related to adolescent suicidal acts (see Prinstein, 2003, for a review). Some research has suggested that peer support might buffer depressed adolescents from suicidal acts or, conversely, that a lack of peer support might combine with depressive symptoms to increase the likelihood of suicidal acts (Lewinsohn et al., 1994). Moreover, suicidal adolescents frequently report social isolation (Negron, Piacentini, Graae, Davies, & Shaffer, 1997) and loneliness (Rossow & Wichstrom, 1994). Finally, there is some evidence that adolescents are at increased risk of engaging in suicidal acts if someone in their school commits suicide, particularly if they were close to that person (Brent et al., 1989).

Summary

An array of demographic, diagnostic, psychological, suicide-relevant, and social variables serve as correlates of and risk factors for adolescent suicidal acts. However, no one variable can be regarded as a reliable predictor for future suicidal acts because the vast majority of individuals with these characteristics do not attempt suicide. Nevertheless, this brief summary of the literature suggests that diagnoses of major depression (particularly when comorbid with conduct disorder or a substance use problem), deficient coping skills, and lack of family cohesion set the stage for adolescent suicidal acts. Impulsivity may also facilitate suicidal acts, particularly in the context of acute stressors that adolescents view as the "last straw" or when adolescents are actively using alcohol or drugs (cf. Esposito, Spirito, & Overholser, 2003). Although poor peer functioning and support are not necessarily direct precursors to suicidal acts, the presence of a stable peer support system can often deter depressed adolescents from attempting suicide (cf. Prinstein, 2003). Any adolescent who has a history of suicide attempts should be monitored especially closely for future suicidal behavior.

COGNITIVE THERAPY PROTOCOL AND CASE EXAMPLE

To address the important public health issue of teen suicide, many research groups are adapting cognitive and behavioral strategies to treat suicidal adolescent patients (e.g., CBT TASA Team, 2008; King et al., 2006). David Goldston at Duke University is also adapting cognitive behavior therapy for the treatment of suicidal adolescents. We have taken important pieces from some of these treatments and integrated them with our intervention described in chapters 6 through 9.

Many of the components of cognitive therapy for suicidal adults also apply to suicidal adolescents, including the major activities that take place in the three phases of treatment. However, as therapy progresses, the clinician must be mindful of several issues that are specific to adolescent populations. For example, family members often play a more central role in the treatment of suicidal adolescents than they do in the treatment of suicidal adults. Of course, involvement of family members makes confidentiality a particularly important issue to address in the first session of cognitive therapy with suicidal adolescent patients. In addition, at times it can be particularly difficult to engage adolescent patients in treatment, so clinicians must be creative as they work toward developing a trusting therapeutic relationship. Finally, there is a substantial association between suicidal and nonsuicidal self-injury behavior in adolescents (e.g., Nock, Joiner, Gordon, Lloyd-Richardson, & Prinstein, 2006); thus, we include a brief discussion of nonsuicidal self-injury behavior in this section.

Early Phase of Treatment

Although the main structure of the early phase of treatment for adolescent patients is similar to that for adult patients, in this section we highlight some special issues that arise in conducting cognitive therapy for suicidal adolescent patients. Specifically, we describe the manner in which treatment is adapted for suicidal adolescent patients in terms of (a) addressing confidentiality, (b) engaging the patient in treatment, (c) conducting an assessment of the presenting problem, (d) including family members, and (e) developing the safety plan. We also consider the manner in which the information gathered in the early phase of treatment is used to formulate a cognitive case conceptualization and establish a treatment plan. In this and the other sections describing the cognitive therapy protocol, we present the case of Jill, who represents an amalgam of female suicidal adolescent patients seen by cognitive therapists.

Addressing Confidentiality

A critical issue to consider in working with adolescents is confidentiality, as most adolescent patients do not refer themselves for treatment and are usually brought to treatment by their parents. The clinician must address this issue directly at the beginning of treatment so that adolescents can perceive that the clinician is trustworthy and that issues discussed are kept private. However, as with adult patients, adolescents should be informed that confidentiality will be broken if the clinician judges that they are a danger to themselves or others. One issue that is different with adolescent patients, as compared to adult patients, is that parents are informed if there is a substantial increase in suicide ideation, even if these patients are not at imminent risk of hurting themselves, and they require a higher level of care. This is so because parents often play a central role in the safety plan and are called on to monitor their child's behavior between sessions. In addition, physical and sexual abuse must be reported to the appropriate authorities, as required by state law, if an adolescent patient divulges that he or she is a perpetrator or victim. Finally, parents are usually informed of treatment goals, general progress toward those goals, and any changes to the treatment plan. Whenever the clinician judges that it is appropriate to disclose information to parents or other professionals, he or she works collaboratively with the adolescent patient to determine a plan for the manner in which this information will be shared.

Engaging Patients in Treatment

Empirical research has demonstrated that approximately 45% of adolescents who attempt suicide do not attend even one psychotherapy session after an emergency department visit (Pillay & Wassenaar, 1995; Taylor & Stansfeld, 1984) and that the median number of psychotherapy sessions of those who do attend is three (Trautman, Stewart, & Morishima, 1993). These statistics are particularly concerning in light of the fact that adolescents who drop out of therapy are at much greater risk for reattempting than those who do not (Boergers & Spirito, 2003).

Adolescents often do not initiate psychological treatment and may regard others as imposing treatment on them. Thus, rapport building is a crucial first step in the treatment of suicidal adolescents to prevent premature dropout and maximize the effectiveness of the specific cognitive therapy strategies. Rapport building should occur before adolescents describe the sequence of events that led up to the suicidal crisis, as they may be reluctant to discuss intimate details unless a trusting therapeutic relationship has been established. Clinicians can be as creative as they like in engaging adolescent patients in treatment. Every effort should be made to demonstrate that the process of therapy is indeed collaborative and that their perspectives are respected, valued, and necessary for a successful outcome. Issues of most therapeutic value to the clinician are interspersed with discussion of issues important to adolescents, even if those issues seem trivial or unrelated to issues that are relevant to the suicidal crisis. As a result, we have observed that it sometimes takes longer with adolescent patients than with adult patients to obtain the relevant information to develop a cognitive case conceptualization.

Conducting an Assessment of the Presenting Problem

As discussed in chapter 7, the cognitive case conceptualization is derived from the psychological assessment and the description of the sequence of events that occurred before the suicidal crisis. Both the psychological assessment and the timeline of events leading to the suicidal crisis can be obtained from interviews with adolescent patients and their family members. The following is a description of some of the information obtained from Jill and her mother during the intake process.

> Jill is a 16-year-old Caucasian high school sophomore who presented for outpatient psychotherapy following 3 days of inpatient hospitalization. She had recently attempted suicide—her first attempt—by cutting her wrists with scissors in the bathroom at her house. Jill indicated that she made the attempt soon after her boyfriend of 4 weeks had dumped her. She claimed that she loved him and continued to have strong feelings toward him, although he made it clear that his feelings were not mutual, and he had since started another romantic relationship with a girl he had been seeing concurrently without Jill's knowledge. Jill claimed that she would do anything to win him back and left multiple cell phone messages for him throughout the day of her attempt. She did not view her suicide attempt as a "big deal" but could not rule out the possibility that she would make a similar attempt if it became clear that her boyfriend had left her for good. Although she denied most symptoms of depression, she admitted that she had been down since her boyfriend broke up with her. Thus, Jill was assigned a provisional diagnosis of depressive disorder, not otherwise specified.
>
> Jill lives with her mother and has no siblings. She rarely has contact with her biological father. Jill has two relatively close girlfriends at school, but she otherwise perceived herself to be unpopular and isolated from her peers. She admitted that she is a relatively poor student (i.e., C average with several Ds and occasional Bs and Fs) and is involved in no school activities. Over the past year, Jill has started to go "cruising" (i.e., driving up and down the main street of her home town and congregating in parking lots) with older boys from her high school, and has recently begun to go out with young men in their 20s. When she was questioned about alcohol use, her response was vague, but she made comments suggesting that she would have a few beers while she was out. Jill lost her virginity soon after she started cruising, and at the time of the intake interview, she reported having had sex with 15 high school boys or young

men over the past year. These sexual incidents were mainly one-night stands, and she did not maintain a romantic relationship with any of these individuals for more than 1 week. Jill did not view her sexual activity as problematic, saying that she feels good when she has sex and enjoys the attention she receives from boys and young men.

Jill is characterized by several risk factors for engaging in a future suicidal act. Although she has not been not diagnosed with a major psychiatric disorder, her interpersonal style suggested to the clinician who conducted the intake interview that she was, potentially, minimizing her symptoms. The diagnosis of depressive disorder, not otherwise specified, was assigned, but the clinician resolved to continue to assess for a major affective disorder and conduct disorder, both of which are risk factors for future suicidal behavior in adolescents. Jill engages in risky behavior (i.e., cruising and promiscuity), which raises the possibility that she is an impulsive person who often uses poor judgment even if a diagnosis of conduct disorder is not warranted. Jill also admitted that future suicidal behavior would be contingent on her boyfriend taking her back—a possibility that seemed unlikely. Moreover, she has few meaningful social connections with family and close friends, suggesting that she is socially isolated.

The timeline of events leading to adolescent patients' suicidal crisis often begins with an external situation that is overwhelming to them. The most common triggers for adolescent suicidal crises are parent–child conflict (for adolescents younger than 16 years of age) or romantic conflict or disruption of a romantic relationship (for adolescents 16 years of age or older; Brent, Baugher, Bridge, Chen, & Chiappetta, 1999). Other precipitants for attempts include legal or disciplinary problems (Brent et al., 1999) and physical or sexual abuse (Cohen-Sandler, Berman, & King, 1982). Occasionally, it is difficult to determine the precipitant of the sequence of events that led to the suicidal crisis. In these cases, the trigger might be internal (e.g., a cognition) or the accumulation of many stressors. We encourage clinicians to work slowly and systematically with adolescents to identify situational and internal triggers for suicidal crises so that these patients can recognize similar triggers in the future.

Even after adolescent patients have developed rapport with their clinician, many are reluctant to engage in this exercise. Some adolescents may have difficulty tolerating the distress associated with the discussion of painful, overwhelming, embarrassing, or shameful events, or they may become impatient because they have had to talk about their suicidal crisis with several people already. Other adolescents are easily frustrated because so many questions are asked when they are recalling the sequence of events that led to the crisis. As we mentioned in previous chapters on cognitive therapy for adult patients, it is essential that clinicians provide a clear rationale for this exercise and demonstrate optimal levels of empathy as patients describe their painful experiences. To make the exercise more bearable, some adolescents find it helpful to imagine that they are describing a sequence of events in a movie. As they describe the movie, they can be instructed to replay the events in slow motion so that the details can be fully described (cf. CBT TASA Team, 2008). Another helpful approach is for the clinician and adolescent, together, to draw the sequence of events and their reactions on pieces of paper, perhaps using different colors for the events, thoughts, emotions, and behaviors. Not only does this approach help adolescents to sort out the timing of events, it also focuses their attention on a collaborative project with the clinician. Moreover, the drawing is useful because it can be referenced throughout the course of therapy. As various strategies for managing suicidal crises are introduced, the clinician can go back to the drawing and ask adolescents where in the sequence of events a particular strategy would be helpful in resolving the suicidal crisis.

Jill was reluctant to disclose the timeline of events leading up to her suicidal crisis, showing a defiant attitude toward her clinician. Her clinician was able to construct a preliminary timeline by giving Jill a menu of choices of thoughts, feelings, and behaviors at each step and allowing Jill to choose which one best characterized her situation. They identified the trigger as her boyfriend calling to break up with her. He was especially mean spirited in stating that he had really never liked her and that he was seeing someone else at the same time. Jill's cognitive reaction was "How can he do this to me? I can't stand to be alone again," and her emotional reaction was panic. Jill's feeling of despair and sense of desperation spiraled when she imagined herself not having a date to the homecoming dance and being ostracized from the people with whom she cruised, as her boyfriend had been part of that group. These images and emotions led to the thought "I'll show him! I'll kill myself, and it will all be his fault." During the gathering of information for the timeline of events, the clinician determined that this sequence took place over the course of only a few minutes after Jill received the telephone call from her boyfriend.

Inclusion of Family Members

There are several important reasons for involving family members in the treatment of suicidal adolescents. First, family members may help to retain adolescents in treatment by encouraging them to attend therapy sessions and, in many instances, providing transportation to sessions. Second, family members can provide additional information about the events that transpired before the suicidal crisis, which can further develop the cognitive case conceptualization and guide treatment planning. Third, family members can facilitate the implementation of the safety plan by monitoring their child for increases in suicide ideation, helping to identify the warning signs, assisting their child with coping strategies, and contacting mental health professionals during a crisis. They often provide emotional support as adolescents go through treatment and in times in which adolescents experience acute distress. Finally, family members can remove or limit access to lethal means (CBT TASA Team, 2008).

Specific family members who participate in treatment are usually one or both of the adolescent's parents or legal guardians who have the ability to engage in treatment in a supportive role. In Jill's case, her mother participated in treatment. Family members with significant mental health or substance use problems should be referred to another qualified provider for treatment, given that the focus of this treatment is on the adolescent. Usually, the clinician meets with family members after the first session with the adolescent. A separate meeting with family members is recommended because some may be angry or resentful toward the adolescent, and it is not helpful for them to express those feelings in front of teens who are still in crisis. This meeting provides an opportunity for family members to articulate their reactions to the suicidal crisis and for clinicians to help them decide what is and is not within their control in addressing distorted perceptions of responsibility for their child's suicidal act. In addition, family members may feel guilty about not being aware of the warning signs before the suicidal crisis; thus, they may benefit from an understanding that adolescents often hide or conceal their feelings.

Family members should also have the opportunity in this session to describe the sequence of events that occurred before the suicidal crisis. The clinician uses similar prompts and questions as those used when obtaining the timeline of events from the adolescent. As family members describe these events, it is essential to ask questions about the consequences and responses of the family and the adolescent's social environment (i.e., peers) to determine factors that might inadvertently be reinforcing or exacerbating the suicidal crisis. Clinicians can help the family to identify vulnerability factors that may have contributed to the suicidal crisis and that may help lower the adolescent's risk for future crises.

After this session, the scheduling of additional sessions with family members is determined on a case-by-case basis. For some adolescents, treatment is focused on individual issues, and family members are informed of progress periodically, such as in the last 10 minutes of prearranged sessions. In other cases, it is clear that family dysfunction was a precipitant of the suicidal crisis, and the clinician uses family-based strategies across the course of treatment with both the adolescent and one or more family members. Finally, other adolescents require treatment with an individual focus but remain in crisis or at high risk. In these cases, family members are more actively involved in treatment to ensure patient safety.

Developing a Safety Plan

As we mentioned in chapter 6, a safety plan should be developed for suicidal patients during the first session. The safety plan includes a list of warning signs, self-help strategies, and information for contacting family members, mental health professionals, and emergency services. The safety plan for adolescent patients (cf. CBT TASA Team, 2008) is very similar to that for adults. The adolescent safety plan should always include information for contacting a responsible adult (e.g., parent) to discuss any suicide ideation. Although contact with friends can be an important distraction strategy and may lower suicide risk, adolescents should be encouraged to disclose any suicidal thoughts to a responsible adult rather than to a peer.

Family members may either receive a copy of the adolescent's safety plan or develop a tailored version that describes the responsibilities of the family. The first step of this family safety plan is to determine how to make the adolescent's home as safe as possible, such as by removing or securing knives or medications (CBT TASA Team, 2008). Every effort must be made to remove firearms from the environment, as research has shown that adolescents may use firearms in suicide attempts if they are available (Marzuk et al., 1992). The clinician should follow the procedures for removing firearms as described in chapter 6. In addition, the identification of warning signs that can be observed by others is another critical component of the family safety plan. Observable warning signs listed on the family safety plan may be different than the warning signs that are listed on the adolescent safety plan. The remainder of the family safety plan should include (a) strategies for talking to adolescents about their suicide ideation, (b) a plan for monitoring adolescents to ensure that they are not left unattended, and (c) circumstances for contacting mental health professionals or emergency services and appropriate contact information.

> Toward the end of the first session, Jill's clinician suggested that they develop a safety plan. Jill balked at this idea, stating, "I'm not going to do anything, OK?!" The clinician recognized that this statement was different than Jill's indication earlier in the session that she would attempt suicide if she determined that she could not rekindle her relationship with her boyfriend; thus, he continued to regard the safety plan as a central component of the early phase of treatment, but he realized that he would have to be creative in approaching the activity in a way that Jill could tolerate.
>
> The clinician backed off from the therapeutic intervention for the moment and instead engaged more casually with Jill, with the goal of finding out things she likes to do. It turned out that the clinician was familiar with a television show that Jill watched religiously, so they spent time talking about the plot and speculating about the characters. After this exchange, the clinician stated, "You are really a big fan of this show! I wonder if watching this show would be one thing that you could do when you are feeling frustrated about your boyfriend or anything else that is not going your way." Jill appeared to be pleasantly surprised that her clinician knew as much as he did about this television show and agreed that this would be helpful. The clinician took this moment of increased rapport to ask Jill what else she could do to take her mind off of

things that frustrate or upset her, and she indicated that she could call her two girlfriends on the phone, go outside and play with her dog, and try out new hairstyles that are shown in her teen magazines. Although Jill also mentioned that she could log on to her myspace.com and facebook.com profiles and talk to friends, it became evident that these activities actually have the potential to escalate her distress because she can see what her boyfriend has posted about her and with whom he has been interacting. Thus, Jill reluctantly agreed that she should stay away from these activities when she is already upset. In all, Jill agreed to try engaging in the four activities (i.e., watching her favorite television show, calling her girlfriends, playing with her dog, styling her hair) in times of distress, and the clinician agreed to table the remainder of the safety plan until the next session.

The clinician judged that it was important to meet separately with Jill's mother as soon as possible, as Jill was unable to complete the entire safety plan in session, and she was uncooperative throughout most of the session. One major aim of this session with Jill's mother was to develop a family safety plan. Jill's mother agreed to put all medications, usually kept in the bathroom, into a locked chest in her bedroom. She also agreed to put sharp objects in this chest, including the scissors in their home office and extra razor blades. Jill's mother identified warning signs that indicate that her daughter is headed for trouble, including withdrawal, irritability, eating very little, and locking herself in her room. These were the behaviors that Jill exhibited before her recent suicide attempt.

Jill's mother admitted that she has difficulty talking to Jill about what is generally going on in her life, let alone about her suicide ideation and intent. She stated that she has felt increasingly distant from Jill over the past year, which corresponds to the time in which Jill became associated with the cruising crowd. The clinician noted this as an issue that might be addressed in the intermediate phase of treatment using family-based strategies; for the purpose of the safety plan, Jill's mother decided that she would approach conversations with Jill by disclosing some of her own struggles with fitting in as an adolescent and modeling effective ways to talk about these issues. Jill's mother also indicated that monitoring Jill when she is not home is a major problem, as she is a single mother who works a full-time job and has a substantial commute. The clinician problem solved with Jill's mother about this issue, and it was determined that Jill's mother could arrange for her older sister (i.e., Jill's aunt) to spend time at their home in the late afternoon when Jill got home from school. Finally, the clinician worked with Jill's mother to identify circumstances when a professional should be called, including acute distress that does not abate with the other interventions on the safety plan and explicit indications of suicide ideation with suicidal intent.

Developing a Cognitive Case Conceptualization

The cognitive model of suicidal acts for adults we described in chapter 3 can be used as a starting point in conceptualizing suicidal crises in adolescent patients. As stated earlier in this chapter, research has shown that impulsivity and problem solving deficits are associated with adolescent suicidal acts and likely serve as distal vulnerability factors and as psychological variables that exacerbate a suicidal crisis once it has been put in motion. Because the vast majority of adolescent suicidal patients have at least one Axis I psychiatric disorder, it is likely that negative schemas associated with those pathologies are activated and exert negative influences. In contrast to the literature on suicidal adults, there is less consistent evidence that suicidal adolescents are characterized by a pervasive sense of hopelessness (e.g., Gould et al., 1996). Thus, for adolescents, it is possible that suicide-relevant schemas other than those related to hopelessness, such as perceived unbearability, become activated during periods of distress. When such suicide-relevant schemas are activated, we predict that adolescents will fall into the same spiral of state hopelessness, attentional fixation, and suicide ideation. We suspect that adolescents may be particularly vulnerable to attentional fixation and have even more difficulty than adults in breaking out of it, depending on their stage of cognitive development. In addition, family interactions and the family environment must be included in the cognitive case conceptualization because the family environment often contributes, either directly or indirectly, to adolescents' distress and crises. Conversely, it is also helpful to identify positive aspects of the family environment that may facilitate treatment engagement and implementation of the strategies learned in therapy. The following is a description of the relevant components of Jill's cognitive case conceptualization, presented in Figure 11.1.

> Jill's family environment contributed to the development of many psychological factors that created a context for her recent suicidal crisis to emerge. Her father left the family when Jill was 4 years old, soon after an argument that she overheard in which he accused her mother of getting pregnant to trap him in the relationship. After he left, her mother was emotionally unavailable to Jill as she was dealing with her own grief about the loss of her relationship and the stress associated with being a single parent. Jill blamed herself for the fact that her father left and for her mother's unhappiness. She had always been a shy child, but she withdrew further after this event, which prevented her from developing meaningful friendships with children in her preschool and the social skills necessary to manage peer relationships as she got older. As a result, Jill developed the core belief that she is unlovable. This core belief strengthened throughout childhood and adolescence, as she had a distant relationship with her mother and almost no relationship with her father, and she was neglected by her classmates. Because she had few relationships, she did not learn how to solve the problems that inevitably arise in relationships, and at times, she used poor judgment and made friends with troublemakers because she was desperate to feel like someone liked her.

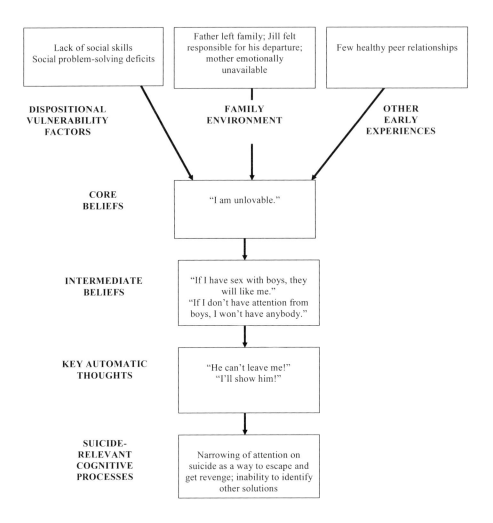

Figure 11.1. Jill's cognitive case conceptualization.

A major change in her perceptions of relationships occurred when Jill began to get attention from the boys with whom she cruised, particularly after she became sexually active. She developed the intermediate beliefs "If I have sex with [name of boy], then he will like me" and "If I don't have attention from boys, then I won't have anybody." However, as with many casual relationships during this stage of development, her relationships with these boys were short lived, and she often found herself in the position in which she was hoping that a long-term relationship would emerge from a brief sexual liaison, whereas her sexual partners were hoping for an easy one-night stand. When it was clear that a long-term relationship would not develop, she vacillated between automatic thoughts such as "He can't leave me! I'll have no one!" and "I'll show him! I'll get laid tonight by someone else." These automatic thoughts were associated with depressed and angry moods, respectively, but not usually with suicide ideation. The suicidal crisis that brought Jill into treatment developed when the boy with whom she had actually entered into a longer term relationship broke up with her, magnifying the intensity of her automatic thoughts, acutely activating her unlovability core belief and leading her to conclude that she would never find anyone again, which, in turn, narrowed her attention on suicide as a method of escape and revenge.

Establishing Treatment Goals

Although we view cognitive factors as playing a central role in the unfolding of a suicidal crisis with adolescent patients, the treatment plan that is derived from the cognitive case conceptualization for adolescents is often different than that for adults because there is a greater emphasis on the behavioral components and family issues. This distinction is so for two reasons: (a) Many adolescent patients have not reached a cognitive developmental level at which they can gain an adequate level of insight into the relation between cognition and suicidal acts, and (b) We cannot fully separate adolescents' worlds from the family environment in which they live. Often, behavioral and family-based interventions ultimately promote cognitive change (e.g., the use of distraction skills to help patients see that they can handle a suicidal crisis). In general, clinicians discuss possible intervention choices with adolescent patients to foster a collaborative stance and secure their commitment to treatment. In most instances, clinicians also discuss these choices with family members to incorporate their perceptions of the most important points of intervention and secure their commitment to helping adolescents implement the cognitive and behavioral coping strategies in their lives (CBT TASA Team, 2008). The clinician works with the family to determine the frequency and duration of check-ins with family members and circumstances in which it is appropriate to increase the involvement of family members.

> Jill's mother was on board with the overarching goal of treatment to be on suicide prevention; Jill was less convinced that this was an important goal and continued to perceive that she was being forced to attend sessions. However, Jill responded positively when the clinician empathized with her feelings about and perceptions of treatment and assured her that it was important to focus on issues that she believed would improve her life circumstances. Jill let down her guard and indicated that she would like to have a boyfriend who likes her for her, not just because she would have sex with him. The clinician then proposed two major goals for treatment: (a) developing strategies for managing distress and that would prevent the escalation of suicidal crises, and (b) developing healthy relationships with others, particularly members of the opposite sex. The clinician articulated the latter goal in broad terms, as the cognitive case conceptualization suggested that strengthening the mother–daughter relationship also had the potential to improve Jill's well-being and re-

duce the likelihood of a future suicidal act. In addition, the clinician reasoned that this goal would help to modify Jill's unlovability core belief that provided the context for cognitions and behaviors associated with suicidal crises. To ensure that Jill was committed to these goals, the clinician asked her to speculate how achieving these goals would make a difference in her life. Jill reluctantly admitted that they might help her to "deal with things better."

Intermediate Phase of Treatment

Through cognitive case conceptualization and treatment planning, the clinician, adolescent patients, and their families develop a better understanding of patients' motivations to kill themselves and the skills deficits that were present during the suicidal crisis. Clinicians who work with suicidal adolescent patients use many of the strategies that were described in chapters 5 and 8 during the intermediate phase of treatment. Next, we present some strategies that are especially useful or indicated when working with adolescent patients. We organize these strategies in four main categories: (a) developing coping strategies, which includes adaptation of the cognitive, emotional, and behavioral strategies presented in chapter 8; (b) increasing reasons for living, a central intervention in the treatment of nearly all suicidal patients; (c) improving family relationships; and (d) modifying nonsuicidal self-injury behavior.

Developing Coping Strategies

Although the clinician who works with suicidal adolescent patients is prepared with the wide array of strategies described in chapters 5 and 8, he or she will often find that these patients respond best to behavioral and affective coping skills, particularly at the beginning of treatment when the therapeutic relationship is still being developed. For example, many suicidal adolescents respond to interventions that stimulate the engagement in pleasurable activities. Family members can also play a role in implementing this strategy, either by engaging in pleasurable activities with their child or by providing transportation so that their child can engage in these activities with peers.

By the time Jill reached the intermediate phase of treatment, she had been able to complete a full safety plan, and she provided a description of the events that led up to her recent suicidal crisis. The therapeutic relationship had improved to some degree, although at times she continued to be withdrawn and disengaged. Her clinician noticed that she had an especially difficult time identifying the thoughts and beliefs that were activated during the suicidal crisis. Thus, he reasoned that behavioral and affective coping strategies would be most effective in helping Jill to develop methods for managing distress. He worked with Jill to expand the list of pleasurable activities she had started on her safety plan. In the process of identifying other pleasurable activities, Jill indicated that she enjoys dancing, but that she does not go to school dances because she does not want to go alone. Together, Jill, her mother, and her clinician brainstormed outlets for Jill to dance, and it was decided that Jill's aunt (who now spent time with her after school) could take her to a jazz dance class twice a week. The clinician reasoned that not only would this be another pleasurable activity in which Jill could regularly engage, but that it might also give her experience with success, which she was not having academically or socially.

Affective coping strategies are designed to help adolescents maintain emotional control so that other cognitive and behavioral coping skills may be used during a crisis. Adolescent patients often report that their emotions seemed to escalate out of control during the period of time before the suicidal crisis. To facilitate greater awareness of one's level of emotional distress, the clinician introduces the concept of the Emotions Thermometer, emphasizing the idea that one's emotional temperature is similar to the outside temperature (cf. CBT TASA Team, 2008; Curry et al., 2005; Rotheram-Borus, Piacentini, Miller, Graae, & Castro-Blanco, 1994; see Figure 11.2). Adolescents are informed that this task may help them in becoming skillful at noticing what types of situations tend to increase their emotional temperature and at identifying their emotional "boiling point" or "point of no return." In other words, the general goal of this strategy is to manage or regulate emotions by learning to "take your temperature" and then to take steps to lower the temperature before reaching the boiling point.

The clinician starts by using a blank 0 to 100 thermometer and asking adolescents to name the way they feel when they are about to lose control, such as *stressed*, *frustrated*, or *angry*. As indicated in Figure 11.2, the upper end of the Emotions Thermometer is labeled with the terms that the adolescent identifies (e.g., *hot, angry, anxious*), and the lower end is labeled *feeling in control* or *calm* and *cool*. At each interval of 10, patients are asked to identify physiological symptoms, thoughts, or behavioral indicators ranging from 0 (*completely in control*) to 100 (*completely out of control*). Examples of these various labels include *feeling tense, talking loud, feeling agitated, feeling heart pounding, cursing, yelling,* and "*I can't take it anymore.*"

After these labels are developed, adolescents identify and mark on the thermometer the highest point on this scale at which they are upset but can still stay in control (i.e., at the 50° point). Next, the boiling point is marked on the thermometer (e.g., 60°–100°), and specific steps are identified to avoid the boiling point, such as taking a deep breath or counting from 1 to 10. Finally, adolescents are asked to select a point to serve as a signal that they need to do something to calm down before they get to the previously identified boiling point. This is the point at which they are still able to use strategies to avoid an outburst or explosion, and it is labeled the *action point*. In many instances, there is more than one action point, and the clinician con-

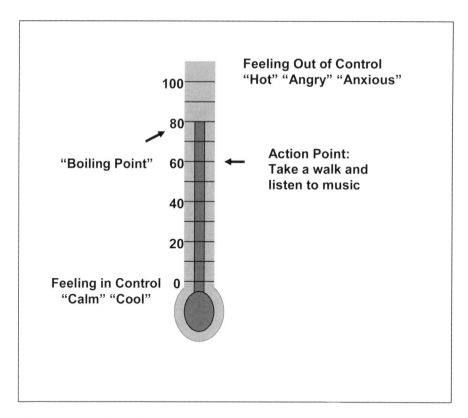

Figure 11.2. Emotions thermometer.

tinues to work with adolescents to identify specific steps they can take at different points to control escalation. Such strategies may include the affective coping strategies described in chapter 8 or other distracting, pleasant activities that have been helpful in the past.

> Jill reluctantly agreed to use the Emotions Thermometer. Although she complained that it was for babies, it quickly became evident that she needed a visual image to help her identify crucial points at which she must intervene before her emotions are overwhelming. Jill identified two action points—one at a level of 30, and the other at a level of 70. Because her emotions escalated so quickly during the recent suicidal crisis, it was reasoned that it would be helpful to implement some of the coping strategies even at times in which her distress was only at a mild to moderate level. Jill agreed that when her level of distress reached a "temperature" of 30, she would watch one of her favorite television shows or rollerblade around the block. In contrast, a level of 70 signaled impending crisis for Jill. It was agreed that if she reached a level of 70, she would talk to her mother, who had been, concurrently, learning ways to help Jill deescalate her emotions. Her mother had made arrangements at work to be available to take calls if Jill contacted her during the day.

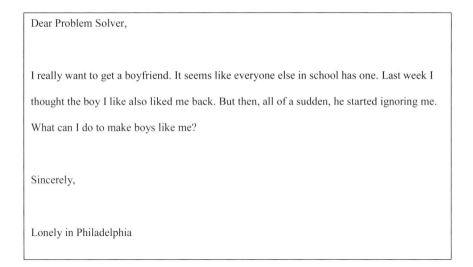

Dear Problem Solver,

I really want to get a boyfriend. It seems like everyone else in school has one. Last week I thought the boy I like also liked me back. But then, all of a sudden, he started ignoring me. What can I do to make boys like me?

Sincerely,

Lonely in Philadelphia

Figure 11.3. Example of a problem solving letter.

The empirical literature suggests that although suicidal adolescents can generate solutions to their problems, they tend to get overwhelmed by them, lack the confidence that they are able to effectively address them, and at times, view suicide as the only way to solve their problems (Esposito, Johnson, et al., 2003). Moreover, in our cognitive model, problem solving deficits play a distal vulnerability role, but they may also exacerbate attentional fixation during a suicidal crisis. Thus, problem solving is an important component of cognitive therapy for suicidal adolescent patients that facilitates active coping with distress. As with any of the specific intervention strategies, the clinician should take care to discuss the rationale for focusing on problem solving to ensure that adolescents are on board. The important concept to communicate is that suicidal behavior is actually a way of coping with their problem(s). Clinicians should first validate the thoughts and feelings that led to the suicidal act, but they should also communicate that the focus of treatment is to help patients develop more adaptive ways to solve their problems.

Some adolescents learn problem solving strategies more effectively after they have distanced themselves from their own problems, as these problems are still fresh and overwhelming and can agitate them in session. Using examples from other real people or fictional characters can be helpful in teaching this skill. Thus, a creative strategy for facilitating a focus on problem solving strategies in session is to use *problem solving letters*, which are hypothetical letters written by teens to a problem solving expert such as those seen in columns in teen magazines (CBT TASA Team, 2008; Curry et al., 2005; see Figure 11.3). Clinicians can have a wide array of these letters on hand, and they can choose a particular letter depending on the clinical needs of the patient. Together, the clinician and teen read the letter and give advice to the letter writer.

Finally, we encourage clinicians to use the cognitive strategies described in chapters 5 and 8 whenever a negative thought or belief associated with the recent suicidal crisis becomes evident in session. Many adolescents have difficulty systematically identifying and evaluating problematic cognitions. In these instances, it is often helpful to conduct a role play. One type of role play involves adolescent patients playing a friend who is in a similar situation, which often helps them to distance themselves from their highly charged emotions. The clinician systematically asks the questions described in chapter 5 to help adolescent patients gain perspective. As these patients gain some experience in using these cognitive strategies, the clinician can suggest a reverse role play, such that the clinician plays the role of the patient and the patient plays the role of the clinician, and they attempt to evaluate a negative cognition associated with distress. When helpful alternative responses to negative cognitions are identified, it is important to write them on a coping card so that adolescents can consult them in times of crisis. For adolescents who continue to have difficulty with these cognitive strategies, it is often helpful to devise a coping card with one or more concrete positive statements (e.g., "Don't let them get to me! I know I'm a good person!").

When it was clear that Jill had amassed a number of behavioral and affective coping strategies to manage distress and that she was able to implement those strategies in her life, her clinician revisited the second goal of treatment—developing healthy relationships with others, particularly with members of the opposite sex. On the basis of the cognitive case conceptualization, her clinician speculated that Jill's core belief of unlovability is associated with poor relationship choices, as she uses sex as a way to feel cared for by boys. In the seventh cognitive therapy session, Jill's clinician attempted to use cognitive strategies to begin to modify her unlovability core belief and asked her to list reasons why she has sex with boys in the context of uncommitted or newly developed relationships. At first, she was defensive, replying, "What do you mean why? It feels good! I like it! And it's no big deal anyway—everyone does it." Her clinician judged that it would damage the therapeutic relationship to challenge the notion that "everyone does it," so instead, he gently asked, "What would it be like if you decided not to be like everyone else and have sex?" For the first time in the course of treatment, Jill became tearful and expressed concern that boys would not like her and that she would be excluded from the group. Later in the session, she acknowledged that having casual sex often left her feeling worse about herself because she felt used and knew deep down that her partners did not really care for her. Moreover, she identified an instance of an acquaintance in her homeroom who had been in a relationship with her boyfriend for more than a year but had not yet had sex. Through this discussion, the clinician helped Jill to develop the alternative response, "There are other ways for boys to like me besides having sex," and they brainstormed healthy ways to initiate opposite-sex relationships. At the end of the session, Jill wrote the alternative response and the list she and her clinician developed on a coping card.

Increasing Reasons for Living

As with adults, suicidal crises often escalate when adolescents conclude that they have nothing to live for. Earlier in the book, we described one cognitive strategy for patients to remind themselves of reasons for living—the Hope Kit—that can be adapted for use with suicidal adolescent patients. Items that adolescent patients have placed in their Hope Kit include pictures of friends or family members or instant messages, e-mails, or notes from friends. Some adolescents may not agree to construct a Hope Kit but are responsive to exercises with a similar intent that use age-appropriate media, such as constructing a collage, putting together a scrapbook, or developing a Web page. Songs or pictures of friends or family that offer a sense of hope can be stored on a cell phone or other multimedia device and used during a suicidal crisis. One adolescent created "Hope Shoes" by decorating a pair of high-top sneakers with mementos that provided meaning in her life.

Improving Family Relationships

Problems in family relationships are important to address in treatment with suicidal adolescents because there is evidence that family conflict and poor family cohesion are associated with poor treatment compliance (see Boergers & Spirito, 2003, for a review). Whereas cognitive therapy for suicidal adult patients focuses on family problems in the context of helping patients to improve their social support networks, treatment with suicidal adolescent patients directly focuses on improving family functioning when clinically indicated. The main goals of the family component of treatment are to (a) improve family communication, (b) improve the family's problem solving ability, (c) manage adolescents' oppositional or uncooperative behavior, and (d) increase family engagement and commitment (cf. Berman, Jobes, & Silverman, 2006; CBT TASA Team, 2008; Wells & Curry, 2000). From the perspective of our cognitive model, these goals serve to decrease vulnerability factors for future suicidal acts (e.g., family conflict), increase adolescents' sense of support from the family, and reinforce strategies targeted in treatment by having family members model or coach adolescent patients in executing them. Next, we elaborate on the most commonly used family-based strategy—improving family communication.

Younger adolescents most commonly cite family problems as the trigger for their suicide attempt (Spirito, Overholser, & Stark, 1989). Therefore, teaching effective communication skills is important for encouraging adolescent patients to seek help and support appropriately, handle interpersonal conflicts, and ultimately facilitate effective communication skills in other relationships. Families are often uncomfortable when talking about the events associated with a current or previous suicidal crisis, and thus sometimes avoid talking about these issues or overreact when these issues are introduced. Talking openly about precursors to the suicidal crisis can habituate family members to the discomfort associated with this subject matter and can help them to learn that it is appropriate to deal directly with this taboo topic. Moreover, discussion can be focused on the family safety plan so that family members can develop a sense of confidence that they would be able to cope effectively with a future suicidal crisis should it arise.

When the source of family conflict is introduced in session, it often becomes evident that the adolescent and parents alike become agitated, and renewed conflict quickly escalates. When this occurs, it is helpful for the clinician to assist the family in negotiating a truce around "hot topics" or possible precipitants to future suicidal crises (CBT TASA Team, 2008; Curry et al., 2005). That is, the clinician can give permission for adolescents and their parents to disengage around that issue until they have learned how to disagree without it leading to a suicidal crisis. Once the family agrees to the truce, it is important to rehearse with the family what they will each do if the truce breaks down (e.g., give permission to leave the room so as not to continue the argument).

> Although Jill and her mother rarely had overt conflicts, they admitted that they had been emotionally disengaged for many years. Moreover, it was clear that Jill's mother was overwhelmed with the recent crisis and had difficulty identifying ways to help Jill improve her life circumstances and ensure her safety. On the basis of this clinical presentation, the clinician reasoned that Jill and her mother would benefit from a focus on family problem solving strategies. To address their emotional detachment, the clinician encouraged Jill and her mother to brainstorm activities that they would both enjoy doing together. They identified activities such as shopping, renting DVDs, going to ballet performances, and riding bicycles. Jill's mother expressed interest in these activities but indicated that she was concerned about time, given that she is a single mother and handles all of the household responsibilities on her own. The clinician guided her in generating ways to overcome that obstacle, such as letting some of the housework go on occasion and asking Jill to pitch in. Moreover, he encouraged them to identify a plan to spend time together on a regular basis. Jill and her mother decided that they would reserve Sunday afternoons for mother–daughter time.
>
> To enhance Jill's mother's ability to deal with Jill's distress, the clinician asked Jill to articulate what her mother could do that would be most helpful in resolving the crisis. Jill indicated that her mother often overreacts when she is upset, which only escalates her distress. Thus, the clinician integrated a focus on effective family communication skills. Jill

asked her mother to assist in self-soothing, such as by preparing her favorite meal or watching television with her, rather than bombarding her with tons of questions. Jill's mother agreed to take this approach, but she expressed a need to have some indication that the strategies are working and that Jill is not planning on hurting herself. Jill made the agreement to explicitly tell her mother that she is no longer in crisis or acute distress.

Modifying Nonsuicidal Self-Injury Behavior

Empirical research has shown that up to 55% of adolescent suicide attempters engage in nonsuicidal self-injury behavior (see discussion in DiFilippo, Esposito, Overholser, & Spirito, 2003). In a study of adolescents who were admitted to an inpatient unit for self-injury behavior, 70% reported a lifetime history of at least one suicide attempt, and 55% reported multiple attempts (Nock et al., 2006). Given the association of self-injury behavior and suicide attempts among adolescents, treatments that focus on suicide prevention may also need to focus on the treatment of self-injury behavior (cf. CBT TASA Team, 2008). As we discussed in chapter 3, Joiner (2005) suggested that people may become more courageous, competent, and willing to make suicide attempts with repeated engagement in nonsuicidal self-injury behavior. Thus, treatment is needed to decrease this behavior because individuals may habituate to the fear and physical pain associated with self-injury and, as a result, may be at greater risk for suicidal acts.

The most common methods of self-injury include cutting the skin (often on the inside of the arms and legs) and burning the skin (Favazza, 1996), but clinicians working with suicidal adolescent patients often observe other types of self-injury, including punching, hitting, or scratching; choking or constricting of the airway; self-biting of hands, limbs, tongue, lips, or arms; picking at wounds, ulcerations, sutures, or blemishes; burning the skin, including cigarette burns, and self-incendiarism; stabbing oneself with wire, pins, nails, or pens; ingesting corrosive chemicals, batteries, or pins; or pinching or clamping with clothespins or paperclips (Favazza, 1996; Whitlock, Eckenrode, & Silverman, 2006). Adolescents who engage in these types of behaviors often report that they do so as a way to regulate or control intense emotions (Fox & Hawton, 2004; Spandler, 1996). Specifically, they may do so to feel better or to reduce the emotional tension that is usually experienced as extreme distress, anxiety, or anger. Others may engage in this behavior to distract themselves from emotional pain or to mask emotional pain with physical pain. Cognitive behavioral approaches to treating nonsuicidal self-injury behavior in adolescents have been adapted by Barbara Stanley (CBT TASA Team, 2008) and Miller, Rathus, and Linehan (2007), and we encourage clinicians to adopt some of these specific strategies as indicated by the cognitive case conceptualization.

Later Phase of Treatment

As with the protocol for suicidal adults, the later phase of treatment consists of four main components: consolidation of skills, the relapse prevention protocol, review of progress toward treatment goals, and preparation for termination. The implementation of the relapse prevention protocol for adolescents is very similar to the relapse prevention protocol for adults. However, our clinical experience suggests that adolescents may be more reluctant to engage in the guided imagery exercise than are adults. One strategy for increasing the likelihood that adolescents would be willing to participate in the relapse prevention protocol is to present the rationale for these exercises very early in treatment (CBT TASA Team, 2008). Adolescent patients are informed that by imagining the suicidal crisis and reliving the pain, they will have the opportunity to assess whether the coping skills learned during treatment can be recalled and implemented. Before completing the guided imagery exercise, the clinician and patient should review all of the skills that were learned during therapy. The clinician should encourage adolescent patients to indicate which skills are the easiest to do and which skills are going to be the most effective in preventing a future suicidal act. The clinician then follows the instructions for the relapse prevention task we described in chapter 9. After the relapse prevention protocol has been conducted, the clinician evaluates for suicide risk and works collaboratively with adolescents to develop an action plan to address any suicide ideation that emerges during the course of this exercise.

If adolescent patients successfully complete the relapse prevention protocol, then they may be ready to end the acute suicide prevention phase of treatment. As in the protocol for adults, the discussion of therapy termination or shift to a continuation phase of treatment should include the following: (a) reviewing progress toward the treatment goals, including the occurrence of additional suicide attempts or self-injury behavior; (b) reviewing the specific coping strategies that were learned during treatment; (c) determining the strategies that have been the most helpful and those most likely to be used during a future suicidal crisis; (d) discussing general plans for the disposition, including a discussion of the treatment plan, the frequency of sessions, and possible referrals for further treatment of specific problems; and (e) identifying any roadblocks or challenges to ending of this phase of treatment. The clinician should educate patients that fluctuations in mood are to be expected and that they should not be equated with relapse. The clinician and adolescent patient anticipate future situations that might trigger suicidal crises and plan ways to handle those situations. The safety plan is reviewed, and the clinician elicits adolescents' commitment to use the safety plan in times of crisis. Finally, the clinician often has a final session with family members to review the safety plan and discuss any potential concerns about setbacks.

> Jill's treatment lasted a total of 20 sessions. She experienced another
> crisis midway through treatment when she learned that a new boy for

whom she developed feelings did not have the same feelings for her. Although Jill did not make another suicide attempt during that crisis, she and her mother admitted that they had difficulty working through it and that many of the strategies learned to that point in treatment did not seem to be effective. When the clinician asked Jill whether she used her safety plan, she indicated that she "just couldn't" and that she knew nothing would work. Thus, the clinician revised the cognitive case conceptualization to include a helplessness core belief (i.e., "I am ineffective") in addition to her unlovability core belief, and he proceeded to use cognitive and problem solving strategies to address this belief. One activity in particular that Jill enjoyed was a modification of the Hope Kit to remind her of reasons for living, including reminders that she is indeed lovable and effective. Specifically, she stored pictures of these reminders on her camera phone so that she would have access to them wherever she is. She included pictures of her mother, her dog (for whom she was the primary caretaker), the dance studio (at which she was excelling at this new activity), her two girlfriends, and her favorite teen idol.

The clinician had doubts that Jill would agree to participate in the relapse prevention protocol, given the defiance he had witnessed many times throughout treatment, and he was pleasantly surprised when she readily gave her consent. When she imagined the suicidal crisis that brought her into treatment, she presented a much richer picture of the sequence of events that led to the crisis, particularly the cognitions and emotions she had been experiencing. She identified several coping skills that would have helped her to manage that crisis, including reviewing her safety plan, distracting herself with pleasurable activities, reading her coping cards, and calling her mother. For the final part of the relapse prevention protocol, Jill imagined that she was in another committed relationship with a boy in her school and that he abruptly broke it off. Jill imagined using many of the same coping skills to manage distress over that future breakup, including a new alternative response: "There are other fish in the sea." In the last session of treatment, Jill noted, "It's lame to get so upset over one dumb boy," and her mother expressed gratefulness that she was educated about warning signs for suicidal behavior in adolescents and ways to resolve suicidal crises. After treatment ended, Jill was referred to group therapy for adolescent girls with low self-esteem. Three months later, she saw her clinician in the hallway of the clinic, and she mentioned that she has been attending the group and could not believe that there were so many other girls in her situation.

SUMMARY AND INTEGRATION

The cognitive approach to the treatment of suicidal adolescents is similar to the cognitive approach to the treatment of suicidal adults; however, there are several important issues that are more likely to arise when treating suicidal adolescents. First, adolescents may be more reluctant to engage in treatment and to talk about the events surrounding the suicidal crisis. Therefore, more emphasis is placed on building rapport with the adolescent during the early sessions. Second, suicidal adolescents may be more likely to overestimate the lethality of their attempt and more likely to engage in nonsuicidal self-injury behavior. Thus, careful monitoring of all self-injury behavior is in order. Third, the cognitive and behavioral strategies that are used with suicidal adults, such as developing safety plans, teaching problem solving skills, and identifying reasons for living, may need to be adapted so that adolescents will find them to be more pleasurable and easier to use (e.g., making a Hope Kit using images stored on one's cell phone). Fourth, adolescents may prefer to engage in behavioral or affective strategies than in cognitive strategies, especially during the early phase of treatment. Finally, family members are much more likely to be involved in treatment. Given that family dysfunction may be an immediate precursor to a suicidal crisis, treatment strategies that strengthen family communication and problem solving, improve contingency management, decrease hostility, and improve emotional engagement are often required. However, it should also be recognized that the family interactions are usually not uniformly problematic and that family members are often a valuable resource for adolescents in providing support and assisting them in developing important skills to prevent future suicidal acts.

12

COGNITIVE THERAPY FOR SUICIDAL OLDER ADULTS

Older adults have a higher rate of suicide than any other age group in the United States. Statistics obtained from the Centers for Disease Control and Prevention (CDC; 2008) indicate that between 1999 and 2005, more than 5,000 adults per year 65 years of age or older died by suicide. The rate of suicide for this age group was 15.05 per 100,000 people, compared to the rate of 10.18 per 100,000 for individuals younger than 65. Moreover, suicide rates continue to increase with age among elderly people; for example, the suicide rate was approximately 17.77 per 100,000 people for adults older than 85. Although older people constituted approximately 12% of the population in the United States during this time period, they accounted for approximately 16% of all suicides. Thus, as Americans continue to age, the raw number of suicides is also likely to increase.

This chapter describes the adaptation of cognitive therapy for suicide prevention to the treatment of suicidal older adults. First, we provide an overview of the correlates of and risk factors for suicidal acts among older people, highlighting variables that are similar to those that are important in understanding suicidal acts in younger populations and those that are more common in older adults. Second, we briefly review the evidence-based treatments for suicidal elders to educate the reader about the psychosocial treatments that have been evaluated to date for this population. Third, we describe the application of cognitive therapy for suicidal older adults. As in the previous chapters describing this intervention approach, the discussion of the cognitive therapy protocol is organized by the early, intermediate, and later phases of treatment and includes a case example.

SUICIDE IDEATION AND SUICIDAL ACTS IN OLDER ADULTS

Given the high rates of suicide among older adults, there is a pressing need to identify the risk factors associated with suicidal acts in this population. As stated in chapter 2, the identification of specific, quantifiable risk factors is essential for developing and implementing effective suicide prevention strategies. However, there have been relatively few epidemiological studies with older adults, in contrast to the large number of studies of risk factors for suicide in younger populations. Nearly all of the studies in this literature have used cross-sectional research designs to identify correlates of suicidal acts in older adults rather than longitudinal designs to identify specific risk factors. In addition, the psychological autopsy method (which is also called the retrospective case controlled method) has been used to identify correlates of suicide in older adults. Researchers who use this method construct a detailed description of the victim's psychological status before death, including psychiatric symptomatology, behavior, and life circumstances, by interviewing knowledgeable informants (e.g., family members), reviewing available clinical records, and working with mental health professionals with expertise in postmortem studies to develop a comprehensive case formulation (e.g., D. C. Clark & Horton-Deutsch, 1992). The studies reviewed in this section focus on (a) demographic variables, (b) diagnostic variables, (c) psychological variables, and (d) suicide-relevant variables that have been identified as correlates in cross-sectional or psychological autopsy studies and as risk factors in prospective studies.

Demographic Variables

There are even greater gender and racial discrepancies in the rates of suicide in older adults than in those in younger adults. According to statistics from the CDC, men account for approximately 85% of suicides among adults age 65 years or older. In contrast, men account for approximately 76% of suicides among adults between the ages of 40 and 60 years (CDC, 2008). Important racial differences also emerge in the rates of suicide among older adults. For example, among adults age 65 years and older, the suicide rate for Caucasians was 16.22 per 100,000, whereas the suicide rates were 5.05 per 100,000 for African Americans and 9.76 per 100,000 for American Indians and Alaskan Natives. In contrast, for younger adults between the ages of 21 and 30, the suicide rate was 13.08 per 100,000 for Caucasians, 9.87 per 100,000 for African Americans, and 19.70 per 100,000 for American Indians and Alaskan Natives (CDC, 2008). Caucasian men older than age 85 have the highest suicide rate (54.03 per 100,000) when all gender, racial, and age groups are considered (CDC, 2008). Moreover, the suicide rate for older men who are divorced or widowed is much higher than that for older men who are married (Buda & Tsuang, 1990; Li, 1995). These statistics suggest that interventions that target older Caucasian men who are divorced or widowed are especially warranted.

Diagnostic Variables

The loss of a spouse or partner is only one of the many potential risk factors for suicide in older adults. With increasing age comes the onset of medical disorders that are likely to have a profound impact on quality of life and psychological adjustment. It is often assumed that physical illness is a risk factor for suicide in older adults (Conwell, Duberstein, & Caine, 2002). Although estimates of standardized mortality ratios suggest that many major medical illnesses are indeed associated with suicide risk (see E. C. Harris & Barraclough, 1994), some prospective studies have failed to find an association between medical illness or physical impairment and suicide (e.g., Turvey et al., 2002). One methodological problem with many of these studies is that they do not control for the presence of psychiatric disturbance or other psychological risk factors, making it difficult to determine the degree to which physical illness confers unique risk for suicidal acts. Some psychological autopsy studies have examined the association between physical illness and suicide in older adults while controlling for these other variables, but the results have been mixed (e.g., Beautrais, 2002; Waern et al., 2002). In general, the pattern of results in this literature suggests that although physical illness may be associated with suicide in older adults, much, if not all, of the suicide risk related to physical disorders may be mediated by psychological factors.

One psychological factor that accounts for the association between medical illness and late-life suicide is the presence of a depressive disorder (for reviews, see Conwell et al., 2002; Pearson & Brown, 2000; Szanto et al., 2002). Results from psychological autopsy studies have indicated that depression is one of the most common correlates of suicide in older adults (Conwell & Brent, 1995; Conwell et al., 1996). More specifically, Conwell et al. (1996) found that the most common psychiatric disorder in older suicide victims was a single episode of nonpsychotic, major depressive disorder without comorbid psychiatric disturbance. In contrast, other psychiatric disorders, including psychotic disorders, personality disorders, and substance use disorders, appear to have a more limited association with suicide in older adults than with suicide in younger adults (see Conwell et al., 2002, for a review).

Psychological Variables

Negative life events that are commonly experienced among elderly people, such as physical illness, restricted mobility, death of a loved one, financial difficulties, and loss of professional roles, may be associated with psychological variables such as hopelessness, complicated grief, and a lack of perceived social support (e.g., Byrne & Raphael, 1999; Rubenowitz, Waern, Wilhelmson, & Allebeck, 2001). Hopelessness is especially prevalent among older people in the context of life events that are dominated by interpersonal loss. Our clinical experience suggests that older adults who live alone or have multiple medical conditions are particularly vulnerable to feeling hopeless. Empirical research has indicated that hopelessness is related to suicide ideation (Uncapher, Gallagher-Thompson, Osgood, & Bonger, 1998) and suicidal acts (Rifai, George, Stack, Mann, & Reynolds, 1994) in older adults. Moreover, Ross, Bernstein, Trent, Henderson, and Paganini-Hill (1990) found that a single item asking about hopelessness was associated with death by suicide in a sample of older adults in a retirement community who were followed prospectively. Although depression and hopelessness are closely linked, results from some studies have suggested that hopelessness is independently associated with suicidal acts. For example, Szanto, Reynolds, Conwell, Begley, and Houck (1998) reported that a high degree of hopelessness persisting after the remission of depression was associated with a history of suicide attempts in elderly patients. Because several studies have found an association between hopelessness and suicidal acts in older adults, it follows logically that treatments focusing on decreasing hopelessness may help to reduce the risk of suicide in this population.

Loneliness and grief following the death of a spouse are common experiences in older adults (see Carr, Nesse, & Wortman, 2005). In a landmark psychological autopsy study of older adults in Great Britain, Barraclough (1971) found that living alone was a correlate of suicide. This study raised the possibility that loneliness is a risk factor for suicide in older adults, as loneliness is often experienced by those who live alone (Conwell, 2001). More recent controlled psychological autopsy studies have found that loneliness is a correlate of suicide (e.g., Heikkinen & Lönnqvist, 1995; Waern, Rubenowitz, & Wilhelmson, 2003). In addition to loneliness, complicated grief following the death of a loved one has been associated with suicidal acts in older adults (e.g., Szanto et al., 2006), with suicide risk being highest in the 1st year after a death (MacMahon & Pugh, 1985). Complicated grief, a syndrome that is distinct from bereavement-related depression, includes symptoms such as intrusive thoughts about the deceased, avoidance of reminders of the deceased, survivor guilt, and lack of acceptance of the death. In a group of older adults whose spouse had died, patients who had high scores on a scale of complicated grief were more likely to report suicide ideation than patients who had low scores on this scale (Szanto, Prigerson, Houck, & Reynolds, 1997). Although these studies indicated that loneliness and grief may be associated with suicide, it is unclear whether this relation is mediated by other risk factors, such as depression.

Suicide-Relevant Variables

In contrast to the literature on younger populations, there is limited research that has established suicide attempts as a risk factor for suicide among older people (cf. Dombrovski, Szanto, & Reynolds, 2005). However, in one of the very few prospective studies of older adults, Hawton and Harriss (2006) reported that intentional self-injury behavior, with and without suicide intent, was a significant independent risk factor for suicide. Specifically, older adults who had a history of a self-injury behavior were four times more likely to kill themselves than those without a history of self-injury behavior. In general, older adults have a lower lifetime prevalence of suicide attempts than younger adults (Mościcki et al., 1988) and are less likely to report new incidents of suicide attempts than are younger adults (Kuo, Gallo, & Tien, 2001). Despite the lower prevalence of suicide attempts among older adults, late-life suicide attempts tend to be more lethal than attempts made by younger adults (for review, see Dombrovski et al., 2005). Several characteristics of older individuals and the methods they use increase the probability of a fatal outcome (Szanto et al., 2002). For example, attempts made by older adults with health problems have a high probability of being successful because their bodies are fragile and have difficulty recovering from self-injury. Attempts made by older adults who live alone have a high probability of being successful because of the low likelihood of rescue. In addition, older adults are more likely to use a firearm to kill themselves than are younger populations (CDC, 2008).

Clinically, we have observed that many suicidal older adults report that they would fail to take precautions to maintain their health, such as discontinuing their medication (i.e., a passive attempt), rather than make an active attempt, such as an overdose. As a result, it is possible that some suicidal acts in older adults are drawn out over time instead of taking place in a single instance. Clinicians working with older populations should carefully assess for suicide attempts that involve a failure to act in some way that could result in death. Regardless of whether the attempt is active or passive, it is important to keep in mind that the potentially lethal behavior must involve an implicit or explicit intent to kill oneself to be considered a suicide attempt (see chap. 1).

Although suicide ideation has been associated with greater risk of attempts in older adults, there is limited prospective research establishing suicide ideation as a risk factor for suicide (Dombrovski et al., 2005). In one exception, G. K. Brown et al. (2001) found that older adults who score higher than zero on the Scale for Suicide Ideation were 15 times more likely to die by suicide than those who score zero on this measure. A retrospective case control study found that nearly 40% of older adult suicide victims had told a health professional that they had a desire to die or kill themselves in the year before their death (Waern, Beskow, Runeson, & Skoog, 1999). Moreover, 75% of this sample had communicated to a family member or acquaintance a desire to die or kill themselves. Together, these studies provide modest support that suicide ideation is a risk factor for suicide in older people.

Despite the evidence that suicide ideation is associated with suicide in older adults, Duberstein et al. (1999) found that increasing age was associated with the endorsement of lower levels of depression and suicide ideation, an interesting finding in light of the fact that the sample under consideration was depressed inpatients whose hospitalization was precipitated by a suicide attempt. Epidemiological research has suggested that older adults are less likely to report suicide ideation than younger adults (Gallo, Anthony, & Muthen, 1994; Gallo, Rabins, & Anthony, 1999), and several psychological autopsy studies have indicated that older adults are more reluctant to disclose their intent to commit suicide than are younger adults. For example, Conwell et al. (1998) reported that relative to younger adults who died by suicide, older adults who died by suicide were more likely to have avoided intervention and to have taken precautions against discovery and were less likely to have communicated their intent to others, according to informants who were administered the Suicide Intent Scale. Another psychological autopsy study found that older adults who died by suicide were described by informants as low in a personality trait called *openness to experience*, relative to matched control individuals who died of other causes (Duberstein, Conwell, & Caine, 1994). Individuals with low levels of openness to experience prefer familiar routines, have a restricted range of interests, and exhibit blunted responses toward their environment. Further research has found that low openness to experience among elders may decrease the likelihood that they report suicide ideation, which may, in turn, increase the risk for suicide by undermining clinician attentiveness (Duberstein et al., 2000; Heisel et al., 2006).

Taken together, these studies suggest that clinicians who work with older patients should be vigilant in identifying correlates of suicide, especially among patients who deny suicide ideation. As with younger populations, the evaluation of suicide risk includes a comprehensive assessment of the risk and protective factors for suicide, such as that described in chapter 6. However, we strongly recommend that clinicians obtain collateral information from family members and other health care professionals, especially when older patients steadfastly deny suicide ideation and have the constricted reporting style that is the hallmark of low openness to experience (Heisel et al., 2006).

Summary

Older men, especially widowed older men, constitute a high-risk group for suicide. Many correlates of and risk factors for suicidal acts in older adults, such as depression, hopelessness, and suicide ideation, are the same as for suicidal acts in younger adults. However, older adults are more likely than younger adults to be faced with major life events such as physical illness, restricted mobility, interpersonal loss, and the loss of professional roles that may lead to depression, hopelessness, and suicide ideation. Given the low prevalence of suicide attempts in this population, the application of cognitive therapy for suicidal older adults is less likely to focus on the prevention of repeat suicide attempts. However, there is a pressing need for interventions for older adults who are at risk for suicide, especially because suicidal older adults often engage in highly lethal behaviors even if they have never made a suicide attempt. Thus, interventions such as cognitive therapy that target suicide ideation and other risk factors may be a promising approach for preventing suicide in elderly people. Because there is limited research on the efficacy and effectiveness of cognitive therapy as an intervention for suicidal older adults, in the next section we review the empirical literature on cognitive therapy for depressed elders and on other empirically based treatments for suicidal older adults.

EVIDENCE-BASED TREATMENT OF SUICIDAL OLDER ADULTS

Given that depression is associated with suicide in older adults, it is plausible that the identification and adequate treatment of depression may reduce the risk of suicide in this population. The cognitive behavioral approach to treatment is the most extensively studied psychotherapy for treating depression in older adults. Randomized controlled trials have indicated that cognitive behavior therapy (CBT) is an effective treatment for late-life depression (cf. Laidlaw, Thompson, Dick-Siskin, & Gallagher-Thompson, 2003; Thompson, Gallagher, & Breckenridge, 1987). Specifically, CBT is more effective in decreasing depressive symptoms than usual care (Campbell, 1992; Scott, Tacchi, Jones, & Scott, 1997) and pill placebo (Jarvik, Mintz, Steuer, & Gerner, 1982). Research studies on the comparative efficacy of CBT to other psychotherapies or to medication are limited. In one study, CBT was found to be no more effective in reducing depressive symptoms than dynamic therapy (Steuer et al., 1984). However, a study comparing

CBT to an antidepressant medication (desipramine) in the treatment of major depressive disorder in older adults found that the combination of CBT and medication was more effective in reducing depressive symptoms than medication alone (Thompson, Coon, Gallagher-Thompson, Sommer, & Koin, 2001).

Despite the evidence that depression can be effectively treated in older adults, there is a paucity of randomized controlled trials that have examined whether treatments that reduce depression are also effective for reducing suicide ideation. One of the few studies to have examined this issue was the Prevention of Suicide in Primary Care Elderly: Collaborative Trial (PROS-PECT) study (Bruce et al., 2004). This randomized controlled trial was designed to test the effectiveness of a depression treatment algorithm in primary care settings on reducing depression and suicide ideation. The PROSPECT study examined the effect of including a depression health specialist, usually a nurse practitioner, who assisted the primary care physician in identifying depressed elders and providing assistance in treating these individuals using medication (especially citalopram [Celexa]) or psychotherapy (interpersonal psychotherapy). The intervention was conducted in the primary care setting because research has found that the majority of older adults had seen their primary care physician in the months before committing suicide (see Conwell, 2001; Pearson, Conwell, & Lyness, 1997). Results from this study indicated that patients receiving the intervention had a more favorable course of depression in both the degree and the speed of symptom reduction, as measured by symptom severity, response, and remission, than patients who received usual care. Although the intervention group showed a greater reduction in suicide ideation than the usual care group, a significant proportion (33%) of patients in the intervention group continued to report suicide ideation.

Another study that assessed the effectiveness of a collaborative-care program for late-life depression in primary care settings on suicide ideation was the Improving Mood: Promoting Access to Collaborative Treatment (IMPACT) study (Unützer et al., 2006). In this study, older adults who were diagnosed with major depression and/or dysthymia were randomly assigned to a study intervention or a usual care condition. Participants in the study condition had access to a depression care manager who assisted with the management of antidepressant medication prescribed by their primary care physician and also offered a problem solving behavioral intervention lasting four to eight sessions. Patients in the usual care condition could receive all treatments that were available in the community, including antidepressant treatment or counseling by their primary care physician, as well as referral to specialty mental health care. Study participants randomized to the IMPACT intervention reported significantly lower rates of suicide ideation than usual care participants at all follow-up points. At baseline, 15.3% of those in the intervention condition and 13.3% of those in the usual care condition reported suicide ideation, and at 24 months, 10.1% of those in the intervention condition and 13.9% of those in the usual care condition reported suicide ideation.

Results from both the PROSPECT and the IMPACT studies demonstrate that depressed and suicidal older adults respond to interventions that target depressive symptoms, although there is much room for improvement because a substantial minority of these patients continues to endorse suicide ideation. Despite advances in the development of cognitive therapy that targets suicidal acts in adults, such as that described at length in this volume, very few treatments specifically target suicide ideation among older adults (see Links, Heisel, & Quastel, 2005). One logical starting point would be to adapt cognitive therapy strategies for reducing suicide ideation and other risk factors for suicidal acts in an older adult population. Such targeted interventions are likely to be more efficient and efficacious in decreasing these specific risk factors than interventions that focus more generally on the treatment of psychiatric or emotional disturbance.

COGNITIVE THERAPY PROTOCOL AND CASE EXAMPLE

Our group has adapted the cognitive therapy protocol for suicidal patients, presented earlier in the volume, to meet the specific needs of suicidal older adults. Many of the components of the intervention for older adults are similar to the intervention for younger adults, such as the three phases of treatment and many of the specific strategies. We are currently conducting a preliminary study to assess the feasibility of cognitive therapy with older men who report a recent desire to kill themselves.

The protocol for suicidal older adults incorporates a focus on patients' negative beliefs about themselves, their lives in general, or their experiences that contribute to their hopelessness about the future. To identify the cognitions that are commonly observed in older adults, we conducted a qualitative analysis of the motivations for suicide ideation endorsed by older men receiving cognitive therapy in our studies. The most frequent reasons that were provided by these patients for wanting to kill themselves were associated with their beliefs of worthlessness, uselessness, inadequacy, helplessness, or being a burden to others. Other motivations for suicide included negative life experiences such as health problems, interpersonal conflict or rejection, traumatic experiences, financial difficulties, death of a loved one, retirement, and immobility. Cognitive therapy can be used to (a) modify these beliefs and reactions to negative life experiences using cognitive strategies, (b) develop alternative ways of obtaining pleasure and meaning in life using behavioral strategies, and (c) address specific problems using problem solving strategies. In this section, we discuss aspects of the treatment protocol for suicidal older adults and highlight some of the strategies that we have commonly used with these patients. We illustrate these strategies using the case example of Mr. J, who represents a typical patient enrolled in our study designed to evaluate the efficacy of this intervention.

Early Phase of Treatment

As described earlier in this volume, activities that take place in the early phase of treatment include an assessment of the presenting problem, including patients' motivation for suicide, and the development of a safety plan. The early phase culminates when the clinician develops a cognitive case conceptualization of the patient's clinical presentation and works with the patient to develop a treatment plan.

Conducting an Assessment of the Presenting Problem

The assessment of suicidal older adults is very similar to the assessment of younger adults (see chap. 6). It includes an understanding of the patient's suicide risk, history of the presenting problem, psychiatric and substance use history, medical history, social history, psychiatric diagnoses, and a treatment plan. However, as discussed earlier, older adults may be more reluctant to reveal suicide ideation to the clinician, so the development of a collaborative therapeutic relationship is especially relevant. Moreover, the clinician should be sure to probe about passive suicidal acts, such as failing to adhere to a treatment regimen that will maintain one's health. For patients who are taking psychotropic medication, it is preferable that medications be managed by a psychiatrist rather than a primary care physician because psychiatrists are usually more likely to monitor suicide ideation than are primary care physicians. The following is a description of the information obtained from Mr. J during the early phase of treatment.

> Mr. J is a 73-year-old widowed Caucasian man who was referred for treatment of depression by his primary care physician. Approximately 3 months before his seeking treatment, his wife died of a chronic illness. He reported feeling lethargic, unmotivated, depressed, and indifferent about living since that time. Mr. J admitted that he often felt guilty that he did not spend enough leisure time with his wife while she was alive and that he becomes teary and melancholic while reminiscing about his late wife and their life together. He also reported that he had thoughts about ceasing all his medications so that his life would not be prolonged. He viewed death as providing a way to end his loneliness, to escape from his numerous medical problems, and to be reunited with his wife in heaven.
>
> Mr. J was the oldest of six siblings. He described his childhood as one filled with hardship and poverty. His father worked for the steel industry as an unskilled laborer but lost his job after an injury. Subsequently, his father developed a significant alcohol problem. Given the family's financial difficulties, Mr. J delivered newspapers, delivered groceries, and per-

formed odd jobs for a steel manufacturing company as a teenager. At age 17, he joined the army and served in active combat duty in the South Pacific during World War II. Following his discharge from the army, he obtained a bachelor's degree in economics. After graduating from college, Mr. J obtained a managerial position in a grocery store and eventually became a regional manager for a large food corporation. At age 26, he married his wife, whom he had known since childhood. He reported having a loving and faithful relationship with her, and they raised three children together.

The first issue that was associated with the onset of Mr. J's depression and suicide ideation was the death of his wife. Mr. J's wife had been living with cancer for several years and was in considerable pain during that time. Mr. J was her primary caretaker, and much of his daily life revolved around looking after her needs and accompanying her to medical appointments. During the last year of her life, she had several unsuccessful operations that increased the amount of attention she required from him. Mr. J said that he had felt numb and exhausted when she died, but also strangely relieved that she was no longer in pain. However, since her death, he felt increasingly depressed and believed that he no longer had a focus in his life. Given the changes in role responsibilities, he found it increasingly difficult to set meaningful goals for himself and structure his time.

A second problem area involved relationship problems with his children. Approximately 6 months ago, his relationship with his two sons had become strained because of a disagreement over money, as he refused to loan them money for a business investment. He felt angry about his sons' behavior and perceived that his children only wanted him for his money. Although he had taken pride in his ability to provide for his family, he regretted that he had placed so much importance on his income throughout the years and wished that he could have spent more time with his children. His relationship with his daughter was not tense, but he stated that he did not know how to go about getting closer to her, as he usually communicated with his daughter through his wife. Mr. J admitted that he had expected that he and his children would "come together" after the death of his wife, but instead he regarded himself as being even more estranged from them.

A third problem reported by Mr. J was the onset of health problems, which restricted his mobility. His medical problems included diabetes, respiratory difficulties, and perceived memory problems. He was unable to drive or do many chores at home because he was becoming increasingly unsteady, breathless, and dizzy. As a result, he became dependent on his children for transportation, which was difficult because he did not feel comfortable asking them for help. The problems with mobility and transportation contributed to the belief that he is "like a child." Moreover, because he stayed at home most of the time, he had little opportunity to engage in pleasurable activities or look forward to new experiences.

It is evident from this description that Mr. J has many characteristics that are associated with suicidal acts in older adults. After the death of his wife, he became socially isolated. He is experiencing symptoms of psychiatric disturbance, particularly depression. He has recently experienced a number of aversive life stressors, such as the death of his wife and major conflicts with two of his children. He is becoming increasingly disabled by several medical conditions. All of these variables contributed to Mr. J's pervasive sense of hopelessness and perception that life is no longer worth living.

Developing a Safety Plan

The development of the safety plan is one of the first interventions that clinicians can use when treating a suicidal patient. As described in chapter 6, a safety plan is a hierarchically arranged written list of coping strategies that can be used before or during a suicidal crisis. The safety plan consists of four main sections: (a) warning signs that are associated with suicidal crises, (b) coping strategies to manage suicidal crises, (c) friends and family who can be contacted in times of suicidal crises, and (d) professionals who can be contacted in times of suicidal crises. The safety plan helps enhance patients' sense of control over suicidal thoughts and urges and promotes the expectation that they can overcome the desire to commit suicide. In our experience, we have found that older adults are often reluctant to reach out to others, particularly professionals, during a suicidal crisis. In these instances, the clinician can examine the advantages and disadvantages of this step to highlight the benefits of reaching out to others. Moreover, role playing may be particularly effective for modeling how to contact others during these times. Next, we describe the manner in which Mr. J's clinician overcame some of the challenges in developing a safety plan with him.

> Mr. J was initially reluctant to complete a safety plan, as he repeatedly assured his clinician that he was not suicidal. However, he admitted that he often had spells of feeling lonely, weak, and hopeless, and he acknowledged that he did not know how to cope with these feelings now that his mobility was limited. To make the exercise more tolerable for Mr. J, the clinician suggested that they refer to it as a coping plan rather than a safety plan. Mr. J identified several warning signs for hopelessness, including loneliness, boredom, and memories of his wife and their life together. Strategies for coping with these triggers included watching sports on television, looking through his childhood baseball card collection, reading the financial section of the newspaper to track his investments, and going around the corner to get a cup of coffee. Individuals to whom he could reach out included his daughter and a man he often chatted with when he went to the store to get coffee. Mr. J expressed some reluctance to contact these individuals during times of hopelessness, stating that he did not want to burden them with his problems. The clinician worked collaboratively with Mr. J to evaluate his assumption that reach-

ing out to these individuals meant that he automatically has to talk to them about his feelings. Mr. J realized that just having contact with them would help him to feel more connected to others and distract him from his hopelessness, so he agreed to contact them and talk about everyday things. Finally, the clinician listed her contact information and the telephone number of a crisis service. After completing the coping plan, the clinician worked with Mr. J to identify a place to keep it so it would be easily accessible (i.e., his wallet) and identify any obstacles that would prevent him from using it.

Developing a Cognitive Case Conceptualization

As stated previously, a fundamental principle of our treatment is the identification of activating events, cognitions, behaviors, emotions, and situations as they relate to patients' suicide ideation or suicidal acts. As patients provide a narrative description of the events surrounding the onset of suicide ideation, the clinician identifies key automatic thoughts that are central to these episodes. These identified thoughts are integrated into a cognitive case conceptualization of the patient's clinical presentation that includes dispositional vulnerability factors, early experiences, core and intermediate beliefs, key automatic thoughts, and suicide-relevant cognitive processes (see chap. 7).

> The fundamental elements of Mr. J's cognitive case conceptualization of his suicide ideation are displayed in Figure 12.1. Mr. J's early experiences of watching his father's demise and having to work at a young age likely contributed to a potentially dysfunctional attitude that men are supposed to be strong and independent. For most of his life, Mr. J was indeed strong and independent, and not surprisingly he was psychologically healthy. However, now that he experienced the loss of many external (e.g., support from his wife) and internal (e.g., his mobility) resources, he developed a hopelessness-based suicide schema characterized by the core beliefs "I am weak" and "Life will never get better." Thus, his attitude about the necessity of men being strong and independent, developed from his early experiences, served as a dispositional vulnerability factor that activated a hopelessness-based suicide schema when his health and life circumstances threatened his strength and independence.
>
> Given the fact that he was faced with multiple physical problems, Mr. J held the intermediate belief that "If I need help, I will be a burden to others, and I will lose my pride." Each day when he took his pills, he had automatic thoughts such as "What's the use? Nothing will make me independent again." When he had those ideas, he often thought about discontinuing his medication altogether to end life on his own terms. Thus, during these episodes in which he contemplated a passive suicide attempt, he narrowed his attention on suicide as his only option at the expense of considering other ways to redefine his self-worth and identity (i.e., suicide-relevant cognitive processes).

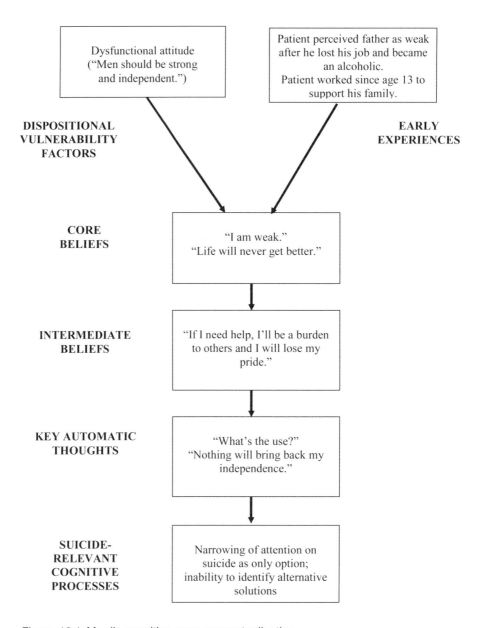

DISPOSITIONAL VULNERABILITY FACTORS

Dysfunctional attitude ("Men should be strong and independent.")

EARLY EXPERIENCES

Patient perceived father as weak after he lost his job and became an alcoholic.
Patient worked since age 13 to support his family.

CORE BELIEFS

"I am weak."
"Life will never get better."

INTERMEDIATE BELIEFS

"If I need help, I'll be a burden to others and I will lose my pride."

KEY AUTOMATIC THOUGHTS

"What's the use?"
"Nothing will bring back my independence."

SUICIDE-RELEVANT COGNITIVE PROCESSES

Narrowing of attention on suicide as only option; inability to identify alternative solutions

Figure 12.1. Mr. J's cognitive case conceptualization.

Establishing Treatment Goals

It is important to assess older adult patients' expectations for treatment to determine whether there are any negative attitudes toward treatment that might interfere with its success. Often, older adults have not participated in psychotherapy and have not developed an understanding of the types of activities and goals that are established in treatment. As with most suicidal elders, the treatment goals should include the reduction of suicide ideation and depressive symptoms and the development of adaptive coping skills to use in times of suicidal crisis. In addition, specific behavioral goals are important for providing an objective measurement of progress in treatment. For example, the clinician could ask, "How would you behave differently if you were less suicidal or less depressed? What would your friends or family members notice about you if you were less depressed or no longer suicidal?" For Mr. J, these goals included being more hopeful, autonomous, and independent, as indicated by increasing participation in social and leisure activities; increasing contact with his family and decreasing the frequency of arguments with his children; and obtaining medical consultation and following treatment recommendations.

Intermediate Phase of Treatment

Clinicians working with suicidal older adults use many of the same strategies we described in chapter 8. However, these strategies are tailored to fit the needs and life circumstances of older adults, such as coping with loss, illness, and physical limitations. Clinicians often work with older adults to recall times when they coped successfully with adversity in the past and to apply the strategies they used previously to their current problems. In this section, we illustrate strategies for increasing reasons for living, improving social resources, developing problem solving strategies, and increasing compliance with other services with Mr. J.

Increasing Reasons for Living

As described earlier in the book, identifying reasons for living is a key strategy in cognitive therapy for suicidal patients because it helps them to counter cognitions characterized by a pervasive sense of hopelessness. This is particularly true for suicidal older adults, who may be struggling with multiple forms of loss. A straightforward exercise is simply to ask patients to list reasons for living and to record those reasons somewhere, such as on a coping card, so they can easily access them during a suicidal crisis. However, many suicidal patients require a more vivid portrayal of these reminders than simple entries on a sheet of paper.

As with younger patients, a Hope Kit may be especially potent in reminding older patients of the reasons for living at times in which they are feeling hopeless or suicidal. The Hope Kit consists of a container that holds mementos (e.g., photographs, letters, souvenirs, prayer cards) that serve as reminders of reasons to live. Anecdotally, older adults have found this activity to be a highly rewarding experience that often leads them to discover reasons to live that had been previously overlooked. It is important for the clinician to work collaboratively with older patients to identify the items that would be most helpful in times of a suicidal crisis. For example, photographs of one's spouse might prompt specific memories of pleasant experiences. But if the spouse is deceased, it also could prompt negative thoughts such as "I'll never have this kind of happiness again." Thus, in session, the clinician can help patients to anticipate the usefulness of the Hope Kit contents in reminding them of reasons to live during suicidal crises. In addition, the clinician can help patients to identify items that remind them of pleasant activities in which they could engage in the future, such as pictures of grandchildren or a schedule of events at the local senior citizen's center.

> Since his retirement, the death of his wife, and the diminished communication with his family, Mr. J struggled to find a purpose in life. Mr. J perceived himself to have been autonomous and goal oriented for most of his life, and he no longer had this strong sense of independence. Mr. J summarized his depleted sense of identity by stating, "I no longer know where I belong." He spent most of the days watching war movies, reminiscing about the past, and ruminating about his current impoverished situation. Therefore, one task of therapy was to help Mr. J articulate reasons for living. Mr. J was able to nominate five reasons for living: (a) to enjoy his relationship with his daughter, (b) to make new friends, (c) to see at least one grandchild married, (d) to meet his great-grandchildren, and (e) to inspire others to "take charge of life." Accordingly, Mr. J collected pictures of his children and grandchildren. He also cut out pictures of places he liked to travel and scenes from magazines. These pictures were placed in a scrapbook, which he enjoyed sharing with others who visited him.

Improving Social Resources

As stated previously, high levels of social isolation and poor social support networks are related to suicide ideation in older adults (Alexopoulos, Bruce, Hull, Sirey, & Kakuma, 1999). Thus, an important strategy in cognitive therapy for suicidal older adults is to develop patients' social resources to decrease levels of hopelessness and to solicit social support in tolerating distress associated with losses, medical problems, and other types of adversity. For example, patients can be encouraged to schedule pleasurable social activities with others and to expand their network of social support. In many instances, clinicians work successfully with older adults to identify specific activities of interest that are sponsored by the local senior center.

In addition, interpersonal conflict with close others can be addressed in session by examining assumptions patients have for their relationships and communication strategies that would be most useful in working through conflict. Many clinicians find that role playing is a useful strategy to help older adults practice and implement communication strategies discussed in session. Whenever possible, family members or caregivers are encouraged to participate in therapy, not only to address interpersonal conflict, but also to educate them about the cognitive and behavioral strategies that patients are developing so that they can help reinforce these strategies in patients' everyday lives.

Improving social resources was a major focus of Mr. J's treatment, as he had experienced social isolation since his wife's death and reported significant conflict in his relationships with his two sons. It was reasoned that focusing on improving social resources would decrease the strength of his core belief that "life will never get better" and increase his reasons for living. Mr. J and his clinician collaboratively decided to address this problem in two ways. First, they brainstormed ways to expand his support network, such as by becoming more active in his local senior citizen's center. Mr. J was initially reluctant to participate in activities at the senior center, stating "That's where old people go." However, he agreed to take on a behavioral experiment, in which he would attend one event that seemed interesting to him and see how it went. At the time of his next session, Mr. J indicated that he saw some people he knew there and that the environment was much different than he had anticipated. Second, Mr. J and his clinician identified strategies for improving his relationships with his children. Mr. J indicated that he felt closest to his daughter and wished he could spend more time with her and his grandchildren. However, he admitted that he did not know how to talk to her about this, as his wife had been the one to arrange visits with his children after they left the home. Thus, the clinician worked with Mr. J to develop communication skills to initiate conversations with his daughter, make requests to visit one another, and negotiate the specifics of the visits. After a few sessions, Mr. J reported that he had a pleasant lunch with his daughter and that they were planning a Sunday dinner at her home with her husband and children.

Improving Mr. J's relationships with his sons proved to be more challenging. He was ambivalent about whether he should make the first step in repairing these relationships. Mr. J felt hurt, resentful, and confused by the fact that they had not contacted him in several weeks to check up on him. He stated, "I have my pride. Children should come to their father, not the other way around." The advantages and disadvantages of contacting his sons were listed, and Mr. J ultimately decided that at this time, he was too uncomfortable to take on this task. Instead, he and his clinician constructed an adaptive response: "Although I wish I had strong relationships with all of my children, I will accept that this is not the case and focus on developing my relationship with my daughter and her family."

Developing Problem Solving Strategies

Older adult patients often benefit from a focus on developing problem solving skills; although many older patients successfully solved problems and managed their lives in the past, they often become overwhelmed with the new life circumstances and roles in which they find themselves. Older patients can be taught to identify life stressors or circumstances that precipitate or contribute to their hopelessness and generate alternative solutions to their problems. The clinician and patient can explore the various possibilities, listing the advantages and disadvantages of each solution until a suitable and concrete plan is created. Coping cards can be created to list the steps of effective problem solving or to evaluate negative cognitions that prevent patients from actively addressing a problem in the first place.

> As a successful businessman, Mr. J had a considerable history of solving problems as they arose in his professional life. By acknowledging these strengths, the clinician was able to collaborate with him in identifying the current problems in his life and generating possible solutions. Specifically, the clinician asked Mr. J what he would advise someone else in his situation to do. In addition, the clinician encouraged him to talk about previous experiences of success and the strategies he used to ensure those successes. When Mr. J discussed these experiences, he began to remember his resources and skills that could be of help in his current situation. For example, Mr. J indicated that he felt uncomfortable depending on his sons for transportation because their relationship was strained and because this arrangement activated the belief that his children need to take care of him. When talking about his achievements in the past, Mr. J recalled that approximately 10 years ago he had volunteered for a senior citizen's transportation service. He decided that using this service would help him to feel more independent.

Increasing Compliance With Other Services

As mentioned earlier in the chapter, late-life depression often occurs in conjunction with the physical illnesses associated with aging. Symptoms associated with depression, including hopelessness and suicide ideation, may interfere with medical compliance and thus worsen health outcomes (Montano, 1999). At the beginning of each session, the clinician assesses patients' adherence to their medical regimen (e.g., keeping medical appointments or taking medication as prescribed). If treatment adherence is identified as a problem, the clinician can use cognitive strategies to examine negative beliefs and behaviors regarding treatment. Once these beliefs have been examined, maladaptive thoughts will be modified and solutions will be generated to overcome the difficulties.

> The key automatic thoughts that prevented Mr. J from attending medical appointments included "What's the use of going to doctors? I'm too old to change. My health problems are irreparable." To address such thoughts, a role playing strategy was adopted, such that the clinician played the role of Mr. J, and Mr. J played the role of a patient advocate. In the context of this exercise, Mr. J was able to identify several reasons for following through with his appointments and complying with his treatment regimen. For example, Mr. J said that he enjoyed sports and wanted to be healthy enough to attend baseball games at the stadium. Furthermore, Mr. J eventually recognized that his health problems were not as bad as those of many other people his age. He could still walk, watch

television, read, and hold conversations, and he wanted to preserve these abilities. With these reasons in mind, Mr. J worked with his clinician to schedule medical appointments and devise specific strategies for complying with treatment recommendations.

Later Phase of Treatment

Treatment may end when patients have made progress toward goals and are no longer experiencing suicide ideation. When the clinician believes that patients have made gains in therapy, a formal assessment of acquired cognitive and behavioral skills is indicated. As with younger adults and adolescents, the relapse prevention protocol serves as an endpoint assessment of patients' ability to apply coping skills during times of acute distress. As stated in chapter 9, the objective of this exercise is to prime as many of the thoughts, images, and feelings associated with previous suicidal crises as possible. The clinician then assesses whether patients are able to respond to problems in an adaptive way. However, the relapse prevention task is somewhat different with suicidal older adults who have not attempted suicide than with younger patients who have. In our experience with most suicidal elders, the level of ideation tends to be less severe and more chronic than with younger populations. The relapse prevention task with older adults often does not have the same level of intensity or degree of focus around a specific activating event.

> Given that Mr. J's suicide ideation had resolved and that his depression was much less severe, the relapse prevention protocol was conducted. Mr. J was asked to imagine the suicidal crisis that brought him into treatment. This was followed by asking Mr. J to provide a detailed description of the specific coping strategies that he found useful during treatment. One useful strategy was to recall his ability to effectively resolve problems when he was younger, which resulted in a tangible positive outcome in that it prompted him to use the transportation service for seniors. In addition, Mr. J indicated that socializing with others at the senior center was a helpful way to decrease his social isolation and, therefore, reduce depression and hopelessness. He also noted that he could always call his daughter during a time of crisis. Mr. J was asked to think of possible scenarios that could possibly lead to him feeling as though life was not worth living. Mr. J was able to recognize that this perceived sense of loss of independence was associated with previous episodes of suicide ideation. During the future-oriented guided imagery exercise, Mr. J imagined that he had another physical illness and that he was no longer able to attend the senior citizen's center. Despite these imagined limitations, Mr. J was able to recognize that he still had the ability to reach out to some friends and family members by calling them. He also thought about his illness being only a temporary setback and that he would be able to return to his previous regimen once his health had improved.

SUMMARY AND INTEGRATION

Epidemiological data have indicated that older adults have relatively higher suicide rates as compared to younger populations and that older men are especially at high risk. Late-life risk for suicide is associated with depression, hopelessness, suicide ideation, complicated grief, social isolation, and loneliness. Despite the prevalence of suicide in older adults, few randomized controlled trials have evaluated the efficacy and effectiveness of treatment with suicidal older adults. Given that cognitive therapy has been one of the most widely studied psychotherapies for the treatment of depression in older people, the use of cognitive therapy to target cognitive risk factors for suicidal acts, such as suicide ideation and hopelessness, is promising. On the basis of the cognitive case conceptualization of the suicidal older adult, the application of cognitive therapy strategies, such as increasing reasons for living, increasing social resources, improving problem solving skills, and increasing compliance with treatments, may help older people to decrease hopelessness and suicide ideation. Most of these strategies are similar to ones described earlier in this book, but they take on a different flavor as older adults attempt to redefine many life roles following losses or the onset of other limitations.

13

COGNITIVE THERAPY FOR SUICIDAL PATIENTS WITH SUBSTANCE DEPENDENCE DISORDERS

As stated in chapter 2, diagnoses of alcohol and drug dependence substantially increase the risk of suicidal acts. For example, G. K. Brown, Tenhave, et al. (2005) noted that 68% of patients who had attempted suicide in their cognitive therapy study had a drug dependence disorder. Aharonovich, Liu, Nunes, and Hasin (2002) found that more than one third of their substance dependent inpatients had attempted suicide at least one time in their lives. Taken as a whole, this empirical literature suggests that it would not be uncommon for clinicians who treat suicidal patients to encounter comorbid substance dependence diagnoses and their associated problems. Individuals with substance dependence disorders are often characterized by many of the factors that research has found to elevate the risk of engaging in a suicidal act (Darke & Ross, 1997, 2002). Moreover, some research has shown that substance abuse problems are a core feature of a distinct pathway to suicidal acts (i.e., externalizing behavior; O'Boyle & Brandon, 1998; Verona, Sachs-Ericsson, & Joiner, 2004). For these reasons, it is logical to target suicide prevention efforts toward substance dependent populations.

This chapter provides a brief overview of the literature on the prevalence of and risk factors for suicidal acts in individuals with substance dependence disorders. In addition, it illustrates the manner in which the cognitive therapy protocol for suicidal patients can be adapted for this population. Issues that are unique to working with suicidal substance dependent patients are highlighted and demonstrated in a case example.

SUICIDE IDEATION AND SUICIDAL ACTS IN PATIENTS WITH SUBSTANCE DEPENDENCE DISORDERS

In this section, we describe the literature on suicide ideation and suicidal acts in people with substance dependence disorders. The majority of the discussion is divided between a focus on people with alcohol dependence and a focus on people with drug dependence. At the end of this section, we highlight two issues that have received less attention in the literature but are relevant to clinicians who work with suicidal patients who have substance dependence disorders—the association between polydrug dependence and suicidal acts and considerations in distinguishing between accidental and intentional overdoses.

Alcohol Dependence

We saw in chapter 2 that a diagnosis of alcohol dependence increases the risk of suicide nearly six times that which would be expected in the general population. This is particularly true for women with alcoholism, whose risk increases to 20 times that which would be expected (E. C. Harris & Barraclough, 1997). Research has shown that between 15% and 50% of patients with alcohol dependence have a lifetime history of suicide attempts (A. T. Beck, Steer, & McElroy, 1982; Cornelius, Salloum, Day, Thase, & Mann, 1996; Koller, Preuss, Bottlender, Wenzel, & Soyka, 2002; Preuss et al., 2002). Unfortunately, few empirical studies have been conducted with the primary purpose of examining correlates of and risk factors for suicidal acts in large samples of alcoholic individuals.

Cornelius et al.'s (1996) in-depth investigation of 41 individuals admitted to a dual diagnosis inpatient unit, 17 of whom had made a suicide attempt during their current depressive episode, provides especially useful insight into the processes at work when alcoholic individuals attempt suicide. Of these attempters, 14 described their attempt as impulsive and regretted making it. Furthermore, 14 of these attempters were drinking at the time of their attempt, with 11 of those 14 admitting that they drank more than usual at the time of their attempt. Cornelius et al. examined patterns of alcohol use before admission and found that the total number of drinks consumed in the week before admission was about one third higher in those who made an attempt relative to those who had not made an attempt. Those who had attempted suicide were more likely to endorse heavy drinking (i.e., more than 70 drinks) in the week before admission. Moreover, the number of days of intoxication during the past month was twice as high in the group of those who had attempted suicide than in the group of those who had not. These results must be interpreted with caution, as they are based on a very small sample size, and estimates of drinking were made retrospectively. However, they raise the possibility that alcoholic individuals are likely to make impulsive attempts during times of especially heavy drinking.

Are suicidal acts made by alcoholic individuals different than the suicidal acts made by nonalcoholic individuals? Research has indicated that alcoholic individuals are characterized by many of the same risk factors for suicidal acts as nonalcoholic individuals, such as age (older age for death by suicide [Conner, Beautrais, & Conwell, 2003]; younger age for suicide attempts [McCloud, Barnaby, Omu, Drummond, & Aboud, 2004; Preuss et al., 2003]), low education and socioeconomic status (Conner, Beautrais, et al., 2003), previous suicide attempts (Motto, 1980; Preuss et al., 2003), depression (Cornelius et al., 1996), psychosis (Conner, Beautrais, et al., 2003), hopelessness (A. T. Beck et al., 1982), and impulsivity (Koller et al., 2002). In his review on alcohol and suicidal behavior, Hufford (2001) pointed out that the lives of many individuals with alcoholism are characterized by chronic marital and family problems associated with excessive drinking and relapse.

In addition to putting individuals at chronic risk for suicidal acts, alcohol ingestion also serves as an immediate precursor to suicidal acts. Hufford (2001) reviewed evidence suggesting that there is a dose–response relation between alcohol use and the likelihood of engaging in a suicidal act, such that the more a person consumes, the greater the risk that he or she will attempt suicide. Alcohol consumption results in a biphasic effect—although the initial effects of drinking often are relaxation and euphoria, eventually the high subsides, and depression sets in. Hufford suggested that it is this second half of the biphasic effect during which individuals are at greatest risk to engage in a suicidal act. Furthermore, it is well established that alcohol intoxication increases aggression, which is part of the externalizing pathway to suicidal acts often observed in addictions populations (Verona et al., 2004). Thus, two potential variables to explain the mechanism by which alcohol ingestion facilitates suicidal behavior is through (a) the depression that sets in after the initial high and (b) increased aggression.

Hufford (2001) raised the interesting possibility that alcohol exacerbates attentional fixation at the time of a suicidal crisis. Not only does alcohol reduce the number of cues to which people attend and encode, but it also disrupts the ability to adequately process the cues that are encoded and obtain accurate meaning from them. These information processing deficiencies lead to *alcohol myopia*, or "short-sightedness in which superficially understood, immediate aspects of experience have disproportionate influence on behavior and emotion, a state in which we can see the trees, but miss the forest altogether" (Steele & Josephs, 1990, p. 923). Thus, alcohol intoxication at the time of the suicidal crisis has the potential to intensify attentional fixation on suicide as the only option by constricting attention even further on suicide-relevant cues and reducing the probability that the person will process non–suicide-relevant cues.

In sum, diagnoses of alcohol dependence clearly increase one's risk of engaging in a suicidal act. Individuals with alcohol dependence are characterized by many of the demographic, diagnostic, and psychological risk factors that characterize suicide attempters in the general population. However, substantial increases in the frequency and volume of alcohol consumed, even in people who are already drinking large quantities of alcohol on a regular basis, are often precursors to suicide attempts. Contemporary research has suggested that suicide attempts made under the influence of alcohol result, at least in part, from a confluence of emotional, behavioral, and cognitive processes, including depression, aggression, and attentional fixation.

Drug Dependence

As we also saw in chapter 2, the diagnosis of a drug dependence disorder substantially increases a person's risk for eventual suicide. However, the precise amount of risk conferred by drug dependence depends on the particular substance being abused. According to Harris and Barraclough's (1997) meta-analysis, the risk for suicide associated with opiate abuse and dependence is 14 times that which would be expected; sedative, hypnotic, or anxiolytic abuse and dependence, 20 times; and marijuana abuse and dependence, 4 times. As we saw with the literature on the association between alcohol problems and suicidal acts, there is a paucity of empirical research that was designed with the primary purpose of identifying the correlates and risk factors for suicidal acts in large samples of drug dependent individuals.

The vast majority of existing studies on this topic focus on samples of opiate dependent patients. Of these studies, the most rigorous and systematic investigations come from Maree Teesson, Shane Darke, and their colleagues in the context of the Australian Treatment Outcome Study (Teesson et al., 2005). This multisite, 3-year longitudinal study followed heroin users who were (a) enrolled in methadone/burenorphine maintenance, (b) receiving detoxification, (c) participating in residential rehabilitation, or (d) not currently enrolled in treatment. Participants completed an extensive battery assessing drug use, general health, health service utilization, psychiatric symptoms, and several indicators of suicide ideation, intent, and attempts. In all, they recruited 535 heroin users in one of the three active treatments and 80 heroin users who were not in treatment and recruited from a needle exchange program.

Analyses conducted on the baseline data (Darke, Ross, Lynskey, & Teesson, 2004) indicated that approximately 34% of the sample reported a history of at least one suicide attempt, with a significant gender difference—44% of female heroin users had attempted suicide, in contrast with 28% of male heroin users. In the month before the baseline assessment, 30% of the sample reported recurrent thoughts of death, 23% reported recurrent thoughts of suicide, 15% reported having a specific plan, and 5% had actually attempted suicide. Characteristics associated with a recent history of attempted suicide included younger age, female gender, less formal secondary education, lifetime and recent polydrug use, current suicide ideation, and diagnoses of major depression, borderline personality disorder, and posttraumatic stress disorder. In other words, individuals who had recently attempted suicide in this study tended to be young female heroin users who exhibited high levels of externalizing behavior and endorsed high levels of psychiatric disturbance.

At the 1-year follow-up assessment (Darke, Williamson, Ross, & Teesson, 2005), 9.1% of participants had made a suicide attempt in the previous 12 months. Approximately two thirds of those participants had a lifetime history of previous attempts. The factors that predicted attempts in the 1st year of follow-up were baseline social isolation, baseline suicide ideation, having made an attempt in the 12 months before enrollment in the study, higher levels of baseline polydrug use, and more treatment episodes over the course of the follow-up period. Although heroin users in the methadone maintenance and residential rehabilitation groups reported significant decreases in suicide ideation, the proportion of patients attempting suicide in the follow-up period did not decline or differ as a function of whether they were receiving treatment. The authors concluded that although addictions treatment programs appeared to reduce some of the concomitants of suicide attempts, such as suicide ideation, they did not decrease the frequency of suicide attempts. These findings suggest that a targeted intervention focused specifically on reducing the likelihood of future attempts would be indicated for this population.

At the 3-year follow-up interval (Darke et al., 2007), a total of 126 suicide attempts were made by the sample, with 4.9% of the heroin users making multiple attempts over the course of 3 years. Predictors of suicide attempts during the follow-up period included a lifetime history of suicide attempts, baseline suicide ideation, social isolation, and baseline polydrug use. Thus, social isolation, baseline suicide ideation, and baseline polydrug use were consistent predictors of attempts at both intervals of the follow-up period. In fact, approximately one in four (24.1%) of the heroin users who endorsed baseline suicide ideation went on to make an attempt during the follow-up period, suggesting that it is important to identify drug dependent individuals with suicide ideation for increased monitoring and targeted treatment to reduce the likelihood that they will engage in a suicidal act. Unlike what was seen at the 1-year follow-up, the frequency of attempts declined substantially at the 3-year follow-up assessment. Darke et al. (2007) speculated that the drop in rate of suicide attempts co-occurred with the general decline in heroin use in the sample, even in those who were recruited from the needle exchange program, suggesting that many participants in the sample were avoiding the pitfalls of a drug-abusing lifestyle that potentially exacerbate the propensity to engage in suicidal acts.

In their review of risk factors for suicidal acts in heroin users, Darke and Ross (2002, p. 1389) concluded,

> Overall, it would appear that . . . the suicide risk factors reported in the general population studies parallel those reported among heroin users. What should be borne in mind, however, is the extremely high prevalence of these risk factors among heroin users. The prevalence of major depression among heroin users is many orders of magnitude that of the general population. Similarly, the social profile of heroin users has been shown repeatedly to be one of predominant unemployment, low educational levels, social isolation, repeated incarceration, high rates of parental alcoholism and psychopathology, and divorce.

In other words, suicidal individuals with drug dependence problems have many of the same characteristics as suicidal individuals without drug dependence problems, but their profiles of risk usually include a greater number and severity of these factors. Moreover, it is likely that many of these risk factors interact with drug use itself (e.g., depression is exacerbated by the effects and consequences of drug use). The one exception is a diagnosis of antisocial personality disorder, which has been found to be a risk factor for engaging in suicidal acts in some studies examining suicidal acts in samples not selected to be particularly high in drug use (Verona, Patrick, & Joiner, 2001) but has not generally emerged as a risk factor in samples of heroin users. Darke and Ross (2002) speculated that many heroin users receive antisocial personality disorder diagnoses because they engage in criminal behavior to satisfy their addiction, which masks those who truly are characterized by psychopathy.

Polydrug Dependence

As seen in the studies by Darke et al. (2004, 2005, 2007) described earlier, polydrug dependence is a variable that puts drug dependent individuals at particular risk for engaging in suicidal acts. Several other studies have also found that polydrug dependence distinguished between substance dependent patients with and without a history of suicide attempts (e.g., Preuss et al., 2002; Roy, 2002) and that it was a risk factor for future attempts (e.g., Preuss et al., 2003). In their meta-analysis, Harris and Barraclough (1997) identified four studies that examined risk of completed suicide in polydrug users. They found that the risk of completed suicide was 20 times that expected, with comorbid opiate and cocaine dependence conferring the greatest risk. Moreover, they found that female polydrug users with a history of suicide attempts were 87 times more likely to die by suicide than would be expected.

Thus, clinicians who see suicidal patients with polydrug dependence should closely monitor suicide ideation and intent across the course of treatment. It is likely that polydrug dependence is associated with severity of psychopathology and personality pathology and with a deviant lifestyle characterized by many of the demographic risk factors associated with suicidal acts.

Special Issue: Distinguishing Between Accidental and Intentional Overdoses

One thorny issue pertaining to the association between substance dependence and suicidal acts is whether overdoses should be classified as suicide attempts. Opinions range from always classifying overdoses as suicide attempts in at-risk populations to only doing so if intent was clearly indicated by the attempter or otherwise discerned by tangible evidence, such as a suicide note. In a study completed before the Australian Treatment Outcome Study, Darke and Ross (2001) found that 92% of heroin users regarded their more recent heroin overdoses as accidental rather than deliberate. When overdoses were deliberate, the vast majority were done with drugs other than heroin, usually benzodiazepines. In fact, a history of deliberate heroin overdose was reported by only 10% of the sample. In an investigation of differences between accidental and deliberate drug overdoses among patients with opiate addictions in methadone maintenance treatment, Best et al. (2000) found that relative to those who had made accidental overdoses, those who had made deliberate overdoses were more likely to endorse symptoms of anxiety, depression, hopelessness, and suicide ideation. Thus, a drug user's profile of relevant risk factors for suicidal acts may provide the background against which a clinician determines that an overdose was indeed a suicide attempt.

Summary

The literature reviewed in this section suggests that individuals with alcohol and drug dependence disorders are at particularly great risk to engage in suicidal acts. In many of the studies examining patients with substance dependence disorders who were receiving some sort of addictions treatment, approximately 15% to 50% had a history of previous suicide attempts (e.g., Aharonovich et al., 2002; A. T. Beck et al., 1982; Cornelius et al., 1996; Darke & Ross, 2001; Roy, 2002, 2003a, 2003b). Psychological autopsy studies have suggested that more than 50% of individuals who died by suicide had some sort of substance dependence disorder, although only a subset of these individuals were receiving treatment for their problems (Kõlves, Värnik, Tooding, & Wasserman, 2006).

One psychological factor that is often implicated in explaining the association between substance dependence and suicidal acts is impulsivity (e.g., Erinoff, Compton, & Volkow, 2004), as many studies have demonstrated that substance dependent patients are more impulsive than healthy control individuals (see Moeller, Barratt, Dougherty, Schmitz, & Swann, 2001). Despite the logic of this explanation, surprisingly few studies have included measures of impulsivity in their investigations of suicidal acts in substance dependent patients. More often, it is inferred that impulsivity is the mechanism by which suicide attempts are made because suicidal substance dependent individuals are particularly likely to be diagnosed with borderline personality disorder, which is characterized by impulsive outbursts (e.g., O'Boyle & Brandon, 1998). We encourage systematic investigations into the traitlike (i.e., distal) and statelike (i.e., proximal) risk factors for suicidal acts in individuals with substance disorder, using the framework described by Hufford (2001). We suspect that diagnoses of substance dependence disorder put individuals at risk for engaging in suicidal acts from a traitlike, or distal, perspective by (a) being associated with other long-standing risk factors; (b) increasing subjective distress; and (c) creating life stress, such as by creating conflict in relationships with family members and close friends. However, it is also likely that being under the influence of alcohol or drugs puts individuals at risk for engaging in suicidal acts from a statelike, or proximal, perspective by (a) clouding judgment, (b) reducing inhibitions and increasing the propensity toward impulsive behavior, (c) increasing depression, and (d) exacerbating attentional fixation on suicide as the only way out.

COGNITIVE THERAPY FOR PATIENTS WITH SUBSTANCE DEPENDENCE DISORDERS

Cognitive therapy has been used to treat patients with substance dependence disorders for more than 15 years (see A. T. Beck, Wright, Newman, & Liese, 1993). The basic principles of cognitive therapy for addictions populations are similar to those of cognitive therapy for other populations—clinicians adhere to a session structure, clinicians help patients to identify and modify automatic thoughts and beliefs that maintain and exacerbate their pathology, and patients develop coping skills for dealing with distress without engaging in maladaptive behavior and for dealing with high-risk situations that put them at risk for relapse. However, A. T. Beck, Wright, et al. (1993) proposed that there are multiple layers of beliefs at work in patients with substance dependence disorders, all of which should be modified in treatment. Not only are these patients often characterized by core beliefs that are typically seen in depressed, anxious, and angry patients, but they also have addictive beliefs that are specific to continued substance use. *Anticipatory beliefs*, for example, are overvalued beliefs that using substances will result in a desired state, satisfaction, or increased efficacy (e.g., "I'm going to have so much fun" "I'll be able to socialize more freely than I would otherwise"). *Relief-oriented beliefs* are beliefs that substance use will relieve an undesirable or aversive state (e.g., "I need to drink to get through this"). *Permissive beliefs* give people permission to use substances, ignoring or minimizing the negative consequences (e.g., "I deserve to have fun every once in awhile"). Substance misuse occurs when internal or external addictions-relevant cues are perceived (e.g., feeling anxious seeing friends who use substances), anticipatory and/or relief-oriented beliefs are activated (e.g., "I need to escape this anxiety" "This will be a great night"), cravings or urges are experienced, and permissive beliefs follow.

Cognitive therapy for substance dependence uses many of the same strategies described in chapter 5, including Socratic questioning, homework assignments, downward arrow questioning, activity scheduling and monitoring, and problem solving. In addition, there is a special focus on coping with urges and cravings. A. T. Beck, Wright, et al. (1993) identified a number of strategies for dealing with urges and cravings, including distraction, coping cards with reminders for staying sober, negative imagery focused on the consequences of relapse, positive imagery focused on successful coping, and relaxation. Cognitive therapists who work with substance dependent patients also focus on the development of *control beliefs* to counteract the addictions beliefs. Control beliefs are beliefs that promote the management of urges and cravings and are formulated by encouraging patients to consider the disadvantages of using drugs and alternative ways to achieve the same desired end (e.g., "I want to achieve the goals I've set for myself, and using will set me back"). They are often practiced through imaginal rehearsal in session, in a similar manner as suicide ideation and urges are addressed through guided imagery in the relapse prevention protocol. Relapse prevention is achieved through identification of high-risk situations and ways to avoid those and cope with addictions beliefs that become activated.

It is well established that the broad spectrum of cognitive behavioral treatment approaches are effective in reducing alcohol and drug use in patients with alcohol and substance dependence disorders (e.g., Roth & Fonagy, 2005), although it must be acknowledged that other treatments, such as programs that facilitate engagement in 12-step programs, motivational interviewing, and even nondirective interactional therapies, are equally as effective in achieving these outcomes (e.g., Kadden, Litt, Cooney, Kabela, & Getter, 2001; Project MATCH Research Group, 1997). Moreover, there is little evidence that cognitive and behavioral approaches achieve their gains through the acquisition of strategies targeted in these treatments (Morgenstern & Longabaugh, 2000), and conversely, patients who are assigned to treatments that do not have a focus on modifying cognitive and behavioral coping strategies exhibit a significant increase in these strategies posttreatment, which is in turn associated with reductions in alcohol and drug use (Litt,

Kadden, Cooney, & Kabela, 2003). Researchers have speculated that structured treatments for addictions are effective when they are administered by clinicians who have a great deal of experience with this population (e.g., Crits-Christoph et al., 1999) or when they take advantage of the opportunity to capitalize on patients' motivation or self-efficacy (Litt et al., 2003), factors that we integrate into the cognitive intervention we describe in the next section.

What we do not know from this literature on cognitive behavioral interventions for alcohol and drug dependent patients, however, is the degree to which these treatments affect variables related to a patient's potential to engage in a suicidal act, such as hopelessness, suicide ideation, and suicidal intent. The majority of studies in this literature focus on indices of alcohol and drug use as primary outcome variables (e.g., percentage of abstinent days, number of days of alcohol or drug use), so it is unclear whether active enrollment in treatment geared toward addictions would reduce the likelihood of patients engaging in a future suicidal act. In one exception, the work reviewed previously by Darke, Teesson, and their colleagues suggests that over a substantial period of time (i.e., 3 years), the number of days enrolled in treatment is associated with decreased rates of attempted suicide, but that there continue to be a substantial minority of patients who are suicidal while they are in treatment. Moreover, van den Bosch, Verheul, Schippers, and van den Brink (2002) reported that dialectical behavior therapy, which includes some cognitive and behavioral components, reduced both suicidal and nonsuicidal self-injury behavior in patients with comorbid borderline personality disorder and substance abuse. Thus, a treatment that is geared specifically to address suicide prevention in this population seems warranted.

COGNITIVE THERAPY PROTOCOL AND CASE EXAMPLE

Suicidal substance dependent patients are a complex population to treat because they have many pressing needs that must be met simultaneously. In fact, it is questionable whether any one setting is ideal for treating these patients. In our experience, many addictions treatment programs will not take these patients because they are viewed as having serious co-occurring mental health issues that these programs are not equipped to address. However, when these patients reach a service that can address their mental health needs, they are often turned away with the rationale that treatment of their substance dependence takes priority. We designed this treatment as one that can be administered by addictions counselors who see patients on an outpatient or intensive outpatient (e.g., three times a week) basis, as researchers have speculated that experience in working with this population is associated with a positive outcome (Crits-Christoph et al., 1999). However, it can also be used by outpatient clinicians who do not work in addictions treatment settings and by clinicians who work in inpatient settings, provided that they have the competence to work with this population.

Clinicians should be aware that there are many points in the recovery process at which patients might report an increase or exacerbation of suicide ideation. For example, many patients report high levels of hopelessness and dejection as they are going through the intake process in an addictions treatment program because they have often recently hit rock bottom and see a long road to recovery. Interestingly, by the end of the intake process many patients report hope for the future because they view themselves as finally doing something to address their problems and are optimistic about the services that they stand to receive (cf. Emery, Steer, & Beck, 1981). In other words, suicide ideation reported at the beginning of the intake process is often fleeting, and hope is instilled when patients are oriented to the comprehensive addictions treatment that they will receive from the program.

However, this hopefulness often does not last for long. Patients quickly see that addictions treatment is hard work and face the reality that they can no longer turn to many, if not all, of the strategies they used to cope with life's stressors and disappointments. As is shown in the case example, many patients with a substance dependence disorder live in recovery houses, in which they are subject to strict rules and routines with privileges that can be obtained slowly over time. In addition, patients begin to face the multitude of problems that have accumulated in their professional, financial, and interpersonal lives. Moreover, patients with histories of suicide ideation or attempts who have lapses are particularly likely to view those setbacks in all-or-nothing terms, which prompts hopeless and defeatist attitudes. Thus, clinicians working with substance dependent patients who are at risk for engaging in a suicidal act must carefully monitor their highs and lows throughout the course of treatment.

The goals of cognitive therapy for suicidal patients with substance dependence disorders are to (a) reduce the likelihood of future suicidal acts, (b) develop strategies for managing suicide ideation and hopelessness, and (c) decrease associated risk factors for engaging in suicidal acts. In other words, the goals for the cognitive therapy suicide protocol with substance dependent patients are the same as the goals of the cognitive therapy suicide protocol with the other patient groups described in this book. What is different about this population, however, is that lapses and relapse are often intricately related to the onset of a suicidal crisis in vulnerable individuals. Thus, it is crucial that, when relevant, the clinician include substance use as a central component of the cognitive case conceptualization and timeline of events leading to the suicidal crisis. Ideally, patients with substance dependence problems will be receiving concurrent addictions treatment that is focused on their substance use. In these instances, the clinician will target the treatment at reducing the likelihood of future suicidal crises and associated risk factors, and interventions targeted toward addictive behavior will be implemented in other contexts. Cognitive and behavioral strategies for modifying addictions beliefs and reducing urges and cravings will be incorporated into treatment to the extent that they have relevance in managing suicidal crises. We recognize, however, that some clinicians will be in a position in which they are called on to address issues associated with both substance dependence and the propensity to engage in future suicidal acts. In these instances, we encourage the clinician to create a hierarchy of treatment problems, beginning with the problem that is most life threatening or dangerous. In most cases, that problem will be reducing the likelihood of a future suicidal act.

The remainder of this section describes the early, intermediate, and later phases of treatment with suicidal patients diagnosed with a substance dependence disorder. Throughout this section, we present the case of Melvin, who represents an amalgam of patients enrolled in intensive, comprehensive outpatient addictions treatment programs and receiving suicide-focused cognitive therapy from addictions counselors in those settings.

Early Phase of Treatment

In a similar manner to our previous chapters on special populations, this section describes how clinicians conduct an assessment of the presenting problem and develop safety plans with suicidal substance dependent patients. In the early phase of treatment, this information is learned and integrated into a cognitive case conceptualization with a focus both on suicide-relevant cognitions and substance use-related cognitions and is directed toward developing a treatment plan.

Conducting an Assessment of the Presenting Problem

As with the other patient populations presented in this book, assessments of suicidal substance dependent patients include the understanding of patients' suicide risk, including vulnerability and protective factors, current problems, psychiatric diagnoses, medical history, and social history. As would be expected, clinicians spend more time with these patients than with other patients in obtaining a detailed history of their substance use, the consequences of their substance use, and their use of substances during previous suicidal crises. Moreover, it is useful to identify periods of sobriety, strategies they used to manage urges and cravings, and factors that contributed to relapse.

In our experience, patients with substance dependence often focus on their moment-by-moment emotional experiences (which, in part, could contribute to both their substance use problems and their propensity to have suicidal crises). Even if they had experienced acute suicide ideation very recently (e.g., the previous day, earlier in the day), some of these patients deny current suicide ideation. In many instances, these patients are reluctant to talk about suicide ideation if they do not perceive themselves to be suicidal at present (e.g., "I was really down and out when I first came here, but I'm fine now. Just get me the treatment I need to stay sober"). Clinicians should carefully assess the frequency of suicide ideation, even if it is fleeting, its intensity, and the degree to which it is associated with intent, plans, and other maladaptive behavior such as the urge to use alcohol or drugs. The following is a description of some of the information obtained from Melvin during his intake interview.

> Melvin is a single, 45-year-old African American man who is participating in court-ordered outpatient addictions treatment. Throughout the weeklong intake and disposition process at the addictions treatment agency, he reported suicide ideation and hopelessness, expressing regret that he has been unable to stay clean despite multiple stays in rehab. He stated that he has abused "every drug you can think of" during his lifetime but that his drugs of choice are crack cocaine and alcohol. Melvin admitted that his substance dependence has damaged his relationship with his current girlfriend and with his young adult children. He has made five suicide attempts in the past, all of which occurred when he was under the influence of drugs or alcohol and when he was experiencing a significant interpersonal crisis, such as a conflict with a significant other or the death of a close family member or friend.
>
> Melvin grew up in a rough area of a large metropolitan city. Although he was surrounded by gang activity and violence, he resisted the temptation to join a gang and was heavily involved in extracurricular activities, playing on the high school baseball team and singing in the church choir. Melvin noted that his father had lofty expectations for him, hoping that he would play college baseball and be the first member of the family to graduate from college. Despite his scholastic and athletic accomplishments, Melvin often felt inferior to his peers and wondered whether they accepted him. To compensate for these insecurities, he often showed off and did outrageous things to get their attention, such as drinking large quantities of alcohol. Melvin claimed that he drank every day after school since he was 14 years old, in large part to fit in with peers in his neighborhood.
>
> Melvin's alcohol abuse did not interfere with his scholarly and athletic performance, and he was admitted to a small state college with a baseball scholarship. However, Melvin admitted that he had a difficult time adjusting to independence away from home, and he began using drugs. He was quickly placed on academic probation, which prevented him from playing on the baseball team, and he failed out of college by the middle of his sophomore year. Melvin returned home to live with his mother, and she died suddenly when he was age 21. He described this period of time as sending him into a "tailspin," and soon after his mother's death he made his first suicide attempt. Since that time, Melvin has lived a transient lifestyle, sometimes working and sometimes not, living with friends, and using alcohol and drugs almost continuously.

Melvin described two main sources of his current suicide ideation. First, he admitted that he perceives himself as a failure because he did not complete college, play college baseball, pursue a meaningful career, or adequately parent his two children. During the assessment, the diagnostician identified two main problems that interfere with his ability to pursue goals consistently and systematically. One problem, of course, was his ongoing substance use. However, the diagnostician also discovered that Melvin had occasional hypomanic episodes that not only exacerbated his substance use problems, but were also associated with risky, impulsive behavior that usually ended up being self-defeating. During these times, he developed elaborate plans for projects that he expected would turn his life around, and he had grandiose views of his ability to achieve these goals. Not surprisingly, he usually did something to thwart those goals, which caused disappointment and dejection and led him back to alcohol and drugs. In addition, he often had arguments with close others during these hypomanic episodes, which damaged these relationships. Melvin admitted that he struggled with numerous severe depressive episodes after these instances. Thus, substance use, risky and impulsive behavior, and grandiosity contributed to his inability to achieve goals in his life, which reinforced his view of himself as a failure and resulted in severe depression. However, he resisted taking medications to manage his hypomania.

Second, at the time of the assessment Melvin was living in a recovery house. In a similar manner as when he was an adolescent, Melvin perceived that he did not fit in with the other men in the home and that they hassled him because he was different. Melvin also believed that the rules of the recovery house were too constricting. He disliked not being able to come and go as he pleased, and he believed that he was required to do too many chores. He stated, "This is what I'm getting sober for?" and expressed doubt that he would be able to live a meaningful life after he was released from the recovery home because he had no money and no permanent residence. Thus, Melvin endorsed substantial hopelessness about the future and could identify very few reasons for living.

As is evidenced in this case profile, Melvin is characterized by many risk factors for suicide attempts and death. He was experiencing symptoms of psychiatric disturbance, particularly hypomanic symptoms, although it also appeared that his social anxiety exacerbated his substance use. The confluence of substance use and interpersonal stressors culminated in multiple suicide attempts. As a result of these chronic problems, he had no permanent residence, had no financial resources, and has alienated others on whom he might otherwise have relied for social support. All of those variables contributed to Melvin's hopelessness and perception that he had few reasons to live.

Developing a Safety Plan

Safety plans are important for suicidal substance-dependent patients because, particularly when they are under the influence of alcohol or drugs, they demonstrate impulsivity, impaired judgment, and a tendency to encode cues that are inconsistent with their focus of attention. Because these patients often experience altered states of consciousness, it is prudent to compose safety plans using simple, straightforward language, perhaps in large type, with highlighting or with other cues that will capture their attention. As stated in chapter 6, safety plans can be laminated so that they do not become torn and can be carried in an easy-to-locate place, such as one's wallet.

Although the main focus of the safety plan is to identify strategies for managing suicidal ideation and urges, patients with a substance dependence disorder often express an interest in listing strategies for managing urges and cravings and/or strategies for avoiding situations that put them at risk for lapses. In some instances, these goals are one and the same when it is determined that lapses are the primary triggers for suicidal crises. However, more often the warning signs and coping strategies are slightly different, and including both foci in the safety plan runs the risk of creating a document that is cumbersome and difficult to use in times of need. We encourage clinicians to focus safety plans specifically on suicidal crises for the sake of brevity. However, if patients find them useful, a logical extension would be for them to create a separate safety plan geared toward managing urges, cravings, and high-risk situations. One benefit of this arrangement is that patients would gain practice in developing and using safety plans.

> Melvin was eager to work on the safety plan at the end of his first cognitive therapy session, stating that he had never been in a treatment like this before and that he had a feeling it would solve his problems. His clinician chose not to focus on these distorted perceptions of therapy at that time, as Melvin expressed hopelessness and mild suicide ideation at the beginning of the session, and she wanted to focus on keeping him safe in between sessions. She also wanted to capitalize on his sense of self-efficacy and motivation to change (cf. Litt et al., 2003). Melvin identified several warning signs for suicide ideation, including (a) feeling worn down at the end of the day after completing his chores at the recovery house, (b) wanting to buy a pack of cigarettes at the store but realizing that he had no money, (c) arguing with his girlfriend, and (d) being reminded of his failed baseball career in college.
>
> Melvin's strategies for coping with these triggers on his own included praying, remembering slogans from Narcotics Anonymous meetings that he had attended awhile ago (e.g., "Play the tape through"), listening to gospel music, and reading the newspaper. Melvin initially indicated that watching baseball games would be a coping strategy for distracting him from suicide ideation and hopelessness, as he was a fan of the local major league team and followed the players' statistics. The clinician conducted a brief advantages–disadvantages analysis of including this strategy on the safety plan, as a few minutes before Melvin had indicated that reminders of his failed baseball career had the potential to induce suicidal crises. He replied that his mood improves when his team wins, but that

he can get in a funk if they lose. Given that Melvin had no control over whether his team wins or loses, his clinician gently provided a menu of alternative coping strategies to consider, such as taking a hot shower and reading the Bible. Melvin enthusiastically indicated that both of those strategies were great ideas and that he wanted to include them on his safety plan.

The clinician encountered some difficulty identifying people that Melvin could call in times of crisis. His mother was deceased, and his relationship with his father had been strained for several years. Although he viewed his girlfriend as a support in some instances, she was somewhat guarded with him because he had not been successful in previous episodes of recovery. Most of the people he considered friends were people who continued to use alcohol and drugs. Eventually, Melvin identified the house manager as someone he could talk to in times of need. He mentioned that he felt an affinity toward this man because this man had been through similar experiences but was now a productive member of society who was giving back to those in need. At the end of the safety plan, the clinician listed her contact information, the phone number for the on-call service, and the phone number for a suicide hotline. Finally, the clinician brainstormed with Melvin places where he could keep the safety plan so that it could be located easily in times of crisis.

Developing a Cognitive Case Conceptualization

As stated in chapter 7, the cognitive case conceptualization integrates patients' cognitions, emotions, and behaviors into a comprehensive understanding of the sequence of events that occur in a suicidal crisis. It incorporates activating events and patients' dispositional vulnerability factors as well as the psychological processes at work at the time of a suicidal crisis. This individualized conceptualization guides the clinician in selecting appropriate strategies to intervene in reducing variables that exacerbate suicidal crises. The following is a description of the relevant components of Melvin's cognitive case conceptualization, presented in Figure 13.1.

Melvin had a number of early experiences during childhood, adolescence, and young adulthood that likely contributed to the development of his dispositional vulnerability factors. For example, his failure to graduate from college and play on the baseball team, as well as the death of his mother, were significant negative life events that could have contributed to the onset of psychiatric disturbance. Psychiatric disturbance, including substance dependence problems and polydrug use, is conceptualized as a dispositional vulnerability factor in this model because, in Melvin's case, it was chronic, long-standing, and severe, and it shaped his core belief that he was a failure. Melvin's perception that he did not fit in with his peers likely contributed to his social anxiety, also a psychiatric condition that contributes to perceptions of failure and unworthiness. In addition to these psychiatric disorders, Melvin was characterized by impulsivity, as evidenced by repeatedly quitting jobs over small mat-

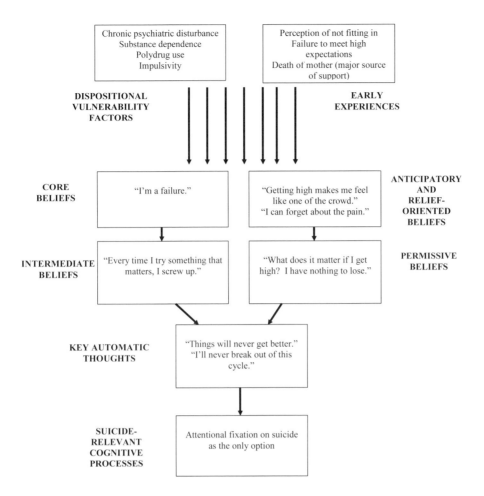

DISPOSITIONAL
VULNERABILITY
FACTORS

Chronic psychiatric disturbance
Substance dependence
Polydrug use
Impulsivity

EARLY
EXPERIENCES

Perception of not fitting in
Failure to meet high
expectations
Death of mother (major source
of support)

CORE
BELIEFS

"I'm a failure."

ANTICIPATORY
AND
RELIEF-
ORIENTED
BELIEFS

"Getting high makes me feel
like one of the crowd."
"I can forget about the pain."

INTERMEDIATE
BELIEFS

"Every time I try something that
matters, I screw up."

PERMISSIVE
BELIEFS

"What does it matter if I get
high? I have nothing to lose."

KEY AUTOMATIC
THOUGHTS

"Things will never get better."
"I'll never break out of this
cycle."

SUICIDE-
RELEVANT
COGNITIVE
PROCESSES

Attentional fixation on suicide
as the only option

Figure 13.1. Melvin's cognitive case conceptualization.

ters with no plan in place to get another job and no money saved. Although these dispositional vulnerability factors are listed separately, in actuality it is likely that they interact to make conditions ripe for the activation of core beliefs and cognitive processes that are relevant to suicidal crises.

Unlike the cognitive case conceptualization presented in chapter 7, the cognitive case conceptualization for suicidal substance dependent patients often contains descriptions of two types of beliefs whose activation have the potential to contribute to suicidal crises. One set of beliefs is the standard combination of core beliefs and intermediate beliefs, which relate to patients' psychiatric disturbance and have the potential to be associated with hopelessness or unbearability. However, a second set of beliefs is relevant to addictions patients—the anticipatory and/or relief-oriented beliefs that set the stage for substance use and the permissive beliefs that facilitate substance use. Together, both sets of beliefs prompt automatic thoughts that are relevant to suicidal crises (and that may be activated in the second part of the biphasic response to the use of some substances, e.g., alcohol; cf. Hufford, 2001). As was described earlier in the chapter, being under the influence of alcohol or drugs has the potential to exacerbate suicide-relevant cognitive biases by further focusing patients' attention on suicide as the only option and reducing the probability that they will encode other, competing cues.

> Melvin's core belief of being a failure was activated frequently, such as when he was faced with the damage he had created for himself during his hypomanic episodes, when he was experiencing a severe depressive episode, and when he used drugs rather than engaging in goal-directed behavior to improve his life. As a result, he developed the intermediate belief "Every time I try to do something that matters, I screw up." Concurrent with the activation of these beliefs, Melvin also experienced the continual activation of addictions beliefs. Although as an adolescent he primarily experienced anticipatory beliefs about using drugs (e.g., "This will help me to fit in with the guys"), as an adult his addictions beliefs were primarily relief-oriented (e.g., "I just want to escape the mess I've made of my life"). As a result, he focused on permissive beliefs (e.g., "What does it matter if I get high again? At this point I have nothing to lose") that facilitated his drug use.
>
> Although drug use improved Melvin's mood for awhile, when he began to come down from his high he became even more depressed and hopeless than he had been previously because his lapse was one more piece of evidence that reinforced the core belief that he is a failure, and he was reminded that his many problems still were not solved. During these times, he had the automatic thoughts, "I will never get out of this cycle. I've screwed up my life." When he had these ideas, he began to consider suicide, and his suicide ideation quickly escalated because he was unable to focus on alternative solutions to his problems. When others were present and he expressed these ideas to them, he would become agitated and belligerent if they tried to talk him out of it, becoming all the more determined to take his own life.

Melvin's cognitive case conceptualization illustrates the interplay between core beliefs, which are often related to patients' psychiatric disturbance, and addictions beliefs. In many cases, continued substance use feeds back into the negative core belief and becomes the final variable that induces a suicidal crisis because of decreased inhibitions, an increased tendency toward aggression and depression, and exacerbated attentional fixation on suicide-relevant cues.

Establishing Treatment Goals

As with most suicidal patients, the overarching goals of cognitive therapy for suicidal substance dependent patients are to reduce suicide ideation and hopelessness and to increase their repertoire of adaptive coping skills to apply in future crises. However, in our experience, these patients are not always on board with these goals. We stated previously that many patients with substance dependence disorders focus on their immediate emotional experiences, failing to acknowledge that they were feeling suicidal or were in crisis in the very recent past. Communicating a clear rationale for the treatment (e.g., being prepared to cope with suicide ideation and hopelessness in the future) can begin to address this issue. In addition, many patients with substance dependence problems are court ordered to receive treatment. Although their court orders are focused on receiving addictions treatment rather than cognitive therapy that is targeted toward reducing the likelihood of suicidal acts, nevertheless, there is potential that these patients will not differentiate among these types of treatments and will view all treatments as being imposed on them. Moreover, patients with substance dependence disorders are sometimes suspicious of clinicians, viewing them as being part of the system (A. T. Beck, Wright, et al., 1993). Thus, the goal-setting process must be handled in a sensitive, collaborative manner.

In some instances, at the beginning of treatment patients concur with a focus on suicide prevention, but they shift their focus in later sessions when they are no longer acutely suicidal. Because these patients are often faced with serious life stressors (e.g., financial duress, homelessness after they are released from the recovery house), they indicate that they have more pressing needs that should assume the focus of treatment. Thus, clinicians should take care to restate the goals of treatment in each session, to assess the degree to which patients are in agreement with these goals, and readjust where necessary. As stated many times in this book, suicidal patients are encouraged to take advantage of the vast array of services that are available to help them address their diverse needs. Thus, the skilled clinician might work with patients to establish the goal of taking advantage of these services (e.g., case management, social services) and to link patients' life stressors back to the potential of a suicidal crisis. The goal of using additional services, then, would be conceptualized as an adaptive step in preventing a future suicidal act.

> Melvin agreed at the beginning of treatment that a focus on suicide prevention would be helpful, as he was feeling hopeless about the future and doubted his ability to make positive changes. He established three specific goals: (a) to reduce hopelessness by identifying and developing additional reasons for living, (b) to develop strategies for managing and preventing future suicidal crises, and (c) to build a healthy social support network consisting of family members and friends who are not struggling with their own addictions. The clinician encouraged Melvin to further delineate specific ways to reduce hopelessness. Because graduating from college was a central focus of his family while growing up, Melvin reasoned that enrolling in the local community college and working toward his associate's degree would give him some purpose in life. The clinician also encouraged Melvin to identify specific individuals with whom he

would like to build relationships. Melvin identified his two younger sisters, who lived in the same city and were raising his nieces and nephews. In addition, he hoped to repair his relationships with his girlfriend and children.

Intermediate Phase of Treatment

The intermediate phase of treatment involves many of the same interventions we described in chapter 8 and other chapters on applications of the protocol for special populations. In our experience, an emphasis on compliance with other services is particularly important in cognitive therapy with suicidal substance dependent patients to support their participation in addictions treatment programs. Moreover, strategies to reduce impulsivity are often a central focus in the intermediate phase of treatment for this population, as impulsivity reduction strategies have the potential to target both an individual's propensity to engage in suicidal acts and the risk of relapse. We illustrate these strategies through our description of the intermediate phase of Melvin's treatment.

Increasing Reasons for Living

Identifying reasons for living is a particularly important task for this population, as these patients are faced with creating an entirely new lifestyle for themselves that is substance free, and many of their former pastimes and friendships will no longer be available to them. In addition, many patients in recovery are faced with a multitude of problems that resulted from their substance use and that they can no longer ignore by being under the influence. Not surprisingly, these patients, like Melvin, are often hopeless and dejected when they realize that there are many areas of their lives that must be rebuilt. Reasons for living can be listed on a coping card to consult in times of distress. Many patients with substance dependence disorders respond well to the Hope Kit, often placing in them letters and pictures of family members and friends with whom they hope to reestablish relationships.

> By the intermediate phase of treatment, Melvin indicated that he was no longer suicidal and that he was optimistic that his friend would help him to get a high-paying job in construction. He had transferred to a different recovery house and assumed the role of assistant house manager. As a house manager, he had many responsibilities, including helping the new residents acclimate to the house and learn the rules. He was only attending approximately half of his scheduled cognitive therapy sessions. When his clinician attempted to focus the session on developing skills to prevent a future suicidal crisis, Melvin expressed doubt that he would ever get that low again, emphasizing that he had been clean for more than a month (the longest period of sobriety in his life) and had a fresh new outlook on life because of renewed faith in God and the promise of a stable, high-paying job.

The clinician asked Melvin to brainstorm possible setbacks that might be associated with future distress and suicide ideation, and Melvin admitted that he would be very disappointed if he did not land the construction job. Thus, the clinician guided Melvin in identifying reasons for living that were not contingent on that particular place of employment. He listed four reasons for living: (a) his faith in God, (b) his children, (c) his favorite baseball team, and (d) helping others in recovery. For homework, he agreed to construct a Hope Kit based on these reasons for living, including a prayer card, pictures of his children, newspaper articles about his baseball team winning games, and a list of the people in the recovery house whom he believed he had helped. All of these activities were geared toward addressing one of the goals for treatment that he identified in the early phase—to reduce hopelessness and to increase reasons for living.

Developing Coping Strategies

A large focus of cognitive therapy for suicidal substance dependent patients is to develop adaptive coping skills for managing adversity and crises. Research has shown that these patients are particularly likely to see drugs and alcohol as a way to cope with depression, as well as other maladaptive strategies that are avoidant, passive, and isolating (Gould et al., 2004). Moreover, many patients with substance dependence disorders have a low frustration tolerance, suggesting that cognitive, emotional, and behavioral strategies for managing symptoms associated with unbearability schemas would be particularly useful for this population. Finally, we can view substance use in the same way we view a suicide attempt—as a maladaptive way to solve life's problems. Thus, most clinicians who work with addictions patients find that problem solving strategies are useful to integrate into the course of treatment. The following is an illustration of the cognitive and behavioral strategies that Melvin developed in cognitive therapy.

> After helping Melvin to identify reasons for living, the clinician used Socratic questioning to achieve a more balanced appraisal of the role the construction job would play in his life. She recognized that Melvin was presenting as mildly hypomanic and that he seemed to be falling into the same pattern as he had described occurring in the past—that he becomes overly invested in one idea that he views as the solution to all of his problems and that he becomes disappointed (and ultimately engages in maladaptive behavior) when his idea does not come to fruition. Therefore, she worked with Melvin to identify other job opportunities to pursue in the event that the construction job did not work out. He brainstormed three other lines of work, and together Melvin and his clinician developed the adaptive response, "I hope I get the construction job, but if it doesn't work out, then there are other jobs I can apply for." Because the process of cognitive restructuring was new for Melvin, the clinician encouraged him to record this adaptive response on a coping

card and add it to his Hope Kit so that it was easily accessible. Using cognitive strategies to modify grandiose cognitions associated with hypomanic symptoms was associated with Melvin's second overarching goal for treatment—to develop skills to manage and prevent future suicidal crises.

In addition, some of Melvin's comments about his performance as assistant house manager led his clinician to conclude that he lacked the problem solving skills that were necessary to execute many of his plans and aspirations, and she suspected that this deficit also contributed to his inability to manage negative life stressors that had triggered previous suicidal crises. When the clinician raised the possibility of focusing on problem solving skills as another strategy for managing and preventing suicidal crises, Melvin was reluctant, claiming that he was a highly effective person and could accomplish anything if he set his mind to it. She did not pursue problem solving in that session so that she did not take an uncollaborative stance and damage the therapeutic relationship. However, two sessions later, Melvin was decidedly more distressed, which he attributed to a difficult new resident in the recovery house. The clinician modeled an effective problem solving approach by guiding Melvin in brainstorming solutions to the problem, weighing the advantages and disadvantages of each solution, deciding on one solution, and identifying ways to evaluate the effectiveness of the solution. She then linked this approach back to the problems he was experiencing when he was suicidal at the beginning of treatment.

Increasing Compliance With Other Services

Patients with substance dependence disorders, in particular, are often in need of additional services. Melvin, for example, went through a comprehensive medical workup to determine the effects of chronic alcohol and drug use on his major internal organs and to be tested for HIV because he had shared needles with other intravenous drugs users in the past. As stated previously, many of these patients require case management and social services to address financial, housing, and vocational needs. Because there is substantial comorbidity between substance dependence and psychiatric disturbance (Darke & Ross, 1997), these patients are often referred to psychiatrists for psychotropic medication management. Moreover, of course, there is available an array of services geared toward recovery from alcohol and drugs, including addictions treatment programs, residential treatment programs, and 12-step programs. Thus, clinicians who work with suicidal substance dependent patients can rely on specialized services to meet the particular needs of the patient and should be well versed in the services that are available in their community.

In addition to referring these patients to relevant services, clinicians also monitor compliance with these services. Patients with substance dependence disorders are notoriously noncompliant with treatment. Only a minority remain abstinent after treatment (e.g., Project MATCH Research Group, 1997), and at least one third use substances enough after treatment that they reenter chemical dependence programs (Farley, Golding, Young, Mulligan, & Minkoff, 2004) or meet criteria for abuse or dependence at follow-up (Xie, McHugo, Fox, & Drake, 2005). We encourage clinicians to work with patients to identify ways in which compliance with various services would reduce factors that were salient in the timeline of events that led to their previous suicidal crisis. For example, if being intoxicated facilitated a previous suicide attempt, then the clinician could conceptualize alcohol treatment as a way to ensure safety in the future.

> When Melvin's attendance in cognitive therapy began to decline, so did his attendance at drug and alcohol groups in his addiction treatment program. His assigned case manager remarked that Melvin had not checked in with him for several weeks. At his sixth cognitive therapy session, Melvin's clinician suggested that they put compliance with his addiction treatment program on the agenda. Melvin indicated that he was still committed to recovery, but that his duties as assistant manager of the recovery house were overwhelming and that often he had difficulty getting away to attend his appointments.
>
> Melvin's clinician revisited the timeline of events that led to his most recent suicidal crisis and asked Melvin to articulate the role that drugs played in that crisis. This intervention reminded Melvin that his drug use has played a central role in previous suicidal crises and that addictions treatment should be a priority for him. He admitted that continuing to engage in addictions treatment was important, not only for preventing future suicidal crises, but also for getting his life on track. His clinician helped him to identify the specific obstacles that prevented him from attending his individual and group drug and alcohol sessions and to brainstorm ways to overcome those obstacles. Melvin identified two ways to increase his participation in addictions treatment: (a) talking to the house manager about either delegating or delaying some of his duties that occur during times his group meets and (b) attending the Narcotics Anonymous meeting at the neighborhood church to receive additional support, particularly on days he was not able to attend sessions at his addictions treatment program. His clinician skillfully illustrated that they were again developing problem solving strategies and asked Melvin to describe how he would apply these strategies to problems he might encounter in the future. In addition, she asked Melvin to describe his perception of the manner in which these problem solving skills would be useful at times he is feeling suicidal. He indicated that he would think carefully to identify the range of possible solutions to his problems rather than conclude that no solution existed.
>
> Melvin's clinician also revisited the role that his hypomanic symptoms play in the timeline of events preceding suicidal crises. Early in the

course of treatment, Melvin had agreed to be evaluated by the agency's psychiatrist so that he could begin taking a mood-stabilizing medication, but he did not keep his appointment. They evaluated the advantages and disadvantages of taking psychotropic medication, and Melvin renewed his commitment to have an evaluation with the psychiatrist.

Improving Social Resources

As is evidenced in the case description of Melvin, patients with a substance dependence disorder are in great need of a strong social support network as they go through recovery, but their networks are often fragile because their substance use did a great deal of damage to many of their close relationships (e.g., Trulsson & Hedin, 2004). Often these relationships are characterized by a lack of trust that accumulated after many years of disappointments and broken promises. Nevertheless, the development and maintenance of close relationships are crucial areas to address when working with suicidal patients to reduce social isolation and provide them with reasons for living. The clinician must strike a balance between instilling hope that some relationships are salvageable and setting realistic expectations for the degree to which people will be receptive to initial efforts to reconnect.

> Melvin readily admitted that his substance use disrupted, if not ruined, a number of his relationships. For example, he indicated that his father had written him off about 20 years ago and that whenever their paths crossed, their interactions were extremely tense and uncomfortable. Given the current state of their relationship, as well as the fact that Melvin held resentment toward his father for holding him to unrealistic standards during childhood, he decided that he would not attempt to repair this relationship at this time. Instead, Melvin expressed an interest in rebuilding relationships with his two sisters, who lived in the area, and his two children, who lived in a nearby state. Melvin's clinician encouraged him to brainstorm ways to establish regular contact with them and regain their trust. Regarding his sisters, Melvin decided that he would attend Sunday morning church services with them, that he would show an interest in being with the family during holidays, and that he would take care not to ask them for money, as he had done in the past only to use it on drugs. Regarding his children, he decided that he would call them at least once a week and that when he completed his time at the recovery home, he would travel by train to visit them. Melvin noted that visiting his children in person might help to regain their trust, as there were many instances in the past when he told them he would visit but did not show up. The clinician then asked Melvin to indicate how these improved relationships would affect his sense of hopelessness about the future. Melvin was able to articulate that having a stronger sense of family would give him a reason to get up in the morning. Thus, the clinician linked these efforts to improve relationships back to reasons for living and added them to his coping card that listed these reasons.

Developing Strategies to Reduce Impulsivity

Although the specific mechanism by which impulsivity operates in substance use and in suicidal crises is unclear, the fact remains that impulsivity is elevated in both substance dependent patients and suicidal patients. Thus, suicidal patients with a substance dependence disorder are particularly likely to be characterized by this dispositional vulnerability factor. Clinicians can work with patients not only to develop strategies to curb impulsivity in their daily lives (i.e., addressing the trait factor), but also to develop strategies to manage impulsivity in times of crisis (i.e., addressing the state factor). Cognitive strategies for reducing impulsivity include the consideration of (a) outcomes of impulsive actions, (b) pros and cons of impulsive actions, (c) vivid images of negative consequences of impulsive actions, and (d) alternative ways of getting intense needs met. Behavioral strategies for reducing impulsivity include (a) waiting a specified period of time before acting, (b) using the "two consult rule"—asking at least two different people whether an intended action is a good idea, (c) controlled breathing, (d) distraction, and (e) keeping close a simple reminder to refrain from particular impulsive actions that would have maladaptive consequences (e.g., a note to oneself reading "Drinking makes things worse in the long run" posted on the refrigerator).

> Throughout the first several sessions of cognitive therapy, Melvin exhibited few instances of impulsive behavior. In fact, in many instances he seemed thoughtful about his recovery, his spirituality, and the life he was trying to build for himself. However, at his seventh session he announced that he had left his recovery house against the judgment of his case manager in his addictions treatment program. He stated that he "just couldn't take it there anymore" and that he was convinced that he would stay sober, as now he had not used alcohol or drugs for about 4 months. However, he did not secure a permanent residence and was back to living for a few days at time with friends, many of whom were still using drugs. Although he claimed that he was staying strong and refraining from using substances, he admitted that he had put himself in a high-risk situation.
>
> Melvin's clinician guided him in identifying the advantages and disadvantages of leaving the recovery house. Although Melvin identified many more advantages than disadvantages, he fixated on the advantage that he had his freedom back because he no longer had to live by the strict rules in place at the recovery house. The clinician encouraged Melvin to consider the short-term benefit of leaving the recovery house versus the long-term benefit of staying sober and transitioning gradually back into the community. She also asked Melvin to consider previous instances in his life in which impulsive decisions such as this resulted in deleterious consequences. Melvin admitted that he was putting himself at risk by remaining in this environment but that he could not bring himself to go back to that recovery house, nor was it likely that they

would take him back because he left against their recommendation. Subsequently, he and his clinician engaged in more problem solving to find an acceptable living situation and continue his outpatient addictions treatment. Throughout this session, the clinician provided the rationale for addressing impulsivity and used Socratic questioning to help Melvin acknowledge its role in previous crises so that he could acknowledge the other side of the coin of the freedom he was enjoying.

Later Phase of Treatment

The activities in the later sessions of cognitive therapy for suicidal substance dependent patients are similar to those in the general protocol described earlier in this book, including consolidation of skills learned in treatment, participation in the relapse prevention protocol, reviewing progress toward treatment goals, and preparation for termination of the acute phase of treatment. In conducting the relapse prevention protocol, clinicians should keep in mind that many of these patients have low frustration tolerance (hence, their propensity to abuse substances to avoid distress) and that they might be especially reluctant to engage in the guided imagery exercises. In addition to being able to communicate a clear rationale for the exercise, it is also helpful to indicate ways in which the relapse prevention protocol has been useful with similar patients in the past (e.g., successful completion gave them the confidence that they would indeed be able to implement the coping strategies when they need them). We also advise clinicians to be prepared with relaxation and breathing exercises to calm these patients before they make a final decision. However, ultimately the decision to engage in the relapse prevention protocol lies with patients, and if they choose not to participate in it, then clinicians should embark on a detailed review of the strategies developed in treatment and solicit specific examples of ways in which patients would implement them.

> Melvin's treatment lasted a total of 12 sessions. Sessions 7, 8, and 9 were focused on solidifying strategies for effective problem solving and reducing impulsivity and on applying those strategies to finding a stable place to live. During the course of those sessions, he found a room to rent in a neighborhood close to the home of one of his sisters, he obtained a part-time job at a convenience store, and he followed through on maintaining contact with his sisters and his children, even planning a visit to see his children on Father's Day. When Melvin moved into the later phase of treatment, he expressed a reluctance to participate in the relapse prevention protocol, saying, "Why go there now? I just want all of that behind me and focus on the future." Although he declined the opportunity to conduct the guided imagery exercises regarding a past suicidal crisis, he agreed to do one for a hypothetical future crisis (i.e., getting laid off from his job). Melvin imagined that his reaction to such a situation would be an increase in hopelessness and despair, as it would activate core beliefs related to failure. He also estimated that the likelihood of his using

drugs again would increase because of boredom. In response, he imagined that he would (a) consult his coping card to remind him of reasons to live other than his job, (b) use problem solving strategies to put together a plan for finding another job, and (c) use the coping strategies on his safety plan (e.g., praying, reading the Bible) at times when he was particularly distressed.

Although Melvin terminated cognitive therapy, he continued to attend one outpatient group in his addictions treatment program and meet with his case manager on a monthly basis. He had begun taking two psychotropic medications—an antidepressant and a mood stabilizer—and he expressed a commitment to stay on that medical regimen. In addition, he began to attend Alcoholics Anonymous meetings at least twice a week. Melvin agreed to schedule a cognitive therapy booster session in 3 months.

SUMMARY AND INTEGRATION

Alcohol and drug abuse and dependence are integral parts of the cognitive case conceptualization of many suicidal patients because diagnoses of alcohol and substance dependence can operate as distal risk factors, an episode of alcohol and drug use can act as a proximal risk factor (e.g., relapse), alcohol and drug use can serve as a coping strategy (albeit maladaptive) to cope with life stressors, and alcohol and drugs might actually serve as the method of a suicide attempt. Patients with a substance dependence disorder are characterized by the same risk factors for suicide attempts and completions as patients without substance dependence problems, but in general, clinicians can expect any individual substance dependent patient to have more risk factors and for the presenting risk factors to be of greater severity. It is well established that suicide ideation and a history of attempts are prevalent in substance dependent patients, and work by Darke, Teesson, and their colleagues has suggested that a substantial minority of substance dependent patients continue to be suicidal even after a year of addictions treatment. Thus, it is logical that an intervention to accompany addictions treatment that is focused on suicide prevention would be especially relevant for this population.

Although the basic cognitive therapy protocol with suicidal substance dependent patients is similar to that used with non–substance dependent patients, as we saw in the protocol for older adults described in chapter 12, it takes on a different flavor. First, addictions-related beliefs must be considered in conjunction with suicide-relevant beliefs and cognitive processes in the cognitive case conceptualization and subsequent selection of intervention strategies. Second, lapses and relapse are often associated with increased distress and suicidal crises, so substance use should be carefully monitored at the beginning of each session in the context of the suicide risk assessment.

Third, these patients can seem especially difficult because their suicide ideation is fleeting or they have difficulty tolerating the pain associated with
focusing on important contributors to their suicidal crises. The research described earlier in this chapter suggests that helping patients to enhance their
(a) self-efficacy about being able to make positive changes in their lives and
(b) motivation to make positive changes might be key in retaining these
patients in therapy, soliciting their collaboration in the treatment process,
and generalizing the strategies to their daily lives.

14

CONCLUSION: A PUBLIC HEALTH MODEL FOR SUICIDE PREVENTION

The following dialogue is from Janice's 6-month booster session with the clinician with whom she worked to develop suicide prevention strategies.

Clinician: Hi Janice, it's been 2 months since I last saw you. [smiles] It's great to see you. [Janice smiles and nods] I would like to talk about how you have been doing during the past few months, to discuss any difficulties that you may have experienced, and to talk about future plans for treatment. Is there anything that you would like to add to this agenda?

Janice: No, that sounds good to me.

Clinician: Is it okay if we talk about the past few months first?

Janice: Sure. Well, I've been doing really well. I was finally able to get a job as a bank teller and save up some money in order to move out of my mother's house. I have my very own apartment. I can't tell you how much better I feel, living on my own.

Clinician: That's wonderful, Janice. I'm really happy for you.

Janice: It hasn't been all that easy. I still have my moments.

Clinician:	Oh, really?
Janice:	Yeah, I still get really upset when my stepfather is critical toward me. But I've learned to recognize that I'm just sensitive to criticism because I have thought of myself as being so worthless for so long.
Clinician:	That's really important for you to be aware of that belief.
Janice:	And I still get really emotional over stupid things to the point that I feel like I'm going to explode.
Clinician:	I'm sorry to hear that, but I certainly understand that you sometimes feel that way. So what do you do when you feel like that?
Janice:	I think about how hard we have worked to deal with those really painful moments. I still have my safety plan, my coping cards, and my Hope Kit.
Clinician:	Ah, that's good.
Janice:	It's almost as if I just have to remember that there are other options for me when I start to think that things are really hopeless. I just hope that I never go to that dark place again, but if I do, I know that I'll get through it.
Clinician:	That's right. You have learned many skills to deal with such a crisis.

As evident from this dialogue, the progress that Janice has made has been clinically meaningful. However, even though she has articulated some of the strategies for managing suicidal crises, there is no guarantee that she will not make another suicide attempt in the future, as there are many aspects of Janice's psychiatric history that put her at chronic risk for engaging in suicidal acts. A fundamental theme of this volume is that the primary focus of cognitive therapy is for the clinician to lower patients' risk for engaging in a future suicidal act by helping them to recognize the warning signs when they are in crisis and to use cognitive, emotional, and/or behavioral coping strategies that are specific to the idiosyncratic cognitive case conceptualization of their suicidal crises. Janice has certainly demonstrated the ability to apply these strategies to her life. Although Janice will remain at higher risk for suicide than most women of her background, her successful completion of cognitive therapy constitutes a major protective factor that, to some degree, counteracts this risk.

As described in the Introduction, suicide is a major public health problem for men and women of all ages and of all races and ethnicities. Raising public awareness of this problem through exposure of the impact of suicide on our lives, our communities, our government, and the media constitutes a national approach for suicide prevention. Families and other individuals who have a loved one who has died from suicide or who has attempted suicide may not feel comfortable discussing this topic in public. Nonetheless, an increased public awareness of the problem may foster those who have experienced this tragedy to come forward and make their concerns known to others. This general awareness also affords the development, testing, and implementation of evidence-based approaches, such as cognitive therapy, for preventing suicide.

According to the National Strategy for Suicide Prevention (U.S. Department of Health & Human Services, 2001), there are five steps for preventing suicide from a public health perspective: (a) surveillance or defining the scope of the problem, (b) assessment of risk and protective factors, (c) developing and testing interventions, (d) implementing and testing evidence-based intervention in the community, and (e) dissemination and program evaluation of suicide prevention efforts (see Figure 14.1). One of the first steps for preventing suicide and suicide attempts is to measure the extent of the problem through surveillance. This is defined as the ongoing, systematic collection, analysis, and interpretation of health data. Although the Centers for Disease Control and Prevention track suicides from state vital statistics offices, there is no current national surveillance for suicide attempts. Reliable estimates of the prevalence and incidence rates of suicide attempts are essential for establishing realistic goals, designing preventive interventions, and evaluating the effectiveness of these programs.

Given that the occurrence of a suicide attempt has been determined to be a major risk factor for suicide, methodologies need to be developed to accurately identify and assess individuals who attempt suicide and who are evaluated within the health care system, especially in emergency departments. There are three potential and important functions of a suicide attempt surveillance system or registry: (a) surveillance, (b) treatment research, and (c) case management. The first function of a suicide attempt registry is to establish a national surveillance system so that the scope and extent of the problem can be assessed. Epidemiological studies of suicide attempts may help us to understand the potential effectiveness of universal, selected, and/or indicated interventions that are designed to reduce the occurrence of suicide attempts in the community. The second function of a registry is to facilitate treatment research so that interventions may be developed and tested that are intended to prevent suicide attempts and deaths by suicide. In this regard, the suicide attempt registry provides the foundation for developing an infrastructure for a clinical trials network so that multisite clinical trials may be conducted. The third function of a suicide attempt registry is to provide an infrastructure for case management services for patients who are at risk for suicide. Individuals who attempt suicide do not often attend outpatient mental health and addiction treatment services after they have been identified and clinically evaluated in the hospital setting. Thus, the registry serves as a basis for the development of an infrastructure that is designed to track and provide outreach

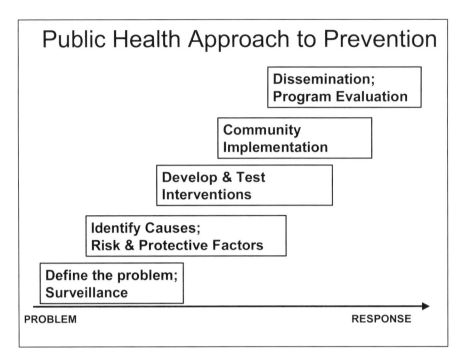

Figure 14.1. A public health model for prevention.

and referral services to patients who are unlikely to attend follow-up psychiatric and addiction treatments.

The adoption of a common nomenclature for suicide ideation and suicidal acts, such as that described in chapter 1, by health care and behavioral health care clinicians is essential for identifying patients who are at risk for suicide and for establishing and maintaining a suicide attempt registry. Moreover, the use of reliable and valid measures of suicide ideation and suicide attempts, as described in chapter 1, along with a comprehensive assessment of the risk and protective factors will not only lead to improved surveillance, but will ultimately save lives.

The second step of our public health model involves identifying the risk and protective factors that are associated with suicide. As discussed in chapter 2, our group has devoted many years to examining the risk factors for suicide. This research has assisted us in establishing the predictive validity of many of our standardized measures of psychopathology, including the Beck Hopelessness Scale, Scale for Suicide Ideation, Suicide Intent Scale, and the Beck Depression Inventory. These widely used measures are some of the few measures of psychopathology that have been empirically demonstrated to measure risk factors for suicide and suicide attempts. This research has helped us to identify those individuals who are at the highest risk for suicide, such as adults who have attempted suicide in the past or those who have had particularly high levels of suicide ideation at the worst point in their lives. Moreover, our group, as well as other researchers, has identified numerous other correlates of and risk factors for suicide attempts and suicide, including demographic, diagnostic, psychiatric history, and other psychological variables. As can be seen in chapter 2, many of these variables have been replicated on numerous occasions using disparate samples and measurement approaches. We call on researchers to design studies that clearly advance the literature by examining these variables (a) prospectively rather than in cross-sectional designs; (b) in a more targeted manner, such as by limiting the analysis to risk factors for suicidal acts in a particular subgroup of interest (e.g., gay, lesbian, or bisexual individuals or veterans); and (c) in light of relevant theory, so that additional constructs can be identified, or so that an integrative theory of suicidal acts can be refined and advanced.

The third step of the public health model entails developing and testing interventions that include clinical strategies to address identified risk factors. We have adopted a general form of cognitive therapy, described in chapter 5, and developed a targeted form of cognitive therapy that was used to address suicidal behavior directly (G. K. Brown, Tenhave, et al., 2005). As described in chapter 4, individuals who attempted suicide were recruited from the emergency department and randomly assigned to receive either cognitive therapy or usual care. The results of this study indicated that those patients who were assigned to cognitive therapy were approximately 50% less likely to try to kill themselves again within 18 months than those who did not receive this intervention. Although the groups did not differ significantly in the frequency and intensity of their suicidal thoughts, those who were assigned to the cognitive therapy condition scored lower on measures of depression severity and hopelessness during the follow-up period. As described in Part II of this volume, cognitive therapy is optimally conducted when flexible scheduling and outreach services are provided. Given the enormous burden for tracking and engaging high-risk patients in treatment, a treatment team approach that includes case management services is highly recommended.

In addition to this research, we have been focused on developing and examining methodologies that address other issues associated with efficacy research, including variables and statistical models associated with mechanisms of change in cognitive therapy. On the basis of the theory described in chapter 3, we have been examining the underlying mechanisms associated with suicidal acts, including cognitive biases (e.g., attentional biases), the tendency to make cognitive distortions (e.g., all-or-nothing thinking), attentional fixation during suicidal crises, and various manifestations of impulsivity (e.g., inability to delay rewards, inability to inhibit responses). We plan to use these data to (a) provide empirical support for the cognitive model described in chapter 3 and (b) develop more refined intervention strategies to modify specific suicide-relevant psychological vulnerability factors and cognitive processes.

The fourth step of the public health model involves implementing interventions in community settings. Given that cognitive therapy was efficacious for preventing suicide attempts when conducted by postdoctoral fellows who received intensive training and supervision, our next study is evaluating the effectiveness of exporting this intervention for patients who attempt suicide and who are referred to community mental health agencies. Specifically, we have trained master's-level community therapists to use this intervention with suicidal patients. Thus, we have embarked on the next step in this line of research, which involves using the experience and findings of the research associated with the third step to further develop intervention programs that can be applied in general settings by a variety of behavioral health professionals. Although the experienced clinician may certainly learn many skills provided in this book for preventing suicide, we have found that didactic training followed by intensive individual and group supervision offers an excellent method for learning cognitive therapy. Specifically, we have found that conducting ratings of audio and video recordings using the Cognitive Therapy Rating Scale (J. E. Young & Beck, 1980) provides a comprehensive assessment of clinicians' strengths and areas for further development. In addition, group supervision provides for a supportive environment when working with challenging patients (see chap. 10).

The fifth and final step of the public health model involves program evaluation and dissemination. The absence of program evaluation is viewed as one of the largest obstacles to the identification and implementation of evidence-based interventions for suicide prevention and for the treatment of mental disorders. Faced with the challenge of transporting research into practice settings, researchers have begun to understand the importance of applying dissemination and organizational theories to the challenge of disseminating treatments into community settings. To date, there have been few attempts to test the applicability of dissemination theories with psychological interventions, and even fewer efforts to manipulate the factors that are thought to be predictive of sustained adoption of an empirically supported treatment. Although this volume is intended to promote the adoption of an empirically supported treatment, we do not yet have access to a systematic, evidence-based approach.

Our recent training efforts have provided us with the opportunity to evaluate the effects of individual and organizational factors on training outcomes and the adoption of cognitive therapy. The aims of this program of research are to (a) measure the adoption of cognitive therapy among clinicians who were trained systematically in this treatment approach, (b) assess barriers to the adoption of cognitive therapy in community settings, (c) learn more about the way in which community-based clinicians adapt cognitive therapy to address the needs of their patients, and (d) compare clinicians' self-reports of their use of cognitive therapy to objective measures of adherence to cognitive therapy.

In conclusion, our cognitive therapy approach has the potential to be a powerful treatment in preventing suicidal acts because of its (a) circumscribed focus, (b) orientation toward involving a treatment team and adjunctive services in treating the patient, and (c) focus on developing concrete cognitive and behavioral strategies that can be used during crises. In fact, it can be said that our theory and the resulting approach to treatment are the result of more than 40 years of work, first initiated by Aaron T. Beck. We have been gratified by the number of clinicians and researchers who have expressed interest in our approach to understanding and treating suicidal patients. This issue is now receiving more attention than it ever has and is being acknowledged by clinicians, researchers, and funding agencies as a problem worthy of attention in its own right, not simply as an extension of a psychiatric diagnosis with which it is associated. Although this book represents the accumulation of our knowledge to this point, our readers can be assured that we are committed to further testing of the intervention, further testing and refining of our theory, developing new and more targeted intervention strategies, and disseminating our treatment to the public.

APPENDIX: OUTLINE OF COGNITIVE THERAPY FOR SUICIDAL PATIENTS

I. Early phase of treatment
   A. Obtain informed consent.
      1. Address confidentiality.
      2. Describe the structure and process of treatment.
      3. Discuss the potential risks and benefits of treatment.
      4. Inform patient of alternative treatments.
   B. Actively engage patient in treatment.
   C. Complete a comprehensive suicide risk assessment.
      1. Assess risk factors (characteristics that create a vulnerability to engaging in suicidal acts).
      2. Assess protective factors (characteristics that reduce the likelihood of engaging in suicidal acts).
      3. Make final determination of suicide risk.
      4. Debrief patient.
   D. Develop a safety plan (hierarchically arranged list of coping skills that patients agree to use in a suicidal crisis).
      1. Recognizing warning signs
      2. Using coping strategies
      3. Contacting family members or friends
      4. Contacting professionals and agencies
   E. Convey a sense of hope.
II. Cognitive case conceptualization
   A. Conduct (or integrate information from) a psychological assessment.*
   B. Construct timeline of the suicidal crisis.*
   C. Develop initial cognitive case conceptualization (application of cognitive theory to understand the cognitive, behavioral, affective, and situational features of patients' suicidal crises).
   D. Engage in treatment planning.
      1. Develop treatment goals.
      2. Select intervention strategies.
III. Intermediate phase of treatment
   A. Continue activities from the early phase of treatment.
      1. Assess suicide risk.
      2. Assess drug and alcohol use.
      3. Assess treatment compliance.

---

*This information is gathered during the early phase of treatment and is compiled into a cognitive case conceptualization at the end of the early phase.

        4. Review and modify safety plan.

  B. Behavioral strategies.

        1. Increase pleasurable activities.

        2. Improve social resources.

        3. Increase compliance with other services.

  C. Affective coping skills.

        1. Physical self-soothing (e.g., muscle relaxation, controlled breathing)

        2. Cognitive self-soothing (e.g., distraction, positive imagery)

        3. Sensory self-soothing (e.g., activities to engage the senses)

  D. Cognitive strategies.

        1. Modify core beliefs.

        2. Identify reasons for living.

        3. Develop coping cards.

        4. Enhance problem solving skills.

        5. Reduce impulsivity.

IV. Later phase of treatment

  A. Review and consolidate skills.

  B. Conduct relapse prevention protocol.

        1. Prepare patient for exercise.

        2. Review past suicidal crisis.

        3. Review past suicidal crisis using skills.

        4. Review a future suicidal crisis.

        5. Debrief patient.

  C. Review progress toward treatment goals.

  D. Engage in additional treatment planning.

        1. Continuation of treatment

        2. Referral

        3. Termination of treatment

REFERENCES

Adams, D. M., & Overholser, J. C. (1992). Suicidal behavior and history of substance abuse. *The American Journal of Drug and Alcohol Abuse, 18,* 343–354.

Addis, M. E., & Jacobson, N. S. (2000). A closer look at the treatment rationale and homework compliance in cognitive-behavioral therapy for depression. *Cognitive Therapy and Research, 24,* 313–326.

Agency for Health Care Policy & Research. (1999). *Evidence report on treatment of depression: Newer pharmacotherapies.* Washington, DC: AHCPR Evidence-Based Practice Centers.

Aharonovich, E., Liu, X., Nunes, E., & Hasin, D. S. (2002). Suicide attempts in substance abusers: Effects of major depression in relation to substance use disorders. *American Journal of Psychiatry, 159,* 1600–1602.

Alexopoulos, G. S., Bruce, M. L., Hull, J., Sirey, J. A., & Kakuma, T. (1999). Clinical determinants of suicidal ideation and behavior in geriatric depression. *Archives of General Psychiatry, 11,* 1048–1053.

Allard, R., Marshall, M., & Plante, M. (1992). Intensive follow-up does not decrease the risk of repeat suicide attempts. *Suicide and Life-Threatening Behavior, 22,* 303–314.

Allebeck, P., & Allgulander, C. (1990). Psychiatric diagnoses as predictors of suicide: A comparison of diagnoses at conscription and in psychiatric care in a cohort of 50,465 young men. *British Journal of Psychiatry, 157,* 339–344.

American Psychiatric Association. (2003). *Practice guideline for the assessment and treatment of patients with suicidal behaviors.* Washington, DC: Author.

American Psychological Association. (2002). Ethical principles of psychologists and code of conduct. *American Psychologist, 57,* 1060–1073.

Anderson, P. S., Tiro, J. A., Price, A. W., Bender, M. A., & Kaslow, N. J. (2002). Additive impact of childhood emotional, physical, and sexual abuse on suicide attempts among low-income African-American women. *Suicide and Life-Threatening Behavior, 32,* 131–138.

Andréasson, S., & Romelsjo, A. (1988). Alcohol and mortality among young men: A longitudinal study of Swedish conscripts. *Scandinavian Journal of Social Medicine, 18,* 9–15.

Andrews, J. A., & Lewinsohn, P. M. (1992). Suicide attempts among older adolescents: Prevalence and co-occurrence with psychiatric disorders. *Journal of the American Academy of Child & Adolescent Psychiatry, 31,* 665–662.

Andriessen, K. (2006). On "intention" in the definition of suicide. *Suicide and Life-Threatening Behavior, 36,* 533–538.

Apter, A., Gothelf, D., Orbach, I., Weizman, R., Ratzoni, G., Har-Even, D., et al. (1995). Correlation of suicidal and violent behavior in different diagnostic categories in hospitalized adolescent patients. *Journal of the American Academy of Child & Adolescent Psychiatry, 34,* 912–918.

Arensman, E., Townsend, E., Hawton, K., Bremner, S., Feldman, E., Goldney, R., et al. (2001). Psychosocial and pharmacological treatment of patients following deliberate self-harm: The methodological issues involved in evaluating effectiveness. *Suicide and Life-Threatening Behavior, 31,* 169–180.

Asarnow, J. R., Carlson, G. A., & Gutherie, D. (1987). Coping strategies, self-perceptions, hopelessness, and perceived family functioning in depressed and suicidal children. *Journal of Consulting and Clinical Psychology, 55,* 361–366.

Asarnow, J. R., & Gutherie, D. (1989). Suicidal behavior, depression, and hopelessness in child psychiatric inpatients: A replication and extension. *Journal of Child Clinical Psychology, 18,* 129–136.

Asnis, G. M., Kaplan, M. L., van Praag, H. M., & Sanderson, W. C. (1994). Homicidal behaviors among psychiatric outpatients. *Hospital Community Psychiatry, 45,* 127–132.

Babor, T. F., Higgins-Biddle, J. C., Saunders, J. B., & Monteiro, M. G. (2001). *The Alcohol Use Disorders Identification Test: Guidelines for use in primary care.* Geneva, Switzerland: World Health Organization.

Baca-Garcia, E., Diaz-Sastre, C., Garcia Resa, E., Blasco, H., Braquehais Conesa, D., Oquendo, M. A., et al. (2005). Suicide attempts and impulsivity. *European Archives of Psychiatry and Clinical Neuroscience, 255,* 152–156.

Barraclough, B. M. (1971). Suicide in the elderly: Recent developments in psychogeriatrics. *British Journal of Psychiatry,* (Suppl. 6), 87–97.

Barratt, E. S. (1959). Anxiety and impulsiveness related to psychomotor efficiency. *Perceptual and Motor Skills, 9,* 191–198.

Barratt, E. S. (1985). Impulsiveness subtraits: Arousal and information processing. In J. T. Spence & C. E. Izard (Eds.), *Motivation, emotion, and personality* (pp. 137–146). Amsterdam: North Holland/Elsevier Science.

Bateman, A., & Fonagy, P. (1999). Effectiveness of partial hospitalization in the treatment of borderline personality disorder: A randomized controlled trial. *American Journal of Psychiatry, 156,* 1563–1569.

Baumeister, R. F. (1990). Suicide as escape from self. *Psychological Review, 97,* 90–113.

Beautrais, A. L. (2001). Subsequent mortality in medically serious suicide attempts: A 5 year follow-up. *Australian and New Zealand Journal of Psychiatry, 37,* 595–599.

Beautrais, A. L. (2002). A case control study of suicide and attempted suicide in older adults. *Suicide and Life-Threatening Behavior, 32,* 1–9.

Beautrais, A. L., Joyce, P. R., Mulder, R. T., Fergusson, D. M., Deavoll, B. J., & Nightengale, S. K. (1996). Prevalence and comorbidity of mental disorders in persons making serious suicide attempts: A case-control study. *American Journal of Psychiatry, 153,* 1009–1014.

Beck, A. T. (1967). *Depression: Causes and treatment.* Philadelphia: University of Pennsylvania Press.

Beck, A. T. (1986). Hopelessness as a predictor of eventual suicide. In J. J. Mann & M. Stanley (Eds.), *Annals of the New York Academy of Sciences: Vol. 487. Psychology and suicidal behavior* (pp. 90–96). New York: New York Academy of Sciences.

Beck, A. T. (1988). Cognitive approaches to panic disorder: Theory and therapy. In S. Rachman & J. D. Maser (Eds.), *Panic: Psychological perspectives* (pp. 91–109). Hillsdale, NJ: Erlbaum.

Beck, A. T. (1996). Beyond belief: A theory of modes, personality, and psychopathology. In P. Salkovskis (Ed.), *Frontiers of cognitive therapy* (pp. 1–25). New York: Guilford Press.

Beck, A. T., Beck, R., & Kovacs, M. (1975). Classification of suicidal behaviors: I. Quantifying intent and medical lethality. *American Journal of Psychiatry, 132,* 285–287.

Beck, A. T., & Bhar, S. S. (in press). Cognitive processes in borderline personality disorder. *Clinical Neuroscience Research.*

Beck, A. T., Brown, G., Berchick, R. J., Stewart, B. L., & Steer, R. A. (1990). Relationship between hopelessness and ultimate suicide: A replication with psychiatric outpatients. *American Journal of Psychiatry, 147,* 190–195.

Beck, A. T., Brown, G. K., & Steer, R. A. (1997). Psychometric characteristics of the Scale for Suicide Ideation with psychiatric outpatients. *Behaviour Research and Therapy, 35,* 1039–1046.

Beck, A. T., Brown, G. K., Steer, R. A., Dahlsgaard, K. K., & Grisham, J. R. (1999). Suicide ideation at its worst point: A predictor of eventual suicide in psychiatric outpatients. *Suicide and Life-Threatening Behavior, 29,* 1–9.

Beck, A. T., Davis, J. H., Frederick, C. J., Perlin, S., Pokorny, A., Schulman, R., et al. (1972). Classification and nomenclature. In H. L. P. Resnik & B. Hathorne (Eds.), *Suicide prevention in the seventies* (pp. 7–12). Washington, DC: U.S. Government Printing Office.

Beck, A. T., & Emery, G. (1985). *Anxiety disorders and phobias: A cognitive perspective.* New York: Basic Books.

Beck, A. T., Freeman, A., Davis, D. D., & Associates (2004). *Cognitive therapy of personality disorders* (2nd ed.). New York: Guilford Press.

Beck, A. T., & Greenberg, R. L. (1974). *Coping with depression.* New York: Institute for Rational Living.

Beck, A. T., Kovacs, M., & Weissman, A. (1975, December 15). Hopelessness and suicidal behavior: An overview. *JAMA, 234,* 1146–1149.

Beck, A. T., Kovacs, M., & Weissman, A. (1979). Assessment of suicidal intention: The Scale for Suicide Ideation. *Journal of Consulting and Clinical Psychology, 47,* 343–352.

Beck, A. T., & Lester, D. (1976). Components of suicidal intent in completed and attempted suicides. *Journal of Psychology, 92,* 35–38.

Beck, A. T., Resnik, H. L., & Lettieri, D. J. (Eds.). (1974). *The prediction of suicide.* Bowie, MD: Charles Press.

Beck, A. T., Rush, A. J., Shaw, B. F., & Emery, G. (1979). *Cognitive therapy of depression.* New York: Guilford Press.

Beck, A. T., Schuyler, D., & Herman, I. (1974). Development of suicidal intent scales. In T. Beck, H. L. Resnik, & D. J. Lettieri (Eds.), *The prediction of suicide* (pp. 45–56). Bowie, MD: Charles Press.

Beck, A. T., & Steer, R. A. (1988). *Manual for the Beck Hopelessness Scale*. San Antonio, TX: Psychological Corporation.

Beck, A. T., & Steer, R. A. (1989). Clinical predictors of eventual suicide: A five to ten year prospective study of suicide attempters. *Journal of Affective Disorders, 17*, 203–209.

Beck, A. T., & Steer, R. A. (1991). *Manual for the Beck Scale for Suicide Ideation*. San Antonio, TX: Psychological Corporation.

Beck, A. T., Steer, R. A., Beck, J. S., & Newman, C. F. (1993). Hopelessness, depression, suicidal ideation, and clinical diagnosis of depression. *Suicide and Life-Threatening Behavior, 23*, 139–145.

Beck, A. T., Steer, R. A., & Brown, G. K. (1996). *Manual for Beck Depression Inventory—II*. San Antonio, TX: Psychological Corporation.

Beck, A. T., Steer, R. A., Kovacs, M., & Garrison, B. (1985). Hopelessness and eventual suicide: A 10-year prospective study of patients hospitalized with suicidal ideation. *American Journal of Psychiatry, 142*, 559–563.

Beck, A. T., Steer, R. A., & McElroy, M. G. (1982). Relationships of hopelessness, depression, and previous suicide attempts to suicidal ideation in alcoholics. *Journal of Studies on Alcohol, 43*, 1042–1046.

Beck, A. T., Steer, R. A., & Ranieri, W. (1998). Scale for Suicide Ideation: Psychometric properties of a self-report version. *Journal of Clinical Psychology, 44*, 499–505.

Beck, A. T., Steer, R. A., Sanderson, W. C., & Skeie, T. M. (1991). Panic disorder and suicidal ideation and behavior: Discrepant findings in psychiatric outpatients. *American Journal of Psychiatry, 148*, 1195–1199.

Beck, A. T., Weissman, A., & Kovacs, M. (1976). Alcoholism, hopelessness, and suicidal behavior. *Journal of Studies on Alcohol, 37*, 66–77.

Beck, A. T., Weissman, A., Lester, D., & Trexler, L. (1974). The measurement of pessimism: The Hopelessness scale. *Journal of Consulting and Clinical Psychology, 42*, 861–865.

Beck, A. T., Weissman, A., Lester, D., & Trexler, L. (1976). Classification of suicidal behaviors: II. Dimensions of suicidal intent. *Archives of General Psychiatry, 33*, 835–837.

Beck, A. T., Wright, F. D., Newman, C. F., & Liese, B. S. (1993). *Cognitive therapy of substance abuse*. New York: Guilford Press.

Beck, J. S. (1995). *Cognitive therapy: Basics and beyond*. New York: Guilford Press.

Beck, R. W., Morris, J. B., & Beck, A. T. (1974). Cross-validation of the Suicidal Intent Scale. *Psychological Reports, 34*, 445–446.

Becker, E. S., Strohbach, D., & Rinck, M. (1999). A specific attentional bias in suicide attempters. *The Journal of Nervous and Mental Disease, 187*, 730–735.

Bedrosian, R. C., & Beck, A. T. (1979). Cognitive aspects of suicidal behavior. *Suicide and Life-Threatening Behavior, 2*, 87–96.

Begg, C., Cho, M., Eastwood, S., Horton, R., Moher, D., Olkin, I., et al. (1996, August 28). Improving the quality of reporting of randomized controlled trials: The CONSORT statement. *JAMA, 276*, 637–639.

Bennewith, O., Stocks, N., Gunnell, D., Peters, T. J., Evans, M. O., & Sharp, D. J. (2002). General practice based intervention to prevent repeat episodes of deliberate self harm: Cluster randomised controlled trial. *British Medical Journal, 324*, 1254–1257.

Bensley, L., Van Eenwyk, J., Spieker, S., & Schoder, J. (1999). Self-reported abuse history and adolescent behavior problems: I. Antisocial and suicidal behaviors. *Journal of Adolescent Health, 24*, 163–172.

Berk, M. S., Henriques, G. R., Warman, D. M., Brown, G. K., & Beck, A. T. (2004). A cognitive therapy intervention for suicide attempters: An overview of the treatment and case examples. *Cognitive and Behavioral Practice, 11*, 265–277.

Berman, A. L., Jobes, D. A., & Silverman, M. M. (2006). *Adolescent suicide: Assessment and intervention* (2nd ed.). Washington, DC: American Psychological Association.

Bertolote, J. M., Fleischmann, A., De Leo, D., & Wasserman, D. (2003). Suicide and mental disorders: Do we know enough? *British Journal of Psychiatry, 183*, 382–383.

Best, D., Gossop, M., Man, L.-H., Finch, E., Greenwood, J., & Strang, J. (2000). Accidental and deliberate overdose among opiate addicts in methadone maintenance treatment: Are deliberate overdoses systematically different? *Drug and Alcohol Review, 19*, 213–216.

Blumenthal, S., Bell, V., Neumann, N. U., Schuttler, R., & Vogel, R. (1989). Mortality and rate of suicide of first admission psychiatric patients: A 5-year follow-up of a prospective longitudinal study. *Psychopathology, 22*, 50–56.

Boergers, J., & Spirito, A. (2003). The outcome of suicide attempts among adolescents. In A. Spirito & J. C. Overholser (Eds.), *Evaluating and treating adolescent suicide attempters: From research to practice* (pp. 261–276). New York: Academic Press.

Boergers, J., Spirito, A., & Donaldson, D. (1998). Reasons for adolescent suicide attempts: Associations with psychological functioning. *Journal of the American Academy of Child & Adolescent Psychiatry, 37*, 277–286.

Bondy, B., Buettner, A., & Zill, P. (2006). Genetics of suicide. *Molecular Psychiatry, 11*, 336–351.

Bongar, B., Maris, R. W., Berman, A. C., & Litman, R. E. (1992). Outpatient standards of care and the suicidal patient. *Suicide and Life-Threatening Behavior, 22*, 453–478.

Borowsky, I., Resnick, M., Ireland, M., & Blum, R. (1990). Suicide attempts among American Indian and Alaska Native youth. *Archives of Pediatrics & Adolescent Medicine, 153*, 573–580.

Bostwick, J. M., & Pankrantz, V. S. (2000). Affective disorders and suicide risk: A reexamination. *American Journal of Psychiatry, 141*, 206–209.

Brent, D. A. (1987). Correlates of the medical lethality of suicide attempts in children and adolescents. *Journal of the American Academy of Child & Adolescent Psychiatry, 26*, 87–89.

Brent, D. A., Baugher, M., Bridge, J., Chen, T., & Chiappetta, L. (1999). Age- and sex-related risk factors for adolescent suicide. *Journal of the American Academy of Child & Adolescent Psychiatry, 38,* 1497–1505.

Brent, D. A., Kerr, M. M., Goldstein, C., Bozigar, J., Wartella, M. E., & Allan, M. J. (1989). An outbreak of suicide and suicidal behavior in high school. *Journal of the American Academy of Child & Adolescent Psychiatry, 32,* 521–529.

Brent, D. A., & Mann, J. J. (2005). Family genetic studies, suicide, and suicidal behavior. *American Journal of Medical Genetics Part C: Seminars in Medical Genetics, 133C,* 13–24.

Brent, D. A., Oquendo, M., Birmaher, B., Greenhill, L., Kolko, D., Stanley, B., et al. (2002). Familial pathways to early-onset suicide attempt: Risk for suicidal behavior in offspring of mood-disordered suicide attempters. *Archives of General Psychiatry, 59,* 801–807.

Brent, D. A., Perper, J. A., Goldstein, C. E., Kolko, D. J., Allan, M. J., Allman, C. J., et al. (1988). Risk factors for adolescent suicide: A comparison of adolescent suicide victims with suicidal inpatients. *Archives of General Psychiatry, 45,* 581–588.

Brent, D. A., Perper, J. A., Moritz, G., Baugher, M., Roth, C., Barach, L., et al. (1993). Familial risk factors for adolescent suicide: A case control study. *Acta Psychiatrica Scandinavica, 89,* 52–58.

Brown, G. K. (2002). *A review of suicide assessment measures for intervention research in adults and older adults* (Technical report submitted to the National Institutes of Mental Health under Contract No. 263-MH914950). Bethesda, MD: National Institute of Mental Health.

Brown, G. K., Beck, A. T., Steer, R. A., & Grisham, J. R. (2000). Risk factors for suicide in psychiatric outpatients: A 20-year prospective study. *Journal of Consulting and Clinical Psychology, 68,* 371–377.

Brown, G. K., Bruce, M. L., Pearson, J. L., & PROSPECT Study Group. (2001). High risk management for elderly suicidal patients in primary care. *International Journal of Geriatric Psychiatry, 16,* 593–601.

Brown, G. K., Henriques, G. R., Ratto, C., & Beck, A. T. (2002). *Cognitive therapy treatment manual for suicide attempters.* Unpublished manuscript, University of Pennsylvania, Philadelphia.

Brown, G. K., Henriques, G. R., Sosdjan, D., & Beck, A. T. (2004). Suicide intent and accurate expectations of lethality: Predictors of medical lethality of suicide attempts. *Journal of Consulting and Clinical Psychology, 72,* 1170–1174.

Brown, G. K., Jeglic, E., Henriques, G. R., & Beck, A. T. (2006). Cognitive therapy, cognition, and suicidal behavior. In T. E. Ellis (Ed.), *Cognition and suicide: Theory, research, and therapy* (pp. 53–74). Washington, DC: American Psychological Association.

Brown, G. K., Steer, R. A., Henriques, G. R., & Beck, A. T. (2005). The internal struggle between the wish to die and the wish to live: A risk factor for suicide. *American Journal of Psychiatry, 162,* 1977–1979.

Brown, G. K., Tenhave, T., Henriques, G. R., Xie, S. X., Hollander, J. E., & Beck, A. T. (2005, August 3). Cognitive therapy for the prevention of suicide attempts: A randomized controlled trial. *JAMA, 294*, 563–570.

Brown, J., Cohen, P., Johnson, J., & Smailes, E. M. (1999). Childhood abuse and neglect: Specificity of effects on adolescent and young adult depression and suicidality. *Journal of the American Academy of Child & Adolescent Psychiatry, 38*, 1490–1496.

Bruce, M. L., Tenhave, T. R., Reynolds, C. F., Katz, K. I., Schulberg, H. C., Mulsant, B. H., et al. (2004, September 1). Reducing suicidal ideation and depressive symptoms in depressed older primary care patients: A randomized controlled trial. *JAMA, 292*, 1081–1091.

Buda, M., & Tsuang, M. T. (1990). The epidemiology of suicide: Implications for clinical practice. In S. J. Blumenthal & D. J. Kupfer (Eds.), *Suicide over the life cycle: Risk factors, assessment, and treatment of suicidal patients* (pp. 17–37). Washington, DC: American Psychiatric Press.

Burdick, K. E., Endick, C. J., & Goldberg, J. F. (2005). Assessing cognitive deficits in bipolar disorder: Are self reports valid? *Psychiatry Research, 136*, 43–50.

Burns, D. D. (1980). *Feeling good: The new mood therapy.* New York: Signet.

Busch, K. A., Clark, D. C., & Fawcett, J. (1993). Clinical features of inpatient suicide. *Psychiatric Annals, 23*, 256–262.

Busch, K. A., Fawcett, J., & Jacobs, D. G. (2003). Clinical correlates of inpatient suicide. *Journal of Clinical Psychiatry, 64*, 14–19.

Byrne, G. J., & Raphael, B. (1999). Depressive symptoms and depressive episodes in recently widowed older men. *International Psychogeriatrics, 11*, 67–74.

Caldwell, C. E., & Gottesman, I. I. (1990). Schizophrenics kill themselves too: A review of risk factors for suicide. *Schizophrenia Bulletin, 16*, 571–589.

Campbell, J. M. (1992). Treating depression in well older adults: Use of diaries in cognitive therapy. *Issues of Mental Health Nursing, 13*, 19–29.

Cantor, C. H., & Slater, P. J. (1995). Marital breakdown, parenthood, and suicide. *Journal of Family Studies, 1*, 91–102.

Carr, D. S., Nesse, R. M., & Wortman, C. B. (Eds.). (2005). *Spousal bereavement in late life.* New York: Springer Publishing Company.

Carter, G. L., Clover, K., Whyte, I. M., Dawson, A. H., & D'Este, C. (2005). Postcards from the EDge project: Randomised controlled trial of an intervention using postcards to reduce repetition of hospital treated deliberate self poisoning. *British Medical Journal, 331*, 805–809.

Carter, G., Reith, D. M., Whyte, I. M., & McPherson, M. (2005). Repeated self-poisoning: Increasing severity of self-harm as a predictor of subsequent suicide. *British Journal of Psychiatry, 186*, 253–257.

CBT TASA Team. (2008). *Cognitive behavioral therapy for adolescent suicide attempters teen manual.* Unpublished manuscript, National Institute of Mental Health.

Cedereke, M., Monti, K., & Ojehagen, A. (2002). Telephone contact with patients in the year after a suicide attempt: Does it affect treatment attendance and outcome? A randomized controlled study. *European Psychiatry, 17*, 82–91.

Centers for Disease Control and Prevention. (2008). *Web-Based Injury Statistics Query and Reporting System (WISQARS)*. Retrieved February 26, 2008, from Centers for Disease Control and Prevention, National Center for Injury and Prevention Control Web site: http://www.cdc.gov/ncipc/WISQARS

Chemtob, C. M., Bauer, G. B., Hamada, R. S., Pelowski, S. R., & Muraoka, M. Y. (1989). Patient suicide: Occupational hazard for psychologists and psychiatrists. *Professional Psychology: Research and Practice, 20,* 294–300.

Chen, Y.-W., & Dilsaver, S. C. (1996). Lifetime rates of suicide attempts among subjects with bipolar and unipolar disorders relative to subjects with other axis I disorders. *Biological Psychiatry, 39,* 896–899.

Cheng, A. T., Chen, T. H., Chen, C. C., & Jenkins, R. (2000). Psychological and psychiatric risk factors for suicide: Case control psychological autopsy study. *British Journal of Psychiatry, 177,* 360–365.

Chowdhury, N., Hicks, R. C., & Kreitman, N. (1973). Evaluation of an after-care service for parasuicide (attempted suicide) patients. *Social Psychiatry, 8,* 67–81.

Clark, D. A., & Beck, A. T. (1999). *Scientific foundations of cognitive theory and therapy of depression.* New York: Wiley.

Clark, D. C., & Horton-Deutsch, S. L. (1992). Assessment in absentia: The value of the psychological autopsy method for studying antecedents of suicide and predicting future suicides. In R. W. Maris, A. L. Berman, J. T. Maltzberger, & R. I. Yufit (Eds.), *Assessment and prediction of suicide* (pp. 145–181). New York: Guilford Press.

Clum, G. A., & Curtin, L. (1993). Validity and reactivity of a system of self-monitoring suicide ideation. *Journal of Psychopathology and Behavioral Assessment, 15,* 375–385.

Clum, G. A., & Febbraro, G. A. R. (2004). Social problem solving and suicide risk. In E. C. Chang, T. J. D'Zurilla, & L. J. Sanna (Eds.), *Social problem solving: Theory, research, and training* (pp. 67–82). Washington, DC: American Psychological Association.

Cohen-Sandler, R., Berman, A. L., & King, R. A. (1982). Life stress and symptomatology: Determinants of suicidal behavior in children. *Journal of the American Academy for Child & Adolescent Psychiatry, 21,* 178–196.

Collins, J. M. (2003). Impact of a patient suicide on clinicians. *Journal of the American Psychiatric Nurses' Association, 9,* 159–162.

Comtois, K. A., & Linehan, M. M. (2006). Psychosocial treatments of suicidal behaviors: A practice-friendly review. *Journal of Clinical Psychology: In Session, 62,* 161–170.

Conner, K. R., Beautrais, A. L., & Conwell, Y. (2003). Moderators of the relationship between alcohol dependence and suicide and medically serious suicide attempts: Analyses of the Canterbury Suicide Project Data. *Alcoholism: Clinical and Experimental Research, 27,* 1156–1161.

Conner, K. R., Duberstein, P. R., Conwell, Y., & Caine, E. D. (2003). Reactive aggression and suicide: Theory and evidence. *Aggression and Violent Behavior, 8,* 413–432.

Conwell, Y. (2001). Suicide in later life: A review and recommendations for prevention. *Suicide and Life-Threatening Behavior, 31,* 32–47.

Conwell, Y., & Brent, D. (1995). Suicide and aging I: Patterns of psychiatric diagnosis. *International Psychogeriatrics, 7,* 149–164.

Conwell, Y., Duberstein, P. R., & Caine, E. D. (2002). Risk factors for suicide in later life. *Biological Psychiatry, 52,* 193–204.

Conwell, Y., Duberstein, P. R., Cox, C., Herrmann, J. H., Forbes, N. T., & Caine, E. D. (1996). Relationships of age and Axis I diagnoses in victims of completed suicide: A psychological autopsy study. *American Journal of Psychiatry, 153,* 1001–1008.

Conwell, Y., Duberstein, P. R., Cox, C., Herrmann, J. H., Forbes, N. T., & Caine, E. D. (1998). Age differences in behaviors leading to completed suicide. *American Journal of Geriatric Psychiatry, 6,* 122–126.

Cornelius, J. R., Salloum, I. M., Day, N. L., Thase, M. E., & Mann, J. J. (1996). Patterns of suicidality and alcohol use in alcoholics with major depression. *Alcoholism: Clinical and Experimental Research, 20,* 1451–1455.

Cotgrove, A., Zirinsky, L., Black, D., & Weston, D. (1995). Secondary prevention of attempted suicide in adolescence. *Journal of Adolescence, 18,* 569–577.

Crits-Christoph, P., Siqueland, L., Blaine, J., Frank, A., Luborsky, L., Onken, L. S., et al. (1999). Psychosocial treatments for cocaine dependence: National Institute on Drug Abuse Collaborative Cocaine Treatment Study. *Archives of General Psychiatry, 56,* 493–502.

Crosby, A. (2007, April). *Development of uniform definitions for self-directed violence surveillance.* Meeting conducted in New Orleans, Louisiana, Etiology and Surveillance Branch, Division of Violence Prevention, National Center for Injury Prevention and Control, Centers for Disease Control and Prevention.

Crumley, F. E. (1990, June 13). Substance abuse and adolescent suicidal behavior. *JAMA, 263,* 3051–3056.

Curry, J. F., Wells, K. C., Brent, D. A., Clarke, G. N., Rohde, P., Albano, A. M., et al. (2005). *Treatment for Adolescents With Depression Study (TADS) cognitive behavior therapy manual: Introduction, rationale, and adolescent sessions.* Unpublished manuscript, Duke University Medical Center. Retrieved January 31, 2007, from https://trialweb.dcri.duke.edu/tads/tad/manuals/TADS_CBT.pdf

Dahlsgaard, K. K., Beck, A. T., & Brown, G. K. (1998). Inadequate response to therapy as a predictor of suicide. *Suicide and Life-Threatening Behavior, 28,* 197–204.

Darke, S., & Ross, J. (1997). Polydrug dependence and psychiatric comorbidity among heroin injectors. *Drug and Alcohol Dependence, 48,* 135–141.

Darke, S., & Ross, J. (2001). The relationship between suicide and heroin overdose among methadone maintenance patients in Sydney, Australia. *Addiction, 96,* 1443–1453.

Darke, S., & Ross, J. (2002). Suicide among heroin users: Rates, risk factors, and methods. *Addiction, 97,* 1383–1394.

Darke, S., Ross, J., Lynskey, M., & Teesson, M. (2004). Attempted suicide among entrants to three treatment modalities in the Australian Treatment Outcome Study (ATOS): Prevalence and risk factors. *Drug and Alcohol Dependence, 73,* 1–10.

Darke, S., Ross, J., Williamson, A., Mills, K. L., Havard, A., & Teesson, M. (2007). Patterns and correlates of attempted suicide by heroin users over a 3-year period: Findings from the Australian treatment study. *Drug and Alcohol Dependence, 87,* 146–152.

Darke, S., Williamson, A., Ross, J., & Teesson, M. (2005). Attempted suicide among heroin users: 12-month outcomes from the Australian Treatment Outcome Study (ATOS). *Drug and Alcohol Dependence, 78,* 177–186.

Dean, P. J., Range, L. M., & Goggin, W. C. (1996). The escape theory of suicide in college students: Testing a model that includes perfectionism. *Suicide and Life-Threatening Behavior, 26,* 181–186.

De Leo, D., Padoani, W., Lönnqvist, J., Kerkhof, A. J. F. M., Bille-Brahe, U., Salander-Renberg, E., et al. (2002). Repetition of suicidal behaviour in elderly Europeans: A prospective longitudinal study. *Journal of Affective Disorders, 72,* 291–295.

de Man, A. F., & Leduc, C. P. (1994). Validity and reliability of a self-report suicide ideation scale for use with adolescents. *Social Behavior and Personality, 22,* 261–266.

Denning, D. G., Conwell, Y., King, D., & Cox, C. (2000). Method choice, intent, and gender in completed suicide. *Suicide and Life-Threatening Behavior, 30,* 282–288.

DiFilippo, J. M., Esposito, C., Overholser, J., & Spirito, A. (2003). High-risk populations. In A. Spirito & J. C. Overholser (Eds.), *Evaluating and treating adolescent suicide attempters: From research to practice* (pp. 229–259). New York: Academic Press.

Dixon, W., Heppner, P., & Anderson, W. (1991). Problem-solving appraisal, stress, hopelessness, and suicide ideation in a college population. *Journal of Counseling Psychology, 38,* 51–56.

Dombrovski, A. Y., Szanto, K., & Reynolds, C. F. (2005). Epidemiology and risk factors for suicide in the elderly: 10-year update. *Aging Health, 1,* 135–145.

Donaldson, D., Spirito, A., & Esposito-Smythers, C. (2005). Treatment for adolescents following a suicide attempt: Results of a pilot trial. *Journal of the American Academy of Child & Adolescent Psychiatry, 44,* 113–120.

Dougherty, D. M., Mathias, C. W., Marsh, D. M., Papageorgiou, T. D., Swann, A. C., & Moeller, F. G. (2004). Laboratory measured behavioral impulsivity relates to suicide attempt history. *Suicide and Life-Threatening Behavior, 34,* 374–385.

Drake, R. E., & Cotton, P. G. (1986). Depression, hopelessness, and suicide in chronic schizophrenia. *British Journal of Psychiatry, 148,* 554–559.

Duberstein, P. R., Conwell, Y., & Caine, E. D. (1994). Age differences in the personality characteristics of suicide completers: Preliminary findings from a psychological autopsy study. *Psychiatry, 57,* 213–224.

Duberstein, P. R., Conwell, Y., Seidlitz, L., Denning, D. G., Cox, C., & Caine, E. D. (2000). Personality traits and suicidal behavior and ideation in depressed inpatients 50 years of age and older. *Journals of Gerontology Series B: Psychological Sciences & Social Sciences, 55*, P18–P26.

Duberstein, P. R., Conwell, Y., Seidlitz, L., Lyness, J. M., Cox, C., & Caine, E. D. (1999). Age and suicidal ideation in older depressed inpatients. *American Journal of Geriatric Psychiatry, 7,* 289–296.

Dubow, E. F., Kausch, D. F., Blum, M. C., Reed, J., & Bush, E. (1989). Correlates of suicidal ideation and attempts in a community sample of junior and senior high school students. *Journal of Clinical Child Psychiatry, 18,* 158–166.

Dyer, J. A. T., & Kreitman, N. (1984). Hopelessness, depression and suicidal intent in parasuicide. *British Journal of Psychiatry, 144,* 127–133.

D'Zurilla, T. J., Chang, E. C., Nottingham, E. J., & Faccini, L. (1998). Social problem solving deficits and hopelessness, depression, and suicide risk in college students and psychiatric inpatients. *Journal of Clinical Psychology, 54,* 1091–1107.

D'Zurilla, T., Nezu, A., & Maydeu-Olivares, A. (2004). Social problem solving: Theory and assessment. In E. Chang, T. D'Zurilla, & C. Sanna (Eds.), *Social problem solving: Theory, research, and training* (pp. 11–27). Washington, DC: American Psychological Association.

Ellis, J. B., & Smith, P. C. (1991). Spiritual well-being, social desirability and reasons for living: Is there a connection? *International Journal of Social Psychiatry, 37,* 57–63.

Ellis, T. E. (2006). Epilogue: What have we learned about cognition and suicide and what more do we need to know? In T. E. Ellis (Ed.), *Cognition and suicide: Theory, research, and therapy* (pp. 369–380). Washington, DC: American Psychological Association.

Ellis, T. E., & Newman, C. F. (1996). *Choosing to live: How to defeat suicide through cognitive therapy.* Oakland, CA: New Harbinger.

Ellis, T. E., & Ratliff, K. G. (1986). Cognitive characteristics of suicidal and non-suicidal psychiatric inpatients. *Cognitive Therapy and Research, 10,* 625–634.

Emery, G. D., Steer, R. A., & Beck, A. T. (1981). Depression, hopelessness, and suicidal intent among heroin addicts. *International Journal of Addictions, 16,* 425–429.

Endicott, P. G., & Ogloff, J. R. P. (2006). Elucidation of impulsivity. *Australian Psychologist, 41,* 3–14.

Erinoff, L., Compton, W. M., & Volkow, N. D. (2004). Drug abuse and suicidal behavior. *Drug and Alcohol Dependence, 76*(Suppl. 1), S1–S2.

Esposito, C., Johnson, B., Wolfsdorf, B. A., & Spirito, A. (2003). Cognitive factors: Hopelessness, coping, and problem solving. In A. Spirito & J. C. Overholser (Eds.), *Evaluating and treating adolescent suicide attempters: From research to practice* (pp. 89–112). New York: Academic Press.

Esposito, C., Spirito, A., & Overholser, J. (2003). Behavioral factors: Impulsive and aggressive behavior. In A. Spirito & J. C. Overholser (Eds.), *Evaluating and treating adolescent suicide attempters: From research to practice* (pp. 147–159). New York: Academic Press.

Evans, J., Evans, M., Morgan, H. G., Hayward, A., & Gunnell, D. (2005). Crisis card following self-harm: 12-month follow-up of a randomized controlled trial. *British Journal of Psychiatry, 187,* 186–187.

Evans, K., Tyrer, P., Catalan, J., Schmidt, U., Davidson, K., Dent, J., et al. (1999). Manual-assisted cognitive-behavior therapy (MACT): A randomized controlled trial of a brief intervention with bibliotherapy in the treatment of recurrent deliberate self-harm. *Psychological Medicine, 29,* 19–25.

Eynan, R., Langley, J., Tolomiczenko, G., Rhodes, A. E., Links, P., Wasylenki, D., et al. (2002). The association between homelessness and suicidal ideation and behaviors: Results of a cross-sectional survey. *Suicide and Life-Threatening Behavior, 32,* 418–442.

Farley, M., Golding, J. M., Young, G., Mulligan, M., & Minkoff, J. R. (2004). Trauma history and relapse probability among patients seeking substance abuse treatment. *Journal of Substance Abuse Treatment, 27,* 161–167.

Faulkner, A. H., & Cranston, K. (1998). Correlates of same-sex behavior in a random sample of Massachusetts high school students. *American Journal of Public Health, 88,* 262–266.

Favazza, A. R. (1996). *Bodies under siege: Self-mutilation and body modification in culture and psychiatry.* Baltimore: Johns Hopkins University Press.

Fawcett, J., Busch, K. A., Jacobs, D., Kravitz, H. M., & Fogg, L. (1997). Suicide: A four-pathway clinical-biochemical model. In D. Stoff & J. Mann (Eds.), *The neurobiology of suicide: From bench to the clinic* (pp. 288–301). New York: New York Academy of Sciences.

Feldman, M., & Wilson, A. (1997). Adolescent suicidality in urban minorities and its relationship to conduct disorders, depression, and separation anxiety. *Journal of the American Academy of Child & Adolescent Psychiatry, 36,* 75–84.

Fenton, W. S., McGlashan, T. H., Vistor, B. J., & Blyer, C. R. (1997). Symptoms, subtype, and suicidality in patients with schizophrenia spectrum disorders. *American Journal of Psychiatry, 154,* 199–204.

Forman, E. M., Berk, M. S., Henriques, G. R., Brown, G. K., & Beck, A. T. (2004). History of multiple suicide attempts as a behavioral marker of severe psychopathology. *American Journal of Psychiatry, 161,* 437–443.

Fox, C., & Hawton, K. (2004). *Deliberate self-harm in adolescence.* London: Jessica Kingsley.

Freedenthal, S. (2007). Challenges in assessing intent to die: Can suicide attempters be trusted? *Omega, 55,* 57–70.

Fremouw, W., Callahan, B., & Kashden, J. (1993). Adolescent suicide risk: Psychological, problem-solving, and environmental factors. *Suicide and Life-Threatening Behavior, 23,* 46–54.

Fridell, E. J., Ojehagen, A., & Träskman-Bendz, L. (1996). A 5-year follow-up study of suicide attempts. *Acta Psychiatrica Scandinavica, 93,* 151–157.

Gallo, J. J., Anthony, J. C., & Muthen, B. O. (1994). Age differences in the symptoms of depression: A latent trait analysis. *Journal of Gerontology, 49,* P251–P264.

Gallo, J. J., Rabins, P. V., & Anthony, J. C. (1999). Sadness in older persons: 13-year follow-up of a community sample in Baltimore, Maryland. *Psychological Medicine, 29,* 341–350.

Garofalo, R., Wolf, R., Cameron, M. S., Kessel, S., Palfrey, J., & DuRant, R. H. (1998). The association between health risk behaviors and sexual orientation among a school-based sample of adolescents. *Pediatrics, 101,* 895–902.

Gibbons, J. S., Butler, J., Urwin, P., & Gibbons, J. L. (1978). Evaluation of a social work service for self-poisoning patients. *British Journal of Psychiatry, 133,* 111–118.

Gilman, S. E., Cochran, S. D., Mays, V. M., Hughes, M., Ostrow, D., & Kessler, R. C. (2001). Risk of psychiatric disorders among individuals reporting same-sex sexual partners in the National Comorbidity Survey. *American Journal of Public Health, 91,* 933–939.

Gispert, M., Davis, M., Marsh, L., & Wheeler, R. (1987). Predictive factors in repeated suicide attempts by adolescents. *Hospital and Community Psychiatry, 38,* 390–393.

Gitlin, J. M. (1999). A psychiatrist's reaction to a patient suicide. *American Journal of Psychiatry, 156,* 1630–1634.

Glick, I. D., Zaninelli, R., Hsu, C., Young, F. K., Weiss, L., Gunay, I., et al. (2004). Patterns of concomitant psychotropic medication use during a 2-year study comparing clozapine and olanzapine for the prevention of suicidal behavior. *Journal of Clinical Psychiatry, 65,* 679–685.

Glowinski, A. L., Bucholz, K. K., Nelson, E. C., Fu, Q., Madden, P., Reich, W., et al. (2001). Suicide attempts in an adolescent female twin sample. *Journal of the American Academy of Child & Adolescent Psychiatry, 40,* 1300–1307.

Goldsmith, S. K., Pellman, T. C., Kleinman, A. M., & Bunney, W. E. (2002). *Reducing suicide: A national imperative.* Washington, DC: National Academies Press.

Goldstein, R. B., Black, D. W., Nasrallah, A., & Winokur, G. (1991). The prediction of suicide: Sensitivity, specificity, and predictive value of a multivariate model applied to suicide among 1906 patients with affective disorders. *Archives of General Psychiatry, 48,* 418–422.

Goldston, D. B. (2003). *Measuring suicidal behavior and risk in children and adolescents.* Washington, DC: American Psychological Association.

Gould, M. S., Fisher, P., Parides, M., Flory, M., & Schaffer, D. (1996). Psychosocial risk factors of child and adolescent completed suicide. *Archives of General Psychiatry, 53,* 1155–1162.

Gould, M. S., & Shaffer, D. (1986). The impact of suicide in television movies. *New England Journal of Medicine, 315,* 690–694.

Gould, M. S., Shaffer, D., Fisher, P., & Garfinkel, R. (1998). Separation/divorce and child and adolescent completed suicide. *Journal of the American Academy of Child & Adolescent Psychiatry, 37,* 155–162.

Gould, M., Velting, D., Kleinman, M., Lucas, C., Thomas, J. G., & Chung, M. (2004). Teenagers' attitudes about coping strategies and help-seeking behavior for suicidality. *Journal of the American Academy of Child & Adolescent Psychiatry, 43,* 1124–1133.

Griffin-Fennell, F., & Williams, M. (2006). Examining the complexities of suicidal behavior in the African American community. *Journal of Black Psychology, 32,* 303–319.

Gunnell, D., & Frankel, S. (1994). Prevention of suicide: Aspirations and evidence. *British Medical Journal, 308,* 1227–1233.

Guthrie, E., Kapur, N., Mackway-Jones, K., Chew-Graham, C., Moorey, J., Mendel, E., et al. (2001). Randomised controlled trial of brief psychological intervention after deliberate self poisoning. *British Medical Journal, 323,* 135–138.

Haring, M., Hewitt, P. L., & Flett, G. L. (2003). Perfectionism and the quality of intimate relationships. *Journal of Marriage and the Family, 65,* 143–158.

Harrington, R., Kerfoot, M., Dyer, E., McNiven, F., Gill, J., Harrington, V., et al. (1998). Randomized trial of a home-based family intervention for children who have deliberately poisoned themselves. *Journal of the American Academy of Child & Adolescent Psychiatry, 37,* 512–518.

Harris, E. C., & Barraclough, B. (1994). Suicide as an outcome for medical disorders. *Medicine Baltimore, 73,* 281–396.

Harris, E. C., & Barraclough, B. (1997). Suicide as an outcome for mental disorders: A meta-analysis. *British Journal of Psychiatry, 170,* 205–228.

Harris, H. E., & Myers, W. C. (1997). Adolescents' misperceptions of the dangerousness of acetaminophen in overdose. *Suicide and Life-Threatening Behavior, 27,* 274–277.

Harriss, L., & Hawton, K. (2005). Suicidal intent in deliberate self-harm and the risk of suicide: The predictive power of the Suicide Intent Scale. *Journal of Affective Disorders, 86,* 225–233.

Harriss, L., Hawton, K., & Zahl, D. (2005). Value of measuring suicidal intent in the assessment of people attending hospital following self-poisoning or self-injury. *British Journal of Psychiatry, 186,* 60–66.

Hausman, K. (2003). Psychiatrists often overwhelmed by a patient's suicide. *Psychiatric News, 38,* 6.

Hawton, K. (1987). Assessment of suicide risk. *British Journal of Psychiatry, 150,* 145–153.

Hawton, K., Arensman, E., Townsend, E., Bremner, S., Feldman, E., Goldney, R., et al. (1998). Deliberate self harm: Systematic review of efficacy of psychosocial and pharmacological treatments in preventing repetition. *British Medical Journal, 317,* 441–447.

Hawton, K., Bancroft, J., Catalan, J., Kingston, B., Stedeford, A., & Welch, N. (1981). Domiciliary and outpatient treatment of self-poisoning patients by medical and nonmedical staff. *Psychological Medicine, 11,* 169–177.

Hawton, K., Cole, D., O'Grady, J., & Osborne, M. (1982). Motivational aspects of deliberate self-poisoning in adolescents. *British Journal of Psychiatry, 141,* 286–291.

Hawton, K., & Harriss, L. (2006). Deliberate self-harm in people aged 60 years and over: Characteristics and outcome of a 20-year cohort. *International Journal of Geriatric Psychiatry, 21,* 572–581.

Hawton, K., Kingsbury, S., Steinhardt, K., James, A., & Fagg, J. (1999). Repetition of deliberate self-harm by adolescents: The role of psychological factors. *Journal of Adolescence, 22,* 369–378.

Hawton, K., McKeown, S., Day, A., Martin, P., O'Connor, M., & Yule, J. (1987). Evaluation of out-patient counseling compared with general practitioner care following overdoses. *Psychological Medicine, 17,* 751–761.

Hawton, K., Sutton, L., Haw, C., Sinclair, J., & Harriss, L. (2005). Suicide and attempted suicide in bipolar disorder: A systematic review of risk factors. *Journal of Clinical Psychiatry, 66,* 693–704.

Hawton, K., Townsend, E., Arensman, E., Gunnell, D., Hazell, P., House, A., et al. (2005). Psychosocial and pharmacological treatments for deliberate self-harm. *Cochrane Database of Systematic Reviews, 3,* CD001764. doi: 10.1002/14651858.CD001764

Hawton, K., Zahl, D., & Weatherall, R. (2003). Suicide following deliberate self-harm: Long-term follow-up of patients who presented to a general hospital. *British Journal of Psychiatry, 182,* 537–542.

Hayes, L. M. (1995). *Prison suicide: An overview and guide to prevention.* Washington, DC: U.S. Department of Justice, National Institute of Corrections.

Heikkinen, M., Aro, H., & Lönnqvist, J. (1994). Recent life events, social support and suicide. *Acta Psychiatrica Scandinavica, 89,* 65–72.

Heikkinen, M. E., Isometsä, E. T., Marttunen, J. J., Aro, H. M., & Lönnqvist, J. K. (1995). Social factors in suicide. *British Journal of Psychiatry, 167,* 747–753.

Heikkinen, M. E., & Lönnqvist, J. K. (1995). Recent life events in elderly suicide: A nationwide study in Finland. *International Psychogeriatrics, 7,* 287–300.

Heila, H., Isometsä, E. T., Henriksson, M. M., Heikkinen, M. E., Marttunen, M. J., & Lönnqvist, J. K. (1997). Suicide and schizophrenia: A nationwide psychological autopsy study on age- and sex-specific clinical characteristics of 92 suicide victims with schizophrenia. *American Journal of Psychiatry, 154,* 1235–1242.

Heisel, M. J., Duberstein, P. R., Conner, K. R., Franus, N., Beckman, A., & Conwell, Y. (2006). Personality and reports of suicide ideation among depressed adults 50 years of age or older. *Journal of Affective Disorders, 90,* 175–180.

Hendin, H., Lipschitz, A., Maltsberger, J. T., Haas, A. P., & Whynecoop, S. (2000). Therapists' reactions to patient suicides. *American Journal of Psychiatry, 157,* 2022–2027.

Henriques, G. R., Beck, A. T., & Brown, G. K. (2003). Cognitive therapy for adolescent and young adult suicide attempters. *American Behavioral Scientist, 46,* 1258–1268.

Henriques, G., Wenzel, A., Brown, G. K., & Beck, A. T. (2005). Suicide attempters' reaction to survival as a risk factor for eventual suicide. *American Journal of Psychiatry, 162,* 2180–2182.

Hepp, U., Wittmann, L., Schnyder, U., & Michel, K. (2004). Psychological and psychosocial interventions after attempted suicide: An overview of treatment studies. *Crisis, 25,* 108–117.

Hewitt, P. L., & Flett, G. L. (1991). Perfectionism in the self and social contexts: Conceptualization, assessment, and association with psychopathology. *Journal of Personality and Social Psychology, 60,* 456–470.

Hewitt, P. L., Flett, G. L., Sherry, S. B., & Caelian, C. (2006). Trait perfectionism dimensions and suicidal behavior. In T. E. Ellis (Ed.), *Cognition and suicide: Theory, research, and therapy* (pp. 215–235). Washington, DC: American Psychological Association.

Hewitt, P. L., Flett, G. L., & Turnbull-Donovan, W. (1992). Perfectionism and suicide potential. *British Journal of Clinical Psychology, 31,* 181–190.

Hewitt, P. L., Flett, G. L., & Weber, C. (1994). Perfectionism, hopelessness, and suicide ideation. *Cognitive Therapy and Research, 18,* 439–468.

Hewitt, P. L., Norton, G. R., Flett, G. L., Callender, L., & Cowan, T. (1998). Dimensions of perfectionism, hopelessness, and attempted suicide in a sample of alcoholics. *Suicide and Life-Threatening Behavior, 28,* 396–406.

Hjelmeland, H., Stiles, T. C., Brille-Brahe, U., Ostamo, A., Renberg, E. S., & Wasserman, D. (1998). Parasuicide: The value of suicidal intent and various motives as predictors of future suicidal behaviour. *Archives of Suicide Research, 4,* 209–225.

Hobson, R. F. (1985). *Forms of feeling.* London: Tavistock.

Hollenbeck, J., Dyl, J., & Spirito, A. (2003). Social factors: Family functioning. In A. Spirito & J. C. Overholser (Eds.), *Evaluating and treating adolescent suicide attempters: From research to practice* (pp. 161–189). New York: Academic Press.

Hollon, S. D., Stewart, M. O., & Strunk, D. (2006). Enduring effects of cognitive behavior therapy in the treatment of depression and anxiety. *Annual Review of Psychology, 57,* 285–315.

Holmstrand, C., Niméus, A., & Träskman-Bendz, L. (2006). Risk factors of future suicide in suicide attempters—A comparison between suicides and matched survivors. *Nordic Journal of Psychiatry, 60,* 162–167.

Hoyer, G., & Lund, E. (1993). Suicide among women related to number of children in marriage. *Archives of General Psychiatry, 50,* 134–157.

Huey, S. J., Henggeler, S. W., Rowland, M. D., Halliday-Boykins, C. A., Cunningham, P. B., Pickrel, S. G., et al. (2004). Multisystemic therapy effects on attempted suicide by youths presenting psychiatric emergencies. *Journal of the American Academy of Child & Adolescent Psychiatry, 43,* 183–190.

Hufford, M. R. (2001). Alcohol and suicidal behavior. *Clinical Psychology Review, 21,* 797–811.

Hughes, D., & Kleespies, P. (2001). Suicide in the medically ill. *Suicide and Life-Threatening Behavior, 31,* 48–59.

Hunter, E. C., & O'Connor, R. C. (2003). Hopelessness and future thinking in parasuicide: The role of perfectionism. *British Journal of Clinical Psychology, 42,* 355–365.

Ingram, R. E., & Kendall, P. C. (1986). Cognitive clinical psychology: Implications of an information processing perspective. In R. E. Ingram (Ed), *Information processing approaches to clinical psychology* (pp. 3–21). San Diego, CA: Academic Press.

Inskip, H. M., Harris, E. C., & Barraclough, B. (1998). Lifetime risk of suicide for affective disorder, alcoholism, and schizophrenia. *British Journal of Psychiatry, 72,* 35–37.

Jarvik, L. F., Mintz, J., Steuer, J., & Gerner, R. (1982). Treating geriatric depression: A 26-week interim analysis. *Journal of the American Geriatrics Society, 30,* 713–717.

Jeglic, E. L., Sharp, I. R., Chapman, J. E., Brown, G. K., & Beck, A. T. (2005). History of family suicide behaviors and negative problem solving in multiple suicide attempters. *Archives of Suicide Research, 9,* 135–146.

Jobes, D. A. (2000). Collaborating to prevent suicide: A clinical-research perspective. *Suicide and Life-Threatening Behavior, 30,* 8–17.

Jobes, D. A. (2006). *Managing suicidal risk: A collaborative approach.* New York: Guilford Press.

Jobes, D. A., Jacoby, A. M., Cimbolic, P., & Hustead, L. A. T. (1997). The assessment and treatment of suicidal clients in a university counseling center. *Journal of Counseling Psychology, 44,* 368–377.

Jobes, D. A., & Mann, R. E. (1999). Reasons for living versus reasons for dying: Examining the internal debate of suicide. *Suicide and Life-Threatening Behavior, 29,* 97–104.

Jobes, D. A., Wong, S. A., Conrad, A., Drozd, J. F., & Neal-Walden, T. (2005). The collaborative assessment and management of suicidality vs. treatment as usual: A retrospective study with suicidal outpatients. *Suicide and Life-Threatening Behavior, 35,* 483–497.

Joe, S., & Kaplan, M. S. (2001). Suicide among African American men. *Suicide and Life-Threatening Behavior, 31,* 106–121.

Joiner, T. E. (2005). *Why people die by suicide.* Cambridge, MA: Harvard University Press.

Joiner, T. E., Brown, J. S., & Wingate, L. R. (2005). The psychology and neurobiology of suicidal behavior. *Annual Review of Psychology, 56,* 287–314.

Joiner, T. E, Conwell, Y., Fitzpatrick, K. K., Witte, T. K., Schmidt, N. B., Merlim, M. T., et al. (2005). Four studies on how past and current suicidality relate even when "everything but the kitchen sink" is covaried. *Journal of Abnormal Psychology, 114,* 291–303.

Joiner, T. E., Pettit, J. W., Walker, R. L., Voelz, Z. R., Cruz, J., Rudd, M. D., et al. (2002). Perceived burdensomeness and suicidality: Two studies on the suicide notes of those attempting and those completing suicide. *Journal of Social and Clinical Psychology, 21,* 531–545.

Joiner, T. E., & Rudd, M. D. (2000). Intensity and duration of suicidal crises vary as a function of previous suicide attempts and negative life events. *Journal of Consulting and Clinical Psychology, 68*, 909–916.

Joiner, T. E., Sachs-Ericsson, N. J., Wingate, L. R., Brown, J. W., Anestis, M. D., & Selby, E. A. (2007). Childhood physical and sexual abuse and lifetime number of suicide attempts: A persistent and theoretically important relationship. *Behaviour Research and Therapy, 45*, 539–547.

Kadden, R. M., Litt, M. D., Cooney, N., Kabela, E., & Getter, H. (2001). Prospective matching of alcoholic clients to cognitive-behavioral or interactional group therapy. *Journal of Studies on Alcohol, 62*, 359–369.

Kaplan, M. S., Huguet, N., McFarland, B. H., & Newsom, J. T. (2007). Suicide among male veterans: A prospective population-based study. *Journal of Epidemiology and Community Health, 61*, 619–624.

Kashden, J., Fremouw, W. J., Callahan, T. S., & Franzen, M. D. (1993). Impulsivity in suicidal and nonsuicidal adolescents. *Journal of Abnormal Child Psychology, 21*, 339–353.

Kazantzis, N., Deane, F. P., & Ronan, K. R. (2000). Homework assignments in cognitive and behavioral therapy: A meta-analysis. *Clinical Psychology: Science and Practice, 7*, 189–202.

Kellerman, A. L., & Reay, D. T. (1986). Protection or peril? An analysis of forearm-related deaths in the home. *New England Journal of Medicine, 327*, 1557–1560.

Kelly, K. T., & Knudson, M. P. (2000). Are no-suicide contracts effective in preventing suicide in suicidal patients seen by primary care physicians? *Archives of Family Medicine, 9*, 1119–1121.

Kessler, R. C., Borges, G., & Walters, E. E. (1999). Prevalence of and risk factors for lifetime suicide attempts in the National Comorbidity Survey. *Archives of General Psychiatry, 56*, 617–626.

King, C. A., Kramer, A., Preuss, L., Kerr, D. C. R., Weisse, L., & Venkataraman, S. (2006). Youth-nominated support team for suicidal adolescents (Version 1): A randomized controlled trial. *Journal of Consulting and Clinical Psychology, 74*, 199–206.

King, C., Raskin, A., Gdowski, C., Butkus, M., & Opipari, L. (1990). Psychosocial factors associated with urban adolescent female suicide attempts. *Journal of the American Academy of Child & Adolescent Psychiatry, 29*, 289–294.

Kingsbury, S., Hawton, K., Steinhardt, K., & James, A. (1999). Do adolescents who take overdoses have specific psychological characteristics? A comparative study with psychiatric and community controls. *Journal of the American Academy of Child & Adolescent Psychiatry, 29*, 289–294.

Kleespies, P. M., & Dettmer, E. L. (2000). The stress of patient emergencies for the clinician: Incidence, impact, and means of coping. *Journal of Clinical Psychology, 56*, 1353–1369.

Koller, G., Preuss, U. W., Bottlender, M., Wenzel, K., & Soyka, M. (2002). Impulsivity and aggression as predictors of suicide attempts in alcoholics. *European Archives of Psychiatry and Clinical Neuroscience, 252*, 155–160.

Kõlves, K., Värnik, A., Tooding, L.-M., & Wasserman, D. (2006). The role of alcohol in suicide: A case-control psychological autopsy study. *Psychological Medicine, 36,* 923–930.

Kosky, R., Silburn, S., & Zubrick, S. (1990). Are children and adolescents who have suicidal thoughts different from those who attempt suicide? *The Journal of Nervous and Mental Disease, 178,* 38–43.

Kovacs, M., & Beck, A. T. (1977). The wish to die and the wish to live in attempted suicides. *Journal of Clinical Psychology, 33,* 361–365.

Kovacs, M., Beck, A. T., & Weissman, A. (1975). Hopelessness: An indicator of suicidal risk. *Suicide, 5,* 98–103.

Kovacs, M., Beck, A. T., & Weissman, A. (1976). The communication of suicidal intent: A reexamination. *Archives of General Psychiatry, 33,* 198–201.

Kposowa, A. J. (2000). Marital status and suicide in the National Longitudinal Mortality Study. *Journal of Epidemiology and Community Health, 54,* 254–261.

Kraemer, H. C., Kazdin, A. E., Offord, D. R., Kessler, R. C., Jensen, P. S., & Kupfer, D. J. (1997). Coming to terms with the terms of risk. *Archives of General Psychiatry, 54,* 337–343.

Kreitman, N. (1979). Reflections on the management of parasuicide. *British Journal of Psychiatry, 135,* 275–277.

Kreitman, N., Carstairs, V., & Duffy, J. (1991). Association of age and social class with suicide among men in Great Britain. *Journal of Epidemiological Community Health, 45,* 195–202.

Kreitman, N., & Philip, A. E. (1969). Parasuicide [Letter to the editor]. *British Journal of Psychiatry, 115,* 746–747.

Krupinski, M., Fischer, A., Grohmann, R., Engel, R., Hollweg, M., & Möller, H.-J. (1998). Risk factors for suicides of inpatients with depressive psychoses. *European Archives of Psychiatry and Clinical Neuroscience, 248,* 141–147.

Kuo, W., Gallo, J. J., & Tien, A. Y. (2001). Incidence of suicide ideation and attempts in adults: The 13-year follow-up of a community sample in Baltimore, Maryland. *Psychological Medicine, 31,* 1181–1191.

Laederach, L., Fischer, W., Bowen, P., & Ladame, F. (1999). Common risk factors in adolescent suicide attempters revisited. *Crisis, 20,* 15–22.

Laidlaw, K., Thompson, L. W., Dick-Siskin, L., & Gallagher-Thompson, D. (2003). *Cognitive behaviour therapy with older people.* New York: Wiley.

Lehnert, K. L., Overholser, J. C., & Spirito, A. (1994). Internalized and externalized anger in adolescent suicide attempters. *Journal of Adolescent Research, 9,* 105–119.

Lester, D., & Beck, A. T. (1975). Attempted suicide: Correlates of increasing medical lethality. *Psychological Reports, 37,* 1236–1238.

Lester, D., Beck, A. T., & Mitchell, B. (1979). Extrapolation from attempted suicides to completed suicides: A test. *Journal of Abnormal Psychology, 88,* 78–80.

Levenson, J. L., & Bostwick, J. M. (2005). Suicidality in the medically ill. *Primary Psychiatry, 12,* 16–18.

Lewinsohn, P. M., Rohde, P., & Seeley, J. R. (1994). Psychosocial risk factors for future adolescent suicide attempts. *Journal of Consulting and Clinical Psychology*, 62, 297–305.

Li, G. (1995). The interaction effect of bereavement and sex on the risk of suicide in the elderly: An historical cohort study. *Social Science Medicine*, 40, 825–828.

Liberman, R. P., & Eckman, T. (1981). Behavior therapy vs. insight-oriented therapy for repeat suicide attempters. *Archives of General Psychiatry*, 38, 1126–1130.

Lindqvist, D., Niméus, A., & Träskman-Bendz, L. (2007). Suicidal intent and psychiatric symptoms among inpatient suicide attempters. *Nordic Journal of Psychiatry*, 61, 27–32.

Linehan, M. M. (1993a). *Cognitive-behavioral treatment of borderline personality disorder.* New York: Guilford Press.

Linehan, M. M. (1993b). *Skills training manual for treating borderline personality disorder.* New York: Guilford Press.

Linehan, M. M. (1997). Behavioral treatments of suicidal behaviors: Definitional obfuscation and treatment outcomes. *Annals of the New York Academy of Sciences*, 836, 302–328.

Linehan, M. M., Armstrong, H. E., Suarez, A., Allmon, D., & Heard, H. L. (1991). Cognitive-behavioral treatment of chronically parasuicidal borderline patients. *Archives of General Psychiatry*, 836, 1060–1064.

Linehan, M. M., Comtois, K. A., Murray, A. M., Brown, M. Z., Gallop, R. J., Heard, H., et al. (2006). Two-year randomized controlled trial and follow-up of dialectical behavior therapy vs therapy by experts for suicidal behaviors and borderline personality disorder. *Archives of General Psychiatry*, 63, 757–766.

Linehan, M. M., Goodstein, J. L., Nielsen, S. L., & Chiles, J. A. (1983). Reasons for staying alive when you are thinking of killing yourself: The Reasons for Living Inventory. *Journal of Consulting and Clinical Psychology*, 51, 276–286.

Links, P. S., Heisel, M. J., & Quastel, A. (2005). Is suicide ideation a surrogate endpoint for geriatric suicide? *Suicide and Life-Threatening Behavior*, 35, 193–205.

Litt, M. D., Kadden, R. M., Cooney, N. L., & Kabela, E. (2003). Coping skills and treatment outcomes in cognitive–behavioral and interactional group therapy for alcoholism. *Journal of Consulting and Clinical Psychology*, 71, 118–128.

Loebel, J. P. (2005). Completed suicide in late life. *Psychiatric Services*, 56, 260–262.

Lönnqvist, J. K. (2000). Psychiatric aspects of suicidal behaviour: depression. In K. Hawton & K. Van Heeringen (Eds.), *The international handbook of suicide and attempted suicide* (pp. 107–120). Chichester, England: Wiley.

Lönnqvist, J. K., Henriksson, M. M., Isometsä, E. T., Marttunen, M. J., Heikkinen, M. E., Aro, H. M., et al. (1995). Mental disorders and suicide prevention. *Psychiatry & Clinical Neurosciences*, 49, S111–S116.

MacLeod, C., Mathews, A. M., & Tata, P. (1986). Attentional bias in emotional disorders. *Journal of Abnormal Psychology*, 95, 15–20.

MacMahon, B., & Pugh, T. F. (1985). Suicide in the widowed. *American Journal of Epidemiology*, 81, 23–31.

Malone, K. M., Oquendo, M. A., Haas, G. L., Ellis, S. P., Li, S., & Mann, J. J. (2000). Protective factors against suicidal acts in major depression: Reasons for living. *American Journal of Psychiatry, 157,* 1084–1088.

Mann, J. J. (2003). Neurobiology of suicidal behaviour. *Nature Reviews Neuroscience, 4,* 819–828.

Mann, J. J., Apter, A., Bertolote, J., Beautrais, A., Currier, D., Haas, A., et al. (2005, October 26). Suicide prevention strategies: A systematic review. *JAMA, 294,* 2064–2074

Mann, J. J., Waternaux, C., Haas, G. L., & Malone, K. M. (1999). Toward a clinical model of suicidal behavior in psychiatric patients. *American Journal of Psychiatry, 156,* 181–189.

Marzuk, P. M., Leon, A. C., Tardiff, K., Morgan, E. B., Stajic, M., & Mann, J. J. (1992). The effect of access to lethal methods of injury on suicide rates. *Archives of General Psychiatry, 49,* 451–458.

Maser, J. D., Akiskal, H. S., Schettler, P., Scheftner, W., Mueller, T., Endicott, J., et al. (2002). Can temperament identify affectively ill patients who engage in lethal or near-lethal suicidal behavior? A 14-year prospective study. *Suicide and Life-Threatening Behavior, 32,* 10–32.

McCabe, S. E., Boyd, C., Cranford, J., Morales, M., & Slayden, J. (2006). A modified version of the Drug Abuse Screening Test among undergraduate students. *Journal of Substance Abuse Treatment, 31,* 297–303.

McCloud, A., Barnaby, B., Omu, N., Drummond, C., & Aboud, A. (2004). Relationship between alcohol use disorders and suicidality in a psychiatric population. *British Journal of Psychiatry, 184,* 439–445.

McHolm, A. E., MacMillan, H. L., & Jamieson, E. (2003). The relationship between childhood physical abuse and suicidality among depressed women: Results from a community sample. *American Journal of Psychiatry, 160,* 933–938.

McLeavey, B. C., Daly, R. J., Ludgate, J. W., & Murray, C. M. (1994). Interpersonal problem-solving skills training in the treatment of self-poisoning patients. *Suicide and Life-Threatening Behavior, 24,* 382–394.

McMillan, D., Gilbody, S., Beresford, E., & Neilly, L. (2007). Can we predict suicide and non-fatal self-harm with the Beck Hopelessness Scale? A meta-analysis. *Psychological Medicine, 37,* 769–778.

McNally, R. J. (1995). Automaticity and the anxiety disorders. *Behaviour Research and Therapy, 33,* 747–754.

Mehlenbeck, R., Spirito, A., Barnett, N., & Overholser, J. (2003). Behavioral factors: Substance use. In A. Spirito & J. C. Overholser (Eds.), *Evaluating and treating adolescent suicide attempters: From research to practice* (pp. 113–145). New York: Academic Press.

Meltzer, H. Y. (2003). Reducing the risk for suicide in schizophrenia and affective disorders. *Journal of Clinical Psychiatry, 64,* 1122–1129.

Meltzer, H. Y., Alphs, L., Green, A. I., Altamura, A. C., Anand, R., Bertoldi, A., et al. (2003). Clozapine treatment for suicidality in schizophrenia: International suicide prevention trial (InterSePT). *Archives of General Psychiatry, 60,* 82–91.

Michaelis, B. H., Goldberg, J. F., Davis, G. P., Singer, T. M., Garno, J. L., & Wenze, S. J. (2004). Dimensions of impulsivity and aggression associated with suicide attempts among bipolar patients: A preliminary study. *Suicide and Life-Threatening Behavior, 34*, 172–176.

Mieczkowski, T. A., Sweeney, J. A., Haas, G. L., Junker, B. W., Brown, R. P., & Mann, J. J. (1993). Factor composition of the Suicide Intent Scale. *Suicide and Life-Threatening Behavior, 23*, 37–45.

Miller, A. L., Rathus, J. H., & Linehan, M. M. (2007). *Dialectical behavior therapy with suicidal adolescents.* New York: Guilford Press.

Minkoff, K., Bergman, E., Beck, A. T., & Beck, R. (1973). Hopelessness, depression, and attempted suicide. *American Journal of Psychiatry, 130*, 455–459.

Moeller, F. G., Barratt, E. S., Dougherty, D. M., Schmitz, J. M., & Swann, A. C. (2001). Psychiatric aspects of impulsivity. *American Journal of Psychiatry, 158*, 1783–1793.

Moher, D., Schulz, K. F., & Altman, D., for the CONSORT Group. (2001, April 18). The CONSORT statement: Revised recommendations for improving the quality of reports of parallel-group randomized trials. *JAMA, 285*, 1987–1991.

Moller, H. J. (1989). Efficacy of different strategies of aftercare for patients who have attempted suicide. *Journal of the Royal Society of Medicine, 82*, 643–647.

Montano, C. B. (1999). Primary care issues related to the treatment of depression in elderly patients. *Journal of Clinical Psychiatry, 60*, 45–51.

Montgomery, D. B., Roberts, A., Green, M., Bullock, T., Baldwin, D., & Montgomery, S. A. (1994). Lack of efficacy of fluoxetine in recurrent brief depression and suicidal attempts. *European Archives of Psychiatry and Clinical Neuroscience, 244*, 211–215.

Montgomery, S. A., Roy, D., & Montgomery, D. B. (1983). The prevention of recurrent suicidal acts. *British Journal of Clinical Pharmacology, 15*, 183–188.

Morgan, H. G., Burns-Cox, C. J., Pocock, H., & Pottle, S. (1975). Deliberate self-harm: Clinical and socio-economic characteristics of 368 patients. *British Journal of Psychiatry, 127*, 564–574.

Morgan, H. G., Jones, E. M., & Owen, J. H. (1993). Secondary prevention of non-fatal deliberate self-harm. *British Journal of Psychiatry, 163*, 111–112.

Morgenstern, J., & Longabaugh, R. (2000). Cognitive-behavioral treatment for alcohol dependence: A review of evidence for its hypothesized mechanisms of action. *Addiction, 95*, 1475–1490.

Mortensen, P. B., & Juel, K. (1993). Mortality and causes of death in first admitted schizophrenic patients. *British Journal of Psychiatry, 163*, 183–189.

Mocecicki, E. K. (1995). Gender differences in completed and attempted suicides. *Annals of Epidemiology, 4*, 152–158.

Mocecicki, E. K. (1999). Epidemiology of suicide. In D. G. Jacobs (Ed.), *The Harvard Medical School guide to suicide assessment intervention* (pp. 40–51). San Francisco: Jossey-Bass.

Mocecicki, E. K., O'Carroll, P., Rae, D. S., Locke, B. Z., Roy, A., & Regier, D. A. (1988). Suicide attempts in the Epidemiologic Catchment Area Study. *Yale Journal of Biology and Medicine, 61,* 259–268.

Motto, J. A. (1976). Suicide prevention for high-risk persons who refuse treatment. *Suicide and Life-Threatening Behavior, 6,* 223–230.

Motto, J. A. (1980). Suicide risk factors in alcohol abuse. *Suicide and Life-Threatening Behavior, 10,* 230–238.

Motto, J. A., & Bostrom, A. G. (2001). A randomized controlled trial of postcrisis suicide prevention. *Psychiatric Services, 52,* 828–833.

Müller-Oerlinghausen, B., Muser-Causemann, B., & Volk, J. (1992). Suicides and parasuicides in a high-risk patient group on and off lithium long-term medication. *Journal of Affective Disorders, 25,* 261–269.

Murphy, G. E. (1984). The prediction of suicide: Why is it so difficult? *American Journal of Psychotherapy, 38,* 341–349.

Murphy, G. E., & Wetzel, R. D. (1982). Family history of suicidal behavior among suicide attempters. *The Journal of Nervous and Mental Disease, 170,* 86–90.

Nakamura, J. W., McLeod, C., & McDermott, J. (1994). Temporal variation in adolescent suicide attempts. *Suicide and Life-Threatening Behavior, 24,* 343–349.

Negron, R., Piacentini, J., Graae, E., Davies, M., & Shaffer, D. (1997). Microanalysis of adolescent suicide attempters and ideators during the acute suicidal episode. *Journal of the American Academy of Child & Adolescent Psychiatry, 36,* 1512–1219.

Niméus, A., Alsen, M., & Träskman-Bendz, L. (2002). High suicidal intent scores indicate future suicide. *Archives of Suicide Research, 6,* 211–219.

Nock, M. K., Joiner, T. E., Gordon, K. H., Lloyd-Richardson, E., & Prinstein, M. J. (2006). Non-suicidal self-injury among adolescents: Diagnostic correlates and relation to suicide attempts. *Psychiatry Research, 144,* 65–72.

Nock, M. K., & Kessler, R. C. (2006). Prevalence of and risk factors for suicide attempts versus suicide gestures: Analysis of the National Comorbidity Survey. *Journal of Abnormal Psychology, 115,* 616–623.

Nordström, P., Åsberg, M., Åberg-Wistedt, A., & Nordin, C. (1995). Attempted suicide predicts suicide risk in mood disorders. *Acta Psychiatrica Scandinavica, 92,* 345–350.

O'Boyle, M., & Brandon, E. A. A. (1998). Suicide attempts, substance abuse, and personality. *Journal of Substance Abuse Treatment, 15,* 353–356.

O'Brien, G., Holton, A., Hurren, K., & Watt, L. (1987). Deliberate self-harm and predictors of out-patient attendance. *British Journal of Psychiatry, 150,* 246–247.

O'Carroll, P. W., Berman, A. L., Maris, R. W., Mościcki, E. K., Tanney, B. L., & Silverman, M. M. (1996). Beyond the Tower of Babel: A nomenclature for suicidology. *Suicide and Life-Threatening Behavior, 26,* 237–252.

O'Connor, R. C. (2007). The relations between perfectionism and suicidality: A systematic review. *Suicide and Life-Threatening Behavior, 37,* 698–714.

O'Connor, R. C., Whyte, M.-C., Fraser, L., Masterton, G., Miles, J., & MacHale, S. (2007). Predicting short-term outcome in well-being following suicidal behaviour: The conjoint effects of social perfectionism and positive future thinking. *Behaviour Research and Therapy, 45,* 1543–1555.

O'Donohue, W. T., & Levensky, E. R. (Eds.). (2006). *Promoting treatment adherence: A practical handbook for health care providers.* London: Sage.

Olson, D. H., Portner, J., & Lavee, Y. (1985). *FACES III.* St. Paul: Family Social Science, University of Minnesota.

Olson, L. M., & Wahab, S. (2006). American Indians and suicide: A neglected area of research. *Trauma, Violence, and Abuse, 7,* 19–33.

Oquendo, M. A., Bongiovi-Garcia, M. W., Galfalvy, H., Goldberg, P. H., Grunebaum, M. F., Burke, A. K., et al. (2007). Sex differences in clinical predictors of suicidal acts after major depression: A prospective study. *American Journal of Psychiatry, 164,* 134–141.

Oquendo, M. A., Dragasti, D., Harkavy-Friedman, J., Dervic, K., Currier, D., Burke, A. K., et al. (2005). Protective factors against suicidal behavior in Latinos. *The Journal of Nervous and Mental Disease, 193,* 438–443.

Oquendo, M. A., Ellis, S. P., Greenwald, S., Malone, K. M., Weissman, M. M., & Mann, J. J. (2001). Ethnic and sex differences in suicide rates relative to major depression in the United States. *American Journal of Psychiatry, 158,* 1652–1658.

Oquendo, M. A., Galfalvy, H., Russo, S., Ellis, S. P., Grunebaum, M. F., Burke, A., et al. (2004). Prospective study of clinical predictors of suicidal acts after a major depressive episode in patients with major depressive disorder or bipolar disorder. *American Journal of Psychiatry, 161,* 1433–1441.

Oquendo, M. A., Kamali, M., Ellis, S. P., Grunebaum, M. F., Malone, K. M., Brodsky, B. S., et al. (2002). Adequacy of antidepressant treatment after discharge and the occurrence of suicidal acts in major depression: A prospective study. *American Journal of Psychiatry, 159,* 1746–1751.

Orbach, I., Bar-Joseph, H., & Dror, N. (1990). Styles of problem solving in suicidal individuals. *Suicide and Life-Threatening Behavior, 20,* 56–64.

Osman, A., Kopper, B. A., Linehan, M. M., Barrios, F. X., Gutierrez, P. M., & Bagge, C. L. (1999). Validation of the Adult Suicidal Ideation Questionnaire and the Reasons for Living Inventory in an adult psychiatric inpatient sample. *Psychological Assessment, 11,* 115–223.

Pallis, D. J., & Sainsbury, P. (1976). The value of assessing suicide intent in attempted suicide. *Psychological Medicine, 6,* 487–492.

Paris, J. (2006). Predicting and preventing suicide: Do we know enough to do either? *Harvard Review of Psychiatry, 14,* 233–240.

Patsiokas, A. T., & Clum, G. A. (1985). Effects of psychotherapeutic strategies in the treatment of suicide attempters. *Psychotherapy, 22,* 281–290.

Patten, S. B. (2000). Selection bias in studies of major depression using clinical subjects. *Journal of Clinical Epidemiology, 53,* 351–357.

Patton, J. H., Stanford, M. S., & Barratt, E. S. (1995). Factor structure of the Barratt Impulsiveness Scale. *Journal of Clinical Psychology, 51,* 768–774.

Pearson, J. L., & Brown, G. K. (2000). Suicide prevention in late life: Directions for science and practice. *Clinical Psychology Review, 20,* 685–705.

Pearson, J. L., Conwell, Y., & Lyness, J. M. (1997). Late-life suicide and depression in the primary care setting. In L. S. Schneider (Ed.), *Developments in geriatric psychiatry: New directions for mental heath services* (pp. 13–38). San Francisco: Jossey-Bass.

Pelkonen, M., Marttunen, M., Pulkkinen, E., Laippala, P., & Aro, H. (1997). Characteristics of out-patient adolescents with suicidal tendencies. *Acta Psychiatrica Scandinavica, 95,* 100–107.

Persons, J. B. (2006). Case formulation-driven psychotherapy. *Clinical Psychology: Science and Practice, 13,* 167–170.

Pfeffer, C. R., Hurt, S. W., Peskin, J. R., & Siefker, C. A. (1995). Suicidal children grow up: Ego functions associated with suicide attempts. *Journal of the American Academy of Child & Adolescent Psychiatry, 38,* 846–851.

Pfeffer, C. R., Newcorn, J., Kaplan, G., Mizruchi, M., & Plutchik, R. (1988). Suicidal behavior in adolescent psychiatric inpatients. *Journal of the American Academy of Child & Adolescent Psychiatry, 27,* 357–361.

Pierce, D. (1987). Deliberate self-harm in the elderly. *International Journal of Geriatric Psychiatry, 2,* 105–110.

Pillay, A. L., & Wassenaar, D. R. (1995). Psychological intervention, spontaneous remission, hopelessness, and psychiatric disturbance in adolescent parasuicides. *Suicide and Life-Threatening Behavior, 25,* 386–392.

Pokorny, A. D. (1983). Prediction of suicide in psychiatric patients. *Archives of General Psychiatry, 40,* 249–257.

Pollock, L. R., & Williams, J. M. G. (2004). Problem-solving in suicide attempters. *Psychological Medicine, 34,* 163–167.

Pope, K., & Tabachnick, B. (1993). Therapists' anger, hate, fear, and sexual feelings: National survey of therapist responses, client characteristics, critical events, formal complaints, and training. *Professional Psychology: Research and Practice, 24,* 142–152.

Posner, K., Brent, D., Lucas, C., Gould, M., Stanley, B., Brown, G., et al. (2007). *Columbia Suicide Severity Rating Scale (C-SSRS).* Unpublished manuscript, Columbia University.

Posner, K., Oquendo, M., Stanley, B., Davies, M., & Gould, M. (2007). Columbia classification algorithm of suicide assessment (C-CASA). *American Journal of Psychiatry, 164,* 1035–1043.

Pratt, D., Piper, M., Appleby, L., Webb, R., & Shaw, J. (2006, July 8). Suicide in recently released prisoners: A population-based cohort study. *Lancet, 368,* 119–123.

Preuss, U. W., Schuckit, M. A., Smith, T. L., Danko, G. P., Bierut, L., Bucholz, K. K., et al. (2002). Comparison of 3190 alcohol-dependent individuals with and without suicide attempts. *Alcoholism: Clinical and Experimental Research, 26,* 471–477.

Preuss, U. W., Schuckit, M. A., Smith, T. L., Danko, G. P., Bucholz, K. K., Hesselbrock, M. N., et al. (2003). Predictors and correlates of suicide attempts over 5 years in 1,237 alcohol-dependent men and women. *American Journal of Psychiatry, 160,* 56–63.

Priester, M. K., & Clum, G. A. (1993). The problem-solving diathesis in depression, hopelessness, and suicide ideation: A longitudinal analysis. *Journal of Psychopathology and Behavioral Assessment, 15,* 239–254.

Prigerson, H. G., Desai, R. A., Lui-Mares, W., & Rosenheck, R. A. (2003). Suicidal ideation and suicide attempts in homeless mentally ill persons. *Social Psychiatry Psychiatric Epidemiology, 38,* 213–219.

Prinstein, M. J. (2003). Social factors: Peer relationships. In A. Spirito & J. C. Overholser (Eds.), *Evaluating and treating adolescent suicide attempters: From research to practice* (pp. 191–213). New York: Academic Press.

Project MATCH Research Group. (1997). Matching alcoholism treatments to client heterogeneity: Project MATCH posttreatment drinking outcomes. *Journal of Studies on Alcohol, 58,* 7–29.

Qin, P., Agerbo, E., Westergård-Nielsen, N., Eriksson, T., & Mortensen, P. B. (2000). Gender differences in risk factors for suicide in Denmark. *British Journal of Psychiatry, 177,* 546–550.

Ramsay, J. R., & Newman, C. F. (2005). After the attempt: Maintaining the therapeutic alliance following a patient's suicide attempt. *Suicide and Life-Threatening Behavior, 35,* 413–424.

Range, L. M., & Penton, S. R. (1994). Hope, hopelessness, and suicidality in college students. *Psychological Reports, 75,* 456–458.

Ranieri, W. F., Steer, R. A., Lavrence, T. I., Rissmiller, D. J., Piper, G. E., & Beck, A. T. (1987). Relationships of depression, hopelessness, and dysfunctional attitudes to suicide ideation in psychiatric patients. *Psychological Reports, 61,* 967–975.

Reid, W. H. (1998). Promises, promises: Don't rely on patients' no-suicide/no-violence "contracts." *Journal of Practical Psychiatry and Behavioral Health, 4,* 316–318.

Reinecke, M. A. (2006). Problem solving: A conceptual approach to suicidality and psychotherapy. In T. E. Ellis (Ed.), *Cognition and suicide: Theory, research, and therapy* (pp. 237–260). Washington, DC: American Psychological Association.

Reinecke, M. A., DuBois, D. L., & Schultz, T. M. (2001). Social problem solving, mood, and suicidality among inpatient adolescents. *Cognitive Therapy and Research, 25,* 743–756.

Remafedi, G., French, S., Story, M., Resnick, M., & Blum, R. (1998). The relationship between suicide risk and sexual orientation: Results of a population-based study. *American Journal of Public Health, 88,* 57–60.

Rich, C. L., Warstadt, G. M., Nemiroff, R. A., Fowler, R. C., & Young, D. (1991). Suicide, stressors, and the life cycle. *American Journal of Psychiatry, 148,* 524–527.

Rifai, A. H., George, C. J., Stack, J. A., Mann, J. J., & Reynolds, C. F. (1994). Hopelessness continues to distinguish suicide attempters after acute treatment of major depression in later-life. *American Journal of Psychiatry, 151,* 1687–1690.

Rogers, P., Watt, A., Gray, N. S., MacCulloch, M., & Gournay, K. (2002). Content of command hallucinations predicts self-harm but not violence in a medium secure unit. *Journal of Forensic Psychiatry, 13,* 251–262.

Ross, R. K., Bernstein, L., Trent, L., Henderson, B. E., & Paganini-Hill, A. (1990). A prospective study of risk factors for traumatic deaths in a retirement community. *Preventive Medicine, 19,* 323–334.

Rossow, I., & Wichstrom, L. (1994). Parasuicide and use of intoxicants among Norwegian adolescents. *Suicide and Life-Threatening Behavior, 24,* 174–183.

Roth, A., & Fonagy, P. (2005). *What works for whom: A critical review of psychotherapy research* (2nd ed.). New York: Guilford Press.

Rotheram-Borus, M. J., Piacentini, J., Miller, S., Graae, F., & Castro-Blanco, D. (1994). Brief cognitive-behavioral treatment for adolescent suicide attempters and their families. *Journal of the American Academy of Child & Adolescent Psychiatry, 33,* 508–517.

Rotheram-Borus, M. J., Trautman, P. D., Dopkins, S., & Shrout, P. (1990). Cognitive style and pleasant activities among female adolescent suicide attempters. *Journal of Consulting and Clinical Psychology, 58,* 554–561.

Rowe, J. L., Conwell, Y., Schulberg, H. C., & Bruce, M. L. (2006). Social support and suicidal ideation in older adults using home healthcare services. *American Journal of Geriatric Psychiatry, 14,* 758–766.

Roy, A. (2001). Serum cholesterol, suicidal behavior, and impulsivity in cocaine-dependent patients. *Psychiatry Research, 101,* 243–247.

Roy, A. (2002). Characteristics of opiate dependent patients who attempt suicide. *Journal of Clinical Psychiatry, 63,* 403–407.

Roy, A. (2003a). Characteristics of drug addicts who attempt suicide. *Psychiatry Research, 121,* 99–103.

Roy, A. (2003b). Distal risk factors for suicidal behavior in alcoholics: Replications and new findings. *Journal of Affective Disorders, 77,* 267–271.

Roy, A., & Janal, M. (2006). Gender in suicide attempt rates and childhood sexual abuse rates: Is there an interaction? *Suicide and Life-Threatening Behavior, 36,* 329–335.

Rubenowitz, E., Waern, M., Wilhelmson, K., & Allebeck, P. (2001). Life events and psychosocial factors in elderly suicides: A case-control study. *Psychological Medicine, 31,* 1193–1202.

Rudd, M. D. (2000). Integrating science into the practice of clinical suicidology: A review of the psychotherapy literature and a research agenda for the future. In R. W. Maris, S. S. Canetto, J. L. McIntosh, & M. M. Silverman (Eds.), *Review of Suicidology 2000* (pp. 49–83). New York: Guilford Press.

Rudd, M. D. (2004). Cognitive therapy for suicidality: An integrative, comprehensive, and practical approach to conceptualization. *Journal of Contemporary Psychotherapy, 34,* 59–72.

Rudd, M. D. (2006). Fluid Vulnerability Theory: A cognitive approach to understanding the process of acute and chronic suicide risk. In T. E. Ellis (Ed.), *Cognition and suicide: Theory, research, and therapy* (pp. 355–368). Washington, DC: American Psychological Association.

Rudd, M. D., Berman, A. L., Joiner, T. E., Nock, M. K., Silverman, M. M., Mandrusiak, M., et al. (2006). Warning signs for suicide: Theory, research, and clinical applications. *Suicide and Life-Threatening Behavior, 36*, 255–262.

Rudd, M. D., Joiner, T., Brown, G. K., Cukrowica, K., Jobes, D., Silverman, M., et al. (in press). Informed consent with suicidal patients: Rethinking risks in (and out of) treatment. *Suicide and Life-Threatening Behavior*.

Rudd, M. D., Joiner, T., & Rajab, M. H. (1996). Relationships among suicide ideators, attempters, and multiple attempters in a young adult sample. *Journal of Abnormal Psychology, 105*, 541–550.

Rudd, M. D., Joiner, T., & Rajab, M. H. (2001). *Treating suicidal behavior: An effective, time-limited approach*. New York: Guilford Press.

Rudd, M. D., Mandrusiak, M., & Joiner, T. E. (2006). The case against no-suicide contracts: The commitment to treatment statement as a practice alternative. *Journal of Clinical Psychology, 62*, 243–251.

Rudd, M. D., Rajab, M. H., & Dahm, P. F. (1994). Problem-solving appraisal in suicide ideators and attempters. *American Journal of Orthopsychiatry, 58*, 562–564.

Rush, A. J., Beck, A. T., Kovacs, M., Weissenburger, J., & Hollon, S. D. (1982). Comparison of the effects of cognitive therapy and pharmacotherapy on hopelessness and self concept. *American Journal of Psychiatry, 139*, 862–866.

Russell, S. T., & Joyner, K. (2001). Adolescent sexual orientation and suicide risk: Evidence from a national study. *American Journal of Public Health, 91*, 1276–1281.

Rychtarik, R. G., McGillicuddy, N. B., Connors, G. J., & Whitney, R. B. (1998). Participant selection biases in a randomized clinical trial of alcoholism treatment settings and intensities. *Alcoholism: Clinical and Experimental Research, 22*, 969–973.

Salkovskis, P. M., Atha, C., & Storer, D. (1990). Cognitive-behavioral problem solving in the treatment of patients who repeatedly attempt suicide. *British Journal of Psychiatry, 157*, 871–876.

Samuelsson, M., Jokinen, J., Nordström, A.-L., & Nordström, P. (2006). CSF 5-HIAA, suicide intent and hopelessness in the prediction of early suicide in male high-risk suicide attempters. *Acta Psychiatrica Scandinavica, 113*, 44–47.

Schotte, D. E., & Clum, G. A. (1982). Suicide ideation in a college population: A test of a model. *Journal of Consulting and Clinical Psychology, 50*, 690–696.

Schotte, D. E., & Clum, G. A. (1987). Problem-solving skills in suicidal psychiatric patients. *Journal of Consulting and Clinical Psychology, 55*, 49–54.

Schotte, D. E., Cools, J., & Payvar, S. (1990). Problem-solving deficits in suicidal patients: Trait vulnerability or state phenomenon? *Journal of Consulting and Clinical Psychology, 58*, 562–564.

Scott, C., Tacchi, M. J., Jones, R., & Scott, J. (1997). Acute and one-year outcome of a randomised controlled trial of brief cognitive therapy for major depressive disorder primary care. *British Journal of Psychiatry, 171*, 131–134.

Shadish, W. R., Matt, G. E., Navarro, A. M., & Phillips, G. (2000). The effects of psychological therapies under clinically representative conditions: A meta-analysis. *Psychological Bulletin, 126*, 512–529.

Shaffer, D., Garland, A., Gould, M., Fisher, P., & Trautman, P. (1988). Preventing teenage suicide: A critical review. *Journal of the Academy of Child & Adolescent Psychiatry, 27*, 675–687.

Shaffer, D., & Pfeffer, C. (2001). Practice parameters for the assessment and treatment of children and adolescents with suicidal behavior. *Journal of the American Academy of Child & Adolescent Psychiatry, 40*, 24S–51S.

Sharma, V., Persad, E., & Kueneman, K. (1998). A closer look at inpatient suicide. *Journal of Affective Disorders, 47*, 123–129.

Shenassa, E. D., Catlin, S. N., & Buka, S. L. (2003). Lethality of firearms relative to other suicide methods: A population based study. *Journal of Epidemiology and Community Health, 57*, 120–124.

Shneidman, E. (1985). *Definition of suicide*. New York: Wiley.

Silver, M. A., Bohnert, M., Beck, A. T., & Marcus, D. (1971). Relation of depression of attempted suicide and seriousness of intent. *Archives of General Psychiatry, 25*, 573–576.

Silverman, M. M. (2006). The language of suicidology. *Suicide and Life-Threatening Behavior, 36*, 519–532.

Silverman, M. M., Berman, A. L., Sanddal, N. D., O'Carroll, P. W., & Joiner, T. E. (2007). Rebuilding the Tower of Babel: A revised nomenclature for the study of suicide and suicidal behaviors. Part I: Background, rationale, and methodology. *Suicide and Life-Threatening Behavior, 37*, 248–263.

Simon, R. I. (2004). *Assessing and managing suicide risk: Guidelines for clinically based risk management*. Washington, DC: American Psychiatric Publishing.

Simon, R. I. (2007). Gun safety management with patients at risk for suicide. *Suicide and Life-Threatening Behavior, 37*, 518–526.

Simon, T., & Crosby, A. (2000). Suicide planning among high school students who report attempting suicide. *Suicide and Life-Threatening Behavior, 30*, 213–221.

Simon, T. R., Swann, A. C., Powell, K. E., Potter, L. B., Kresnow, M. J., & O'Carroll, P. W. (2001). Characteristics of impulsive suicide attempts and attempters. *Suicide and Life-Threatening Behavior, 32*, 49–59.

Skogman, K., Alsen, M., & Ojehagen, A. (2004). Sex differences in risk factors for suicide after attempted suicide—A follow-up study of 1052 suicide attempters. *Social Psychiatry and Psychiatric Epidemiology, 39*, 113–120.

Skogman, K., & Öjehagen, A. (2003). Motives for suicide attempters—The views of the patients. *Archives of Suicide Research, 7*, 193–206.

Slaby, A. E. (1998). Outpatient management of suicidal patients. In B. Bongar, A. L. Berman, R. W. Maris, M. M. Silverman, E. A. Harris, & W. L. Packman (Eds.), *Risk management with suicidal patients* (pp. 34–64). New York: Guilford Press.

Slee, N., Arensman, E., Garnefski, N., & Spinhoven, P. (2007). Cognitive behavioral therapy for deliberate self-harm. *Crisis, 28,* 175–182.

Slee, N., Garnefski, N., van der Leeden, R., Arensman, E., & Spinhoven, P. (2008). Cognitive-behavioural intervention for self-harm: Randomised controlled trial. *British Journal of Psychiatry, 192,* 202–211.

Soloff, P. H., Lis, J. A., Kelly, T., Cornelius, J., & Ulrich, R. (1994). Risk factors for suicidal behavior in borderline personality disorder. *American Journal of Psychiatry, 151,* 1316–1323.

Sorenson, S. B., & Rutter, C. M. (1991). Transgenerational patterns of suicide attempts. *Journal of Consulting and Clinical Psychology, 59,* 861–866.

Sosdjan, D., King, R., Brown, G. K., & Beck, A. T. (2002). *Study case management manual for suicide attempters.* Unpublished manuscript, University of Pennsylvania.

Spandler, H. (1996). *Who's hurting who? Young people, self-harm and suicide.* Manchester, England: 42nd Street.

Spirito, A. (2003). Understanding attempted suicide in adolescence. In A. Spirito & J. C. Overholser (Eds.), *Evaluating and treating adolescent suicide attempters: From research to practice* (pp. 1–18). New York: Academic Press.

Spirito, A., Brown, L., Overholser, J., & Fritz, G. (1989). Attempted suicide in adolescence: A review and critique of the literature. *Clinical Psychology Review, 9,* 335–363.

Spirito, A., Overholser, J. C., & Stark, L. J. (1989). Common pathways and coping strategies II: Findings with adolescent suicide attempters. *Journal of Abnormal Child Psychology, 17,* 213–221.

Stanford, E. J., Goetz, R. R., & Bloom, J. D. (1994). The no harm contract in the emergency assessment of suicidal risk. *Journal of Clinical Psychiatry, 55,* 344–348.

Steblaj, A., Tavcar, R., & Dernovsek, M. Z. (1999). Predictors of suicide in psychiatric hospital. *Acta Psychiatrica Scandinavica, 100,* 383–388.

Steele, C. M., & Josephs, R. A. (1990). Alcohol myopia: Its prized and dangerous effects. *American Psychologist, 45,* 921–933.

Steer, R. A., Rissmiller, D. B., Ranieri, W. F., & Beck, A. T. (1993). Dimensions of suicidal ideation in psychiatric inpatients. *Behavior Research and Therapy, 31,* 229–236.

Stein, D., Apter, A., Ratzoni, G., Har-Even, D., & Avidan, G. (1998). Association between multiple suicide attempts and negative affect in adolescents. *Journal of the American Academy of Child & Adolescent Psychiatry, 37,* 488–494.

Stein, D., Witztum, E., Brom, D., DeNour, A., & Elizur, A. (1992). The association between adolescents' attitudes toward suicide and their psychosocial background and suicidal tendencies. *Adolescence, 27,* 949–959.

Stengel, E., & Cook, N. G. (1958). *Attempted suicide: Its social significance and effects.* London: Chapman & Hall/CRC.

Steuer, J. L., Mintz, J., Hammen, C. L., Hill, M. A., Jarvik, L. F., McCarley, T., et al. (1984). Cognitive–behavioral and psychodynamic group psychotherapy in treatment of geriatric depression. *Journal of Consulting and Clinical Psychology, 52,* 180–189.

Stroebe, M., Stroebe, W., & Abakoumkin, G. (2005). The broken heart: Suicidal ideation in bereavement. *American Journal of Psychiatry, 162,* 2178–2180.

Strohmetz, D. B., Alterman, A. I., & Walter, D. (1990). Subject selection bias in alcoholics volunteering for a treatment study. *Alcoholism: Clinical and Experimental Research, 14,* 736–738.

Strosahl, K., Chiles, J. A., & Linehan, M. (1992). Prediction of suicide intent in hospitalized parasuicides: Reasons for living, hopelessness, and depression. *Comprehensive Psychiatry, 33,* 366–373.

Suokas, J., Suominen, K., Isometsä, E., Ostamo, A., & Lönnqvist, J. (2001). Long-term risk factors for suicide mortality after attempted suicide—Findings of a 14-year follow-up study. *Acta Psychiatrica Scandinavica, 104,* 117–121.

Suominen, K., Henriksson, M., Suokas, J., Isometsä, E., Ostamo, A., & Lönnqvist, J. (1996). Mental disorders and comorbidity in attempted suicide. *Acta Psychiatrica Scandinavica, 94,* 234–240.

Suominen, K., Isometsä, E., Heilä, H., Lönnqvist, J., & Henriksson, M. (2002). General hospital suicides: A psychological autopsy study in Finland. *General Hospital Psychiatry, 24,* 412–416.

Suominen, K., Isometsä, E., Henriksson, M., Ostamo, A., & Lönnqvist, J. (1997). Hopelessness, impulsiveness and intent among suicide attempters with major depression, alcohol dependence, or both. *Acta Psychiatrica Scandinavica, 96,* 142–149.

Swann, A. C., Dougherty, D. M., Pazzaglia, P. J., Pham, M., Steinberg, J., & Moeller, G. (2005). Increased impulsivity associated with severity of suicide attempt history in patients with bipolar disorder. *American Journal of Psychiatry, 162,* 1680–1688.

Szanto, K., Gildengers, A., Mulsant, B. H., Brown, G. K., Alexopoulos, G. S., & Reynolds, C. F. (2002). Identification of suicide ideation and prevention of suicidal behavior in the elderly. *Drugs and Aging, 19,* 11–24.

Szanto, K., Prigerson, H. G., Houck, P. R., & Reynolds, C. F. (1997). Suicidal ideation in elderly bereaved: The role of complicated grief. *Suicide and Life Threatening Behavior, 27,* 194–207.

Szanto, K., Reynolds, C. F., Conwell, Y., Begley, A. E., & Houck, P. (1998). High levels of hopelessness persist in geriatric patients with remitted depression and a history of attempted suicide. *Journal of the American Geriatrics Society, 46,* 1401–1406.

Szanto, K., Reynolds, C. F., Frank, E., Stack, J., Fasiczka, A. L., Miller, M., et al. (1996). Suicide in elderly depressed patients: Is active vs. passive suicidal ideation a clinically valid distinction? *American Journal of Geriatric Psychiatry, 4,* 197–207.

Szanto, K., Shear, M. K., Houck, P. R., Reynolds, C. F., Frank, E., Caroff, K., et al. (2006). Indirect self-destructive behavior and overt suicidality in patients with complicated grief. *Journal of Clinical Psychiatry, 67,* 233–239.

Talbot, N. L., Duberstein, P. R., Cox, C., Denning, D., & Conwell, Y. (2004). Preliminary report on childhood sexual abuse, suicidal ideation, and suicide attempts among middle-aged and older depressed women. *American Journal of Geriatric Psychiatry, 12*, 536–538.

Taylor, E. A., & Stansfeld, S. A. (1984). Children who poison themselves: Prediction of attendance for treatment. *British Journal of Psychiatry, 145*, 132–135.

Teesson, M., Darke, S., Ross, J., Mills, K., Williamson, A., Havard, A., et al. (2005). *The Australian Treatment Outcome Study (ATOS): Heroin.* Retrieved May 2, 2007, from http://notes.med.unsw.edu.au/ndarcweb.nsf/page/Completed%20 Project%20T7%20ATOS

Tejedor, M. C., Diaz, A., Castillon, J. J., & Pericay, J. M. (1999). Attempted suicide: Repetition and survival findings of a follow-up study. *Acta Psychiatrica Scandinavica, 100*, 205–211.

Termansen, P. E., & Bywater, C. (1975). S.A.F.E.R.: A follow-up service for attempted suicide in Vancouver. *Canadian Psychiatric Association Journal, 20*, 29–34.

Thies-Flechtner, K., Müller-Oerlinghausen, B., Seibert, W., Walther, A., & Greil, W. (1996). Effect of prophylactic treatment on suicide risk in patients with major affective disorders: Data from a randomized prospective trial. *Pharmacopsychiatry, 29*, 103–107.

Thompson, L. W., Coon, D. W., Gallagher-Thompson, D., Sommer, B. R., & Koin, D. (2001). Comparison of desipramine and cognitive-behavioral therapy in the treatment of elderly outpatients with mild-to-moderate depression. *American Journal of Geriatric Psychiatry, 9*, 225–240.

Thompson, L. W., Gallagher, D., & Breckenridge, J. S. (1987). Comparative effectiveness of psychotherapies for depressed elders. *Journal of Consulting and Clinical Psychology, 55*, 385–390.

Torhorst, A., Moller, J. J., Burk, F., Kurz, A., Wachter, C., & Lauter, H. (1987). The psychiatric management of parasuicide patients: A controlled clinical study comparing different strategies of outpatient treatment. *Crisis, 8*, 53–61.

Trautman, P. D., Rotheram-Borus, M. J., Dopkins, S., & Lewin, N. (1991). Psychiatric diagnoses in minority female adolescent suicide attempters. *Journal of the American Academy of Child & Adolescent Psychiatry, 30*, 617–622.

Trautman, P. D., Stewart, N., & Morishima, A. (1993). Are adolescent suicide attempters noncompliant with outpatient care? *Journal of the American Academy of Child & Adolescent Psychiatry, 32*, 89–94.

Trout, D. L. (1980). The role of social isolation in suicide. *Suicide and Life-Threatening Behavior, 10*, 10–23.

Trulsson, K., & Hedin, U.-C. (2004). The role of social support when giving up drug abuse: A female perspective. *International Journal of Social Welfare, 13*, 145–157.

Turvey, C. L., Conwell, Y., Jones, M. P., Phillips, C., Simonsick, E., Pearson, J. L., et al. (2002). Risk factors for late-life suicide: A prospective, community-based study. *American Journal of Geriatric Psychiatry, 10*, 398–406.

Tyrer, P., Thompson, S., Schmidt, U., Jones, V., Knapp, M., Davidson, K., et al. (2003). Randomized controlled trial of brief cognitive behaviour therapy versus treatment as usual in recurrent deliberate self-harm: The POPMACT study. *Psychological Medicine, 33,* 969–976.

Uncapher, H., Gallagher-Thompson, D., Osgood, N. J., & Bonger, B. (1998). Hopelessness and suicide ideation in older adults. *Gerontologist, 38,* 62–70.

Unützer, J., Tang, L. Q., Oishi, S., Katon, W., Williams, J. W., Hunkeler, E., et al. (2006). Reducing suicidal ideation in depressed older primary care patients. *Journal of the American Geriatrics Society, 54,* 1550–1556.

U.S. Department of Health & Human Services. (2001). *National strategy for suicide prevention: Goals and objectives for action.* Rockville, MD: U.S. Department of Health & Human Services, Public Health Service.

Vaiva, G., Ducrocq, F., Meyer, P., Mathieu, D., Philippe, A., Libersa, C., et al. (2006). Effect of telephone contact on further suicide attempts in patients discharged from an emergency department: Randomised controlled study. *British Medical Journal, 332,* 1241–1245.

Vanable, P. A., Carey, M. P., Carey, K. B., & Maisto, S. A. (2002). Predictors of participation and attrition in a health promotion study involving psychiatric outpatients. *Journal of Consulting and Clinical Psychology, 70,* 362–368.

VandeCreek, L., & Knapp, S. (2001). *Tarasoff and beyond: Legal and clinical considerations in the treatment of life-endangering patients.* Sarasota, FL: Professional Resource Press/Professional Resource Exchange.

van den Bosch, L. M. C., Verheul, R., Schippers, G. M., & van den Brink, W. (2002). Dialectical behavior therapy of borderline patients with and without substance use problems: Implementation and long-term effects. *Addictive Behaviors, 27,* 911–923.

Van der Sande, R., van Rooijen, L., Buskens, E., Allart, E., Hawton, K., van der Graff, Y., et al. (1997). Intensive in-patient and community intervention versus routine care after attempted suicide: A randomized controlled intervention study. *British Journal of Psychiatry, 171,* 35–41.

Van Heeringen, C., Jannes, S., Buylaert, W., Henderick, H., De Bacquer, D., & Van Remoortel, J. (1995). The management of noncompliance with referral to outpatient after-care among attempted suicide patients: A controlled intervention study. *Psychological Medicine, 25,* 963–970.

Verkes, R. J., Van der Mast, R. C., Hengeveld, M. W., Tuyl, J. P., Zwinderman, A. H., & Van Kempen, G. M. J. (1998). Reduction by paroxetine of suicidal behavior in patients with repeated suicide attempts but not major depression. *American Journal of Psychiatry, 155,* 543–547.

Verona, E., Patrick, C. J., & Joiner, T. E. (2001). Psychopathy, antisocial personality, and suicide risk. *Journal of Abnormal Psychology, 110,* 462–470.

Verona, E., Sachs-Ericsson, N., & Joiner, J. E. (2004). Suicide attempts associated with externalizing psychopathology in an epidemiological sample. *American Journal of Psychiatry, 161,* 444–451.

Vingoe, L., Welch, S., Farrell, M., & Strang, J. (1999). Heroin overdose among treatment sample of injecting drug misusers: Accident or suicidal behaviour? *Journal of Substance Abuse, 4,* 88–91.

Waern, M., Beskow, J., Runeson, B., & Skoog, I. (1999). Suicidal feelings in the last year of life in elderly people who commit suicide. *Lancet, 354,* 917–918.

Waern, M., Rubenowitz, E., Runeson, B., Skoog, I., Wilhelmson, K., & Allebeck, P. (2002). Burden of illness and suicide in elderly people: Case-control study. *British Medical Journal, 324,* 1355–1358.

Waern, M., Rubenowitz, E., & Wilhelmson, K. (2003). Predictors of suicide in the old elderly. *Gerontology, 49,* 328–334.

Wagner, B. M., Wong, S. A., & Jobes, D. A. (2002). Mental health professionals' determinations of adolescent suicide attempts. *Suicide and Life-Threatening Behavior, 32,* 284–300.

Waterhouse, J., & Platt, S. (1990). General hospital admission in the management of parasuicide: A randomised controlled trial. *British Journal of Psychiatry, 156,* 236–242.

Weissman, A., Beck, A. T., & Kovacs, M. (1979). Drug abuse, hopelessness, and suicidal behavior. *International Journal of the Addictions, 14,* 451–464.

Wells, K. C., & Curry, J. F. (2000). *Parent and conjoint parent-adolescent sessions.* Unpublished manuscript, Duke University Medical Center. Retrieved January 31, 2007, from https://trialweb.dcri.duke.edu/tads/tad/manuals/TADS_CBT.pdf

Welu, T. C. (1977). A follow-up program for suicide attempters: Evaluation of effectiveness. *Suicide and Life-Threatening Behavior, 7,* 17–30.

Wenzel, A., Jeglic, E. L., Levy-Mack, H. J., Beck, A. T., & Brown, G. K. (in press). Treatment attitude and therapy outcome in patients with borderline personality disorder. *Journal of Cognitive Psychotherapy.*

Wenzel, A., Sharp, I. R., Sokol, L., & Beck, A. T. (2006). Attentional fixation in panic disorder. *Cognitive Behaviour Therapy, 35,* 65–73.

Wetzel, R. D. (1977). Factor structure of Beck's suicide intent scales. *Psychological Reports, 40,* 295–302.

Wetzler, S., Asnis, G. M., Hyman, R., Virtue, C., Zimmerman, J., & Rathus, J. H. (1996). Characteristics of suicidality among adolescents. *Suicide and Life-Threatening Behavior, 26,* 37–45.

Whitlock, J., Eckenrode, J., & Silverman, D. (2006). Self-injurious behaviors in a college population. *Pediatrics, 117,* 1939–1948.

Wilkinson, G. (1994). Controversies in management: Better treatment of mental illness is a more appropriate aim. *British Medical Journal, 309,* 860–861.

Williams, J. M. G. (1996). Depression and the specificity of autobiographical memory. In D. C. Rubin (Ed.), *Remembering our past: Studies in autobiographical memory* (pp. 244–267). New York: Cambridge University Press.

Williams, J. M. G., Barnhoffer, T., Crane, C., & Duggan, D. S. (2006). The role of overgeneral memory in suicidality. In T. E. Ellis (Ed.), *Cognition and suicide: Theory, research, and therapy* (pp. 173–192). Washington, DC: American Psychiatric Association.

Williams, J. M. G., & Broadbent, K. (1986a). Autobiographical memory in suicide attempters. *Journal of Abnormal Psychology, 95,* 144–149.

Williams, J. M. G., & Broadbent, K. (1986b). Distraction by emotional stimuli: Use of a Stroop task with suicide attempters. *British Journal of Clinical Psychology, 25,* 101–110.

Williams, J. M. G., & Dritschel, B. H. (1988). Emotional disturbance and the specificity of autobiographical memory. *Cognition & Emotion, 2,* 221–234.

Wolfsdorf, B. A., Freeman, J., D'Eramo, K., Overholser, J., & Spirito, A. (2003). Mood states: Depression, anger, and anxiety. In A. Spirito & J. C. Overholser (Eds.), *Evaluating and treating adolescent suicide attempters: From research to practice* (pp. 53–88). New York: Academic Press.

Wood, A., Trainor, G., Rothwell, J., Moore, A., & Harrington, R. (2001). Randomized trial of group therapy for repeated deliberate self-harm in adolescents. *Journal of the American Academy of Child & Adolescent Psychiatry, 40,* 1246–1253.

Wright, J. E., Basco, M. R., & Thase, M. E. (2006). *Learning cognitive-behavior therapy: An illustrated guide.* Washington, DC: American Psychiatric Publishing.

Xie, H., McHugo, G. J., Fox, M. B., & Drake, R. E. (2005). Substance abuse relapse in a ten-year prospective follow-up of clients with mental and substance use disorders. *Psychiatric Services, 56,* 1282–1287.

Yen, S., Shea, M. T., Pagno, M., Sanislow, C. A., Grilo, C. M., McGlashan, T. H., et al. (2003). Axis I and axis II disorders as predictors of prospective suicide attempts: Findings from the collaborative longitudinal personality disorders study. *Journal of Abnormal Psychology, 112,* 375–381.

Young, J. E., & Beck, A. T. (1980). *Manual for the Cognitive Therapy Rating Scale.* Philadelphia: University of Pennsylvania.

Young, M., Fogg, L., Scheftner, W., Fawcett, J., Akiskal, H., & Maser, J. (1996). Stable trait components of hopelessness: Baseline and sensitivity to depression. *Journal of Abnormal Psychology, 105,* 105–165.

Ystgaard, M., Hestetun, I., Loeb, M., & Mehlum, L. (2004). Is there a specific relationship between childhood sexual and physical abuse and repeated suicidal behavior? *Child Abuse & Neglect, 28,* 863–875.

AUTHOR INDEX

Abakoumkin, G., 34
Åberg-Wistedt, A., 38
Aboud, A., 285
Adams, D. M., 175
Addis, M. E., 223
Agency for Health Care Policy & Research, 83
Agerbo, E., 48
Aharonovich, E., 283, 289
Alexopoulos, G. S., 278
Allard, R., 84, 96, 97
Allebeck, P., 37, 266
Allgulander, C., 37
Allmon, D., 82
Alsen, M., 25
Alterman, A. I., 97
Altman, D., 95
American Psychiatric Association (APA), 130, 138, 140, 218, 219
American Psychological Association, 130
Anderson, P. S., 38
Anderson, W., 44, 70
Andréasson, S., 36
Andrews, J. A., 237, 238
Andriessen, K., 17
Anthony, J. C., 268
Appleby, L., 47
Apter, A., 53, 239
Arensman, E., 82, 94n1, 96, 97
Armstrong, H. E., 82
Aro, H., 47, 48, 143, 237
Asarnow, J. R., 238, 239
Åsberg, M., 38
Asnis, G. H., 42
Avidan, G., 239

Babor, T. F., 142
Baca-Garcia, E., 43, 65
Bar-Joseph, H., 44, 70
Barnaby, B., 285
Barnett, N., 237
Barnhoffer, T., 68
Barraclough, B., 35, 36, 37, 38, 265, 266, 284, 286, 288
Barratt, E. S., 42, 43, 290
Basco, M. R., 103, 105

Bateman, A., 88, 95
Bauer, G. B., 228
Baugher, M., 244
Baumeister, R. F., 65
Beautrais, A. L., 33, 34, 35, 38, 39, 265, 285
Beck, A. T., 6, 7, 8, 9, 17, 18, 19, 21, 24, 25, 26, 27, 28, 29, 34, 37, 39, 41, 54, 56, 57, 58, 61, 65, 92, 93, 98, 103, 104, 123, 127, 134, 139, 141, 143, 174, 284, 285, 289, 290, 291, 293, 301, 316
Beck, J. S., 7, 103, 105, 106, 107, 113, 125, 174, 193, 223
Beck, R., 6, 7, 18, 24, 26, 41, 141
Becker, E. S., 67
Bedrosian, R. C., 7
Begg, C., 95
Begley, A. E., 266
Bell, V., 38
Bender, M. A., 38
Bennewith, O., 86
Bensley, L., 240
Berchick, R. J., 8, 41
Beresford, E., 41
Bergman, E., 7, 24, 41
Berk, M. S., 39, 127, 134
Berman, A. L., 16, 17, 47, 48, 215, 244, 257
Bernstein, L., 266
Bertolote, J. M., 35
Beskow, J., 268
Best, D., 289
Bhar, S. S., 104
Black, D., 38, 86
Bloom, J. D., 145
Blum, M. C., 239
Blum, R., 236, 237
Blumenthal, S., 38
Blyer, C. R., 37
Boergers, J., 46, 239, 242, 257
Bohnert, M., 24
Bondy, B., 40, 51
Bongar, B., 215, 229, 230, 266
Borges, G., 3
Borowsky, I., 236
Bostrom, A. G., 80, 81, 84, 85, 92, 95
Bostwick, J. M., 35, 47

357

SUBJECT INDEX

ABOUT THE AUTHORS

Amy Wenzel, PhD, is on the faculty at the University of Pennsylvania, where she conducts research on cognitive approaches to understanding suicidal behavior. She is the recipient of awards from the National Alliance for Research on Schizophrenia and Depression, the American Foundation for Suicide Prevention, and the National Institutes of Health. She has published more than 70 journal articles and chapters and is a coeditor of five books.

Gregory K. Brown, PhD, is a Research Associate Professor of Clinical Psychology in psychiatry at the University of Pennsylvania, where he conducts research on the effectiveness of cognitive therapy with high-risk individuals. He is the recipient of the 2007 Edwin Shneidman Award for outstanding contributions in suicide research from the American Association of Suicidology.

Aaron T. Beck, MD, is professor emeritus of psychiatry at the University of Pennsylvania and is known as "the father of cognitive therapy." He has published more than 500 scientific articles and is author or coauthor of 17 books. He is the recipient of the 2006 Lasker Award (known as "America's Nobel Prize") for Clinical Medical Research.